RÉAUMUR'S
Memoirs on Steel and Iron

RÉAUMUR'S
Memoirs on Steel and Iron

A TRANSLATION
FROM THE ORIGINAL PRINTED IN 1722

By

Anneliese Grünhaldt Sisco

WITH AN INTRODUCTION
AND NOTES BY

Cyril Stanley Smith

THE UNIVERSITY OF CHICAGO PRESS · CHICAGO · ILLINOIS

THE PUBLICATION OF THIS BOOK HAS BEEN MADE POSSIBLE
BY FUNDS GRANTED BY

The American Iron and Steel Institute

Library of Congress Catalog Number: 56-6637

THE UNIVERSITY OF CHICAGO PRESS, CHICAGO 37
Cambridge University Press, London, N.W. 1, England
The University of Toronto Press, Toronto 5, Canada

© *1956 by The University of Chicago Press. Published 1956
Composed and printed by* THE UNIVERSITY OF CHICAGO PRESS,
Chicago, Illinois, U.S.A.

CONTENTS*

I. STEELMAKING

II. SOFTENING CAST IRON

* Réaumur's own Table of Contents is in the back (p. 365), as in the
original.

Contents

INTRODUCTION

I. RÉAUMUR'S LIFE AND WORK[1]

RENÉ ANTOINE FERCHAULT, knight and seigneur of Réaumur, whose name is today widely known only in connection with a thermometric scale and a station on the Paris Metro, was a representative and significant figure in eighteenth-century France. His achievements were many and important, though none was spectacular. His life was a quiet one, unmarked by dramatic incident, but for a dedicated man of science it was full of excitement, of new horizons sighted, and of facts in many fields of science revealed and put in order. To Réaumur basic and applied science were inseparable. He made useful inventions and reduced them to practice. Believing that knowledge should be shared, he wrote up his own work in great detail and took a leading part in the recording and publication of craftsmen's techniques in the manner of the Encyclopedists a generation later.

Réaumur's career as savant and experimenter was made easier by a family background that provided both financial independence and influential friends. He was born in La Rochelle on February 28, 1683. From his father, a lawyer and civil servant who died when the son was two, the young René inherited the family seigneury in the Vendée. By its name he was always known, and for it he retained a deep affection. His mother and her relatives, the prosperous Calais merchant family of Bouchel, supervised the boy's schooling, sending him after his early years in La Ro-

1. The biographical sketch was prepared with the assistance of Alice Kimball Smith. It is based largely upon three sources: Grandjean de Fouchy's eulogy of Réaumur, *Histoire de l'Académie Royale des Sciences*, 1757, pp. 201 ff.; Jean Torlais, *Réaumur, un esprit encyclopédique en dehors de l'Encyclopédie* (Paris, 1936); and Jean Torlais (ed.), *Réaumur, morceaux choisis* (Paris, 1939).

chelle to the Jesuits in Poitiers and then at sixteen to study law at Bourges. The young Réaumur did not matriculate in law as family tradition directed but instead spent the next four years studying mathematics and the sciences. In 1703, at the age of twenty, he was ready for more advanced training in Paris.

There Réaumur was at once introduced into the stimulating circle of the Académie Royale des Sciences by a connection of his mother's, Charles Jean François Hénault, historian and future president of the French parliament. He quickly became a special protégé and friend of the Abbé Bignon, a kind of tutelary angel of scientists and savants, and he continued his mathematical studies under Pierre Varignon, professor in the Collège Mazarin and the Collège Royal. In March of 1708 he was chosen by his master as a student member of the Academy.

The association thus established provided the focus for most of Réaumur's scientific work and personal relationships until his death nearly fifty years later. He was first and foremost an academician at a time when the term implied an interest in whatever was novel and provocative and when Academy members took pride in fulfilling the obligations of citizenship in which the semiofficial character of the society involved them. Scarcely a year passed without his contributing at least one paper, and often more, to its proceedings. Among its members he found some of his closest friends; through it he knew men like Fontenelle and Montesquieu and many of the leading intellectuals in other parts of Europe.

The Academy in Réaumur's day included seventy members, election to the higher categories being nominally in the hands of the king. Ten were honorary members, men of distinction in French public life but not necessarily scientists. Twenty were pensioners who had to be at least twenty-five years old and who received support from the royal treasury. Another twenty were associates, of whom not more than eight might be foreigners; and, finally, there were twenty student members, each chosen by a pensioner.

As Varignon's student it was natural that Réaumur's first memoir to the Academy should deal with the intersection of curves. It was followed by two more papers on the same subject in 1708 and 1709, but thereafter his interest in mathematics ceased. He was already keenly interested in biology, and, deserting his master's field, he presented a paper on shellfish in the autumn of 1708. In May of 1711 the death of Carré created a vacancy among the pensioners, and Réaumur was made a *pensionnaire mécanicien*.

In spite of his youth, as a full-fledged member of the Academy, Réaumur soon assumed an active part in its administration and in the formation of policy. This had originally been intrusted to a president and a vice-president selected by the king from the honorary members, but these officials tended to perform their duties in too perfunctory a fashion, and the scientists had successfully demanded the creation of two other posts, a director and an assistant director, to be filled annually from their own ranks. These offices Réaumur held twenty-one times between 1713 and 1753, eleven times as director and ten as assistant.[2] With his colleagues he considered ministerial requests for what would today be called "research and development" programs, assigned topics to individual members for study, and planned the Wednesday and Saturday meetings of the Academy at which papers were presented and discussed.

Probably it was not a coincidence that Réaumur frequently held office when the Abbé Bignon was president or vice-president. The Abbé, unlike some of the honorary members, took a most active interest in the society, and the unpublished correspondence of these two enthusiastic academicians, as described by Réaumur's biographer, Torlais, shows a happy collaboration between the two friends in the planning of major projects, in filling vacancies in membership, and in the work of Réaumur's own laboratory, which was supported by his pensioner's grant.

In carrying out his own assignments for the Academy, Réaumur became familiar with the natural history and the industry of many parts of France, but he never went beyond her borders. He became known, however, in all the scientific centers of Europe through his writings, his copious correspondence, and his hospitality to visitors to Paris, and he was elected to member-

2. Jean Rozier, *Nouvelle table des articles dans les volumes de l'Académie des Sciences, 1660–1770*, Vol. I (Paris, 1775).

ship in the royal societies of England, Prussia, Sweden, and Russia and in the Royal Institute of Bologna.

To Réaumur's passion for research and his consuming interest in the Academy there seems to have been no rival distraction. He never married, nor is there evidence of any romantic attachments. But his life was by no means that of a recluse or lacking in personal warmth. His Academy eulogist, de Fouchy, declared that he regarded all his knowledge and prestige as a trust held for the use of others, and his generous exercise of this trust endeared him to friends and collaborators alike. So kind and helpful was he in time of illness, continued de Fouchy, that some of his friends claimed they looked forward to having a fever in order to enjoy more of his company. Contemporaries criticized his work, but as a human being he was generally regarded with affection and respect.

These personal qualities, combined with his early scientific success and the right introductions, had opened many doors to Réaumur as a young man, and in the salon of Mme de Tencin he appeared frequently at one time. As he grew older, he took less interest in Parisian society. He moved his household, his laboratory, and his vast collections to suburban Charenton, which bordered the Seine to the southeast of the city. He seldom came into Paris except for the two weekly meetings of the Academy, after which he stayed to dine with his old friend de Boze. The large house in Charenton was always open to men of scientific interests from the humblest worker to the most distinguished foreign visitor. The household included laboratory assistants and illustrators, for the artist and plate-engraver was naturally a distinguished and important collaborator of the scientist before the days of photography. Réaumur used first the experienced Simonneau, who prepared the plates for the present volume, and later Mlle Hélène de Moutier, whom he made residuary legatee of his estate in gratitude for her loyal service.

In Charenton, Réaumur established his aviary and "menagerie" and the biological collections begun with shellfish during youthful holidays at the seashore, to which he had added the increment of his changing interests and ubiquitous curiosity. His favorite recreation was walking in the nearby Bois de Vincennes, which he preferred to the more fashionable route along the Pont Neuf, and he often returned with new specimens to add to his vast collections of insects, butterflies, and birds.

This quiet routine was interrupted only by journeys to the estate in the Vendée, where for two months in the autumn Réaumur established himself with his domestic staff and some of his research assistants. In the secluded village, where the simple manor house still stands, old men tell stories of the seigneur who had a taste for sorcery, who chased insects, and who observed the stars.

Toward the end of his life Réaumur's already ample estate was augmented by inheritance from a friend of the Château de Bermondière in Maine. While spending his holidays there in the autumn of 1757, he suffered a stroke and died on October 17 at the age of seventy-four.

Réaumur's 138 portfolios of unpublished notes and papers and his collections were left to the Academy. The collections were lodged in the Jardin du Roi (now the Jardin des Plantes), where, ironically enough, they became the responsibility of its curator, his young rival, Buffon, who made use of Réaumur's specimens in engraving his own plates.

Réaumur's published contributions to scientific literature during his lifetime had been extensive and diverse. His Academy memoir of 1708 on shellfish was the first of many in the field of marine biology, and these were interspersed among papers that touched on practically every aspect of natural and physical science that was of contemporary concern. There is a preview of his later interest in both insects and metals in an early paper on ductility (*Mémoires de l'Académie Royale des Sciences*, 1713, p. 199), in which he uses the spider's web and gold wire as principal examples and, incidentally, records for the first time the exceedingly high strength of glass fibers.

The Rozier index[3] lists seventy-five papers by Réaumur that

3. *Ibid.*, Vol. III (Paris, 1777).

were published in the *Mémoires* of the Academy. They fall into the following categories:

Porcelain..............	3	
Mathematics............	4	
Metals.................	4	
Geology and mineralogy..	7	Total physical science, 38
Physics (general)........	9	
Thermometry...........	11	
Entomology............	6	
Marine biology.........	14	Total biological science, 32
Other biology...........	12	
Miscellaneous...........	5	
	—	
Total................	75	

These are in addition to a number of brief paragraphs in the *Histoire* of the Academy and works which were published separately, comprising three of the *Descriptions des arts et métiers*, the present book on iron and steel, and the six quarto volumes forming Réaumur's *Mémoires pour servir à l'histoire des insectes*. The last were published between 1734 and 1742 and are generally regarded as Réaumur's most important work. It was his interest in insects that led to close observation of the way in which wasps build their nests from vegetable fibers, and upon this he based proposals which eventually gave rise to the wood-pulp paper industry. This furnishes a good example of the validity of Réaumur's conviction, expressed in the Preface to the present work, that scientific observation cannot be separated into the interesting and the useful. The view that science has both intellectual and practical value was widely shared among French scientists in the eighteenth century, and it found practical expression through the Academy program.

In response to a request in 1675 from the great finance minister, Colbert, the Academy had designated certain of its members to prepare detailed accounts of the various mechanic arts and to examine and report on new machines of all kinds. Réaumur was charged with the editorship of the *Descriptions* soon after he joined the Academy, and this assignment undoubtedly was the start of his interest in metallurgy. Although he himself collected and wrote up a great deal of material for the *Descriptions*, none of it was published during his lifetime. From his predecessor he inherited a number of drawings (the first prepared in 1693) and an illustrated manuscript on type, printing, and bookbinding by M. Jaugeon which had been completed in 1704 and is still preserved in the library of the Institut de France. It was left to the more aggressive editorship of Duhamel du Monceau to bring about the publication of the series,[4] probably in response to the stimulus of the imminent publication of the famous *Encyclopédie* of Denis Diderot and his associates, which had itself been inspired in part by the Academy project and more rapidly brought to fruition. The *Encyclopédie* articles and their accompanying fine plates are of great value to the historian of technology, but the *Descriptions* are usually to be preferred in the fields which they cover, because these accounts are more detailed and are more critically compiled.

The first of the Academy's *Descriptions* appeared in 1761. It was *L'Art du charbonnier* by Duhamel du Monceau, and the last was Salmon's *L'Art du potier d'étain* in 1788. The series includes memoirs by Réaumur on the manufacture of tin plate, on anchors, and on needles and his *Nouvel art d'adoucir le fer fondu*. The last is an enlarged second edition of the second part of the present work and is discussed in more detail in Appendix B. Shorter writings by Réaumur are incorporated in many of the memoirs by other authors, particularly in those on iron and steel, and his influence is evident throughout.

Réaumur's interest in iron and steel began about 1716 and in due course bore fruit in the publication of the present treatise in 1722 and in other metallurgical memoirs which he read before the Academy during the next four years, including his important "Principes de l'art de faire le fer blanc" (*Mém. Acad. Sci.*, 1725, p. 102). After 1726 he published nothing more on metals, and his interest in the field seems to have ceased. The metallurgical work was undertaken largely from a sense of duty to the state, and the government showed its gratitude by granting him

4. A good description of the project is given by A. H. Cole and G. B. Watts, *The Handicrafts of France as Recorded in the "Description des arts et métiers," 1761–88* (Kress Library of Business and Economics, Publication No. 8 [Cambridge, Mass.: Harvard University, 1952]).

a pension of 12,000 *livres*, which, at Réaumur's request, was continued to the Academy after his death for the support of experiments leading to the perfection of the arts.

In spite of this substantial mark of official approval, Réaumur's work on steel was not without its detractors. As de Fouchy admitted in his eulogy, commercial success in making steel came only after many failures, for which Réaumur had been severely criticized. But the criticism, thought de Fouchy, was unjust, because Frenchmen had been exceedingly slow to develop the art and were in no position to reproach the man whose efforts had finally attracted to France much of the commerce in a field formerly monopolized by her neighbors. He also gave Réaumur credit for making possible the production of cheap, well-finished works of iron at a twentieth of the former cost and for making France independent of foreign markets in tin plate.

Réaumur often laid himself open to attack by writing on so many different subjects, but criticism was tempered by the generally high regard in which he was held, and controversy was kept to a minimum by his own reluctance to initiate it. Once he was goaded into taking indirect action when the young Buffon's book on insects disagreed with some of his own cherished convictions and, incidentally, threatened to supplant in popular appeal his own recently published work. His influence was generally recognized behind the Abbé de Lignac's *Lettres à un Américain sur l'histoire générale et particulière de M. Buffon* (Hamburg, 1751), which attacked Buffon's inaccuracies and facile style and praised Réaumur. Réaumur had little to say publicly, but he wrote with some bitterness to a friend regarding Buffon's denial that spiders and other insects had souls and acted intelligently; and he suggested that Buffon scorned the tiny creatures largely because he himself loved them so much. The debate with the Jesuits in which his work in natural history involved him seems to have stirred him less deeply.

Réaumur was, as Torlais so aptly describes him in the subtitle of his biography, "un esprit encyclopédique en dehors de l'Encyclopédie." Although he was essentially unpolitical, and in this respect differed from the Encyclopedists in one of their most notable characteristics, he anticipated them in the scope of his interests and in his avid search for facts. As the emperor of China commented, upon reading the translation which he had ordered of Réaumur's article on silk, "In order to have so great a passion for discovery, the man must be a European."

There was without doubt some incompatibility between the point of view of Réaumur and that of the younger generation of intellectuals for whose work his wide but disciplined curiosity had done so much to prepare the way. He helped to introduce Rousseau into Academy circles but soon began to distrust the younger man. Voltaire expressed admiration of Réaumur as an observer of nature but criticized his technology and leveled some pointed—and, it must be admitted, well-deserved—barbs at his literary style.

With Diderot, too, Réaumur's relations became somewhat strained, largely because of what Réaumur considered to be the virtual theft of the plates which were being prepared for use in the *Descriptions* by agents of the *Encyclopédie*. The work of many years, consisting of a hundred and fifty plates already engraved and many more drawn, was stolen, he claimed in February, 1756, because the carelessness and infidelity of his printer had allowed proofs to be collected and re-engraved for the rival project.[5] The similarity between many of the plates is indeed proof of Réaumur's charge.

When Réaumur refused to allow Diderot to observe an operation for cataract which was being performed under his sponsorship, Diderot wrote caustically that such a famous man did not want spectators when he made his observations so much as he wanted an audience when he talked about them. Yet the *Encyclopédie* article on steel spoke with respect of Réaumur as one whose reputation stemmed largely from his research on the subject, and in the anatomy article he was commended not only for his sweetness of character but also for his valuable work on insects.

Réaumur's long-winded discursive style is exasperating if one is looking for scientific information, but it makes his book in

5. *Diderot et l'Encyclopédie* (catalogue to exhibition at the Bibliothèque Nationale [Paris, 1951]).

general more valuable by reflecting the environment in which he worked. One finds comments on French financial affairs, on the notorious tax farmers, and on taste in the palaces of the rich and many side lights on industrial organization of the period, including a reference to the possibility of mass-producing muskets with accurately shaped interchangeable parts.

Réaumur was writing at the time when the traditionally superb French craftsmanship in iron was decaying, and there is a hint of the horrors to come in his delight that his invention would permit the restoration of sculptured ornateness to cheap metal work. However, he did not wish things to become too cheap, realizing that "we should look with less pleasure and interest at the paintings of the great masters if daubers discovered how to paint similar ones."

It is a remarkable coincidence, probably as much a result of the economic pressures of the times as of Réaumur's own predilections, that his principal contributions to industrial technology—malleable cast iron, improved tin plate, pseudo-porcelain, and paper from wood pulp—were all inventions that allowed easy, cheap production of materials to replace those used by the older type of skilled artisan. These new materials were fabricated without the essential contact of the loving hand of the skilled craftsman and invited exuberant overproduction of ornate atrocities until designers began to understand the spirit of the new methods and producers learned to accept the separation of design from fabrication.

Réaumur had a clear understanding of the social effects of new inventions. He saw that they might be exploited in unsuitable ways and so brought into ill repute. He anticipated that malleable castings would be opposed on the grounds that they would produce technological unemployment, and he countered the objections much as we would today; but instead of discussing automobiles versus hostlers, as we might, he used the example of windmills supplanting waterwheels, which had in their turn displaced the hand grinders of corn. In any case, he said, the coppersmiths need not fear the loss of their jobs if they would only turn to the working of iron. Realizing that it would be more profitable for a workman to do a single, specialized task,

he suggested that there should be custom malleablizers processing at so much a pound the castings made by a common founder,
which could then be finished by the gunsmith, the locksmith,
and others.

Those who attempted to follow Réaumur's metallurgical advice were not always rewarded by immediate profit. For all his
economic insight, he himself lacked managerial skill, and the
works established at Cosne under his direction failed miserably.
The company, Le Manufacture Royal d'Orléans pour Convertir
le Fer en Acier et pour Faire des Ouvrages de Fer et d'Acier
Fondus, was formed shortly after the publication of the present work. To judge from Réaumur's remarks in the *Nouvel art*
(see p. 375), he wasted time and money casting iron into red-hot
molds instead of exploiting his malleablizing process. For making steel neither his furnaces nor his cementation compound had
the simplicity that is desirable in commercial operation. Patriot-
ism prompted the use of local iron instead of the purer Swedish
product, and French steel could not compete successfully with
the finer English product in the eighteenth century.

Frédéric Le Play held Réaumur responsible for the failure of
the French steel industry to develop, because his reputation and
authority inspired unmerited confidence![6] Yet, had Réaumur
been more aggressive commercially, it is unlikely that he would
have developed the scientific imagination to make his initial
discoveries; and, if other Frenchmen had taken the critical approach that he recommended, the few errors in his writings
would have been promptly discovered and discarded.

Réaumur's countryman and contemporary, Voltaire, must
have been reflecting rather general opinion when he wrote to
M. Bertrand (the editor of a dictionary): "You can add in a
second edition of the article 'iron,' that all those who have
wished to undertake the manufacture of cast iron according to
M. Réaumur have been ruined. As soon as he was informed of a
discovery made in a foreign country, he invented it on the spot.

6. *Mémoire sur la fabrication et le commerce des fers à acier dans le nord de l'Europe* (Paris, 1846). Though the author was a competent metallurgist, his book
was principally propaganda for a low tariff on Swedish iron imported into
France.

He has even invented porcelain. One should state too that he was a very good observer."[7] This characteristically biting comment is unperceptive; even if Réaumur did often start with knowledge of a possible end product, he truly originated the means of achieving it, and, above all, he tried to understand the processes and to make them public.

The comments of the English cutler, Henry Horne, are also interesting.[8] He admits that Réaumur was "the first who attempted to reduce the affair of converting iron into steel to a regular science" but then rejects him: "It ought to be observed that Mr. Réaumur wrote his treatise in a great measure to be an amusement for gentlemen, and the appearance of his book entitles it to a place in the genteelest libraries; it is finely printed, the draughts contained in it are inimitably executed; but when you come to examine the vast number of experiments he chooses to mention, I am greatly mistaken, if you do not find many of them extremely trifling." And, he continues, "I do not remember to have met with a single instance where an artist in the steel way has ever professed to have received any benefit from his writings." Yet, even as he inveighs against Réaumur's unnecessarily complicated carburizing compounds, he unconsciously reveals that he has been very deeply influenced by the French master's theoretical concepts.

Most of the many references to Réaumur in metallurgical literature are favorable. The adverse views cited above merely serve to illustrate the difficulty of perceiving the commercial value of scientific work even when it is done with a practical aim. Any new idea needs a prolonged period of development under industrial conditions before it is likely to be profitable, and a different kind of creativeness is usually involved. Despite the initial failure of Réaumur's method of softening cast iron, it was resurrected later, and today there exists a large industry making "malleable" iron castings. His improvements in the making of tin plate were at once successful.

Réaumur's steelmaking methods were indeed less practical than those in secret use in England even before his time, yet his

7. Torlais, *Réaumur*, p. 246.
8. *Essays concerning Iron and Steel* (London, 1773).

ideas on the constitution of steel have come to have enormous value. Simple though the concept now seems—that steel is merely iron plus some diffusing material—Réaumur was the first to express it. It was an essential step in the sequence that led to the understanding of the chemical and physical nature of alloys and to the vast steel industry of today.

II. RÉAUMUR'S POSITION IN THE HISTORY OF SCIENCE

Much of the fascination of metallurgy lies in the rich diversity of its subject matter and in the variety of human motivation to which its study and exploitation have appealed. Although there has always been a solid core of profit-seeking behind metallurgical operations, the aesthetic qualities of the metals themselves, their transmutability or decay into non-metals, and the general distinction of their properties have attracted both theoretical and experimental philosophers.

The vast and interesting literature of the metallurgist reflects these different aspects, often separately, sometimes happily merged. At first it was the actual practitioners in mine and workshop who produced the best books in the field. The purely pragmatic treatises by Biringuccio, Agricola, and Ercker, all of the sixteenth century, would even today serve as clear guides to workable methods of treating metals. Metallurgists are conservative, however, and the beginnings of modern science in the seventeenth century had little immediate effect upon the writing of books on metals. In fact, even in the twentieth century, textbooks on smelting offer chiefly descriptions of furnaces and processes and contain little enough science, despite a fair sprinkling of chemical formulas. Nevertheless, new alloys and new observations on their properties and treatment have usually been the work of men concerned directly with their utilization, though collaboration between scientist and plant operator has often been fruitful. Until very recently the literature of the chemist or physicist, who sees metals as only one of many types of matter, has had little in common with that of the metallurgist, who has tended to see them as unique substances of special interest. Books in which theory and practice are presented in a balanced and integrated way are rare enough even today, and the modern metallurgist may well read with respect the work of Réaumur, who, over two hundred years ago, attempted to combine the science and the art of metallurgy. He was, in fact, one of the first writers on any topic who can be called an applied scientist in the modern sense, and he has the additional distinction of being the first to produce a significant book on iron and steel.

THE LITERARY BACKGROUND

The best metallurgical books that had been published prior to Réaumur's were the general works[9] of Biringuccio,[10] Agricola,[11] and Barba,[12] in which were recorded some descriptions of the operations of smelting and other metallurgical processes. In addition, there were the anonymous *Probierbüchlein*[13] and the fine work of Ercker[14] on assaying, the various "books of secrets,"[15] and the works by the goldsmith Cellini,[16] the locksmith

9. Charles Singer (ed.), *A History of Technology* (Oxford, 1954——). Volume III (in press) will contain a general account of the state of metallurgical knowledge in the two centuries preceding Réaumur.

10. Vannoccio Biringuccio, *De la pirotechnia: Libri x dove ampiamente si tratta non solo di ogni sorte & diuersita di miniere....* (Venice, 1540). English trans. by C. S. Smith and M. T. Gnudi (New York, 1942).

11. Georgius Agricola, *De re metallica libri xii* . . . (Basle, 1556). English trans. by H. C. and L. H. Hoover (London, 1912, and New York, 1950).

12. Alvaro Alonso Barba, *Arte de los metales* ... (Madrid, 1640). English trans. by R. E. Douglass and E. P. Mathewson (New York, 1923).

13. *Brobir buchleyn tzu Gotes lob* . . . (Magdeburg, 1524). English trans. by A. G. Sisco and C. S. Smith entitled *Bergwerk- und Probierbüchlein* (New York, 1949).

14. Lazarus Ercker, *Beschreibung allerfürnemisten mineralischen Ertzt vnnd Berckwercksarten* . . . (Prague, 1574). English trans. by A. G. Sisco and C. S. Smith (Chicago, 1951).

15. For a description of this complicated series of books and pamphlets see John Ferguson, *Bibliographical Notes on Histories of Inventions and Books of Secrets* (Glasgow, 1896), and supplements; and Ernst Darmstaedter, *Berg-, Probir- und Kunstbüchlein* (Munich, 1926).

16. Benvenuto Cellini, *Dve trattati, vno intorno alle otto principali arti del l'oreficeria: L'Altro in materia dell'arte della scultura....* (Florence, 1568). English trans. by C. R. Ashbee (from the Italian ed. edited by Milanesi, 1857) (London, 1898).

Jousse,[17] and the mintmaster Boizard.[18] Despite the overwhelming importance of iron, most metallurgical writers before Réaumur give it only passing attention. The chapters on iron by Biringuccio, Agricola, and Ercker are trivial compared with their detailed treatments of the non-ferrous metals, particularly the precious ones, a difference reflecting the literacy of workers in the different fields and the degree of popular and princely interest in the different metals. Only three books dealing primarily with iron and steel had appeared before Réaumur's: the anonymous and unimportant chapbook *Stahel und eysen;*[19] Dudley's *Mettallum martis,*[20] which was an argument for the use of coal in smelting iron, though not a description of how to do it; and Jousse's *Fidelle ouverture de l'art de serrurier*, which was concerned more with the artistic shaping of iron than its metallurgy. Porta devoted one of the twenty "books" of his *Natural Magick*[21] to the hardening of steel, and there are, of course, innumerable secondary references to ironworking in encyclopedic works of all kinds and in general literature.

These early books were useful because they clearly recorded practice, and practice in this period was far ahead of theory as represented by the virtually meaningless alchemical writings. The science of materials was beginning to develop, however, and a number of chemical authors, notably Glauber,[22] had dealt with some useful topics sometimes impinging on metallurgy. Physicists and philosophers speculated on the reasons underlying the highly diverse behavior of different kinds of matter. Both the Royal Society of London and the French Académie

17. Mathurin Jousse, *La fidelle ouverture de l'art de serrurier ... ensemble un petit traicté de diverses trempes* (La Flèche, 1627).

18. Jean Boizard, *Traité des monoyes, de leurs circonstances et dépendances ...* (Paris, 1696).

19. *Stahel und eysen kunstlich weych und hart zu machen* (Mainz, 1532). The book is related to the second of the *Drey schoner künstreicher Büchlein* (Leipzig, 1532) that is discussed by Darmstaedter, *op. cit.*

20. Dud Dudley, *Mettallum martis* (London, 1665).

21. G. B. della Porta, *Magiae natvralis libri xx . . .* (Naples, 1589). English trans. (London, 1658).

22. Johann Rudolf Glauber, *Furni novi philosophici* (Amsterdam, 1648), and later works.

Royale des Sciences made an effort to gather descriptions of artisans' procedures for their scientific interest. Nevertheless, no one before Réaumur had combined in a metallurgical work the viewpoint of the pure scientist with an interest in what had been, and what could be, achieved in practice. Réaumur tended to be intolerant of the conservatism of artisans; yet at the same time he appreciated the empirical knowledge which their skills represented.

RÉAUMUR AS A SCIENTIST

Réaumur was a man of the kind so well described by the obsolete term "natural philosopher." He had some interest in almost all branches of pure and applied science, and his work reflects this breadth. Although he is known to the common man for his temperature scale and to the learned principally as a biologist, he deserves to be classed among the leaders of both physics and chemistry of his day.

Despite Réaumur's early schooling in mathematics, the majority of his writings reflect only elementary mathematical concepts. In the few places in the present work where simple geometry or arithmetic is needed, he shows no acuity; indeed, in calculating the volume of air in a bellows, he uses a geometric approximation which is both inexact and unnecessarily complicated. Nevertheless, he was the first ever to bother to compute how much air a blast furnace actually uses, and his mathematical training must also account for his awareness of the effect of the scale of operations on their unit cost and of the influence of changing surface-to-volume ratio in experimental samples.

It would be impossible for such a man to be concerned with metallurgical processes and not to consider the nature of heat. Réaumur's experiments on steel led him to his discovery of the difference between specific heats of materials as well as to his work on thermometric scales.[23] He obviously had a clear concept—by no means universal at his time nor for several decades

23. *Mém. Acad. Sci.*, 1730, p. 432; *ibid.*, 1731, p. 250. The degree on Réaumur's temperature scale corresponds to a definite fractional increase in volume above that at the freezing point of water of an alcohol-water mixture of constant-boiling composition. It was the first temperature scale the definition of which depended on the physical properties of matter.

later—of the difference between the amount of heat (which depended on the amount of fuel burned) and its intensity or temperature. He understood the conduction of heat in both refractory and metal. Characteristically, he combined this understanding with a feeling for economics, for he designed his furnaces carefully so that there would be no fuel burning in spaces inaccessible to the surfaces to be heated. He realized the importance of air in combustion and the importance of excluding it during the cementation, yet nowhere is there the least suggestion that the combustion process is a chemical combination of part of the air with the fuel. Also, despite the fact that chimney stacks had been applied to laboratory furnaces a half-century earlier and were soon to become the commonest devices for accelerating combustion, Réaumur urged his cementation furnaces with blast from a bellows.

In a qualitative sense the concept of heat as motion permeates his whole book. In explaining the fact that mercury heats more rapidly than water when hot steel is quenched in it, Réaumur says: "One might suppose that the parts of mercury are more easily set in motion than those of water." He also clearly sensed the kinetic explanation of thermal expansion and of the increasing rates of diffusion at higher temperatures, though in his view it was particles of heat that moved, not the atoms themselves. These experiments and ideas on heat had important consequences, for they influenced Joseph Black, the discoverer of specific and latent heats. In an autobiographical note Black names Réaumur as one of only two chemical authors whom he enjoyed in his youth: "The celebrated Réaumur's method of writing seemed to me to be uncommonly pleasing."[24]

Réaumur was aware that liquid metals, like water, do not on continued heating increase in temperature beyond a fixed temperature, the boiling point. He measured the increase in length of iron and steel on heating several years before the more famous observations of Musschenbroek, and he showed that, when quenched back to room temperature, iron completely recovered its original length but steel only partially so. He weighed steel

24. William Ramsay, *Life and Letters of Joseph Black, M.D.* (London, 1918). We are indebted to Professor Henry Guerlac for calling this to our attention.

before and after quenching and showed that the volume change was not accompanied by an increase in weight, from which he assumed that no added substance had been imbibed from the fire or the water. By similar experiments he showed that cementation of iron in making steel did increase its weight.

In line with his general quantitative approach, Réaumur attempted to measure the hardness of metals by noticing their scratchability with various minerals—a clear anticipation of Mohs's scale—and he devised the first materials-testing machine on record, with which he measured the deflection that a bar of heat-treated steel would undergo before fracture.

The strength of an approach based on a combination of inductive and deductive methods associated with critical experiment was, of course, widely recognized by the beginning of the eighteenth century. Réaumur's expression of the principles and his success in carrying them out are nevertheless outstanding. His procedure in seeking the best preparations for carburizing steel conform to the best practices of controlled chemical experimentation. He says, for example (p. 210), that the method of the scientist is to make an intuitive guess and follow this by experiment to show whether the guess is right or wrong. Men should not be expected to believe a conclusion until they have seen all the experiments from which it arises as a necessary consequence. He realizes that a negative result can be as important as a positive one; and he follows his own admonition to record every detail of an experiment to an extreme that gives his book a long-windedness often painful to the modern reader.

In his appreciation of scientific procedures, Réaumur was clearly influenced by the *Traité de physique* of Jacques Rohault, which had been published in Paris in 1671. Although Réaumur sometimes quotes Rohault to refute him in detail, he had adopted much of his scientific philosophy. Rohault was son-in-law to Clerselier, friend and literary executor of René Descartes, and promoter of the philosopher's ideas. Rohault's book deals with all material science, including astronomy, medicine, and meteorology, in a purely Cartesian manner. It had a great influence on the development of French science. It was, curiously, the critical notes advancing rival Newtonian theories that were appended to the Latin translation of this book by Samuel Clarke that were largely responsible for the popularization of Newtonian physics in England. Rohault divides experiments into three kinds—first, the simple but careful observation of nature; second, the empirical "tryal of any Thing, without knowing all, for seeing what will come to pass; as when, after the manner of Chymists, we make choice of first one subject and then another, and make all the tryals we can think of upon each of them, and carefully remember what we have at any time found to succeed, and the manner in which we arrived at any certain effect";[25] and, third, that kind of experiment which is a consequence of reasoning and is designed specifically to test deductions from theory. Réaumur made good use of all three.

RÉAUMUR'S IDEAS ON THE STRUCTURE OF MATTER

Another important inheritance that Réaumur received from Rohault was his concept of the component parts of matter and their aggregation. In turn, most of this had been derived directly from Descartes. As a philosopher, Descartes was interested in the diversity of natural bodies and their properties, and he fitted these directly into his cosmology.[26]

25. Rohault did not deny that this approach might eventually achieve the goal of the alchemists—transmutation. However, in the absence of any useful guiding theory, he regarded this as almost inconceivably improbable, and he gives a fine statistical analogy: "We must think, that if it be true, that some Chymists have now and then converted Lead into Gold, it was by just such a Hazard, as if a Man should let fall a handful of Sand upon a Table, and the Particles of it should be so ranged that we could read distinctly on it a whole page of *Virgil's Aenead*." This quotation and that above are from John Clarke's English translation of the *Traité de physique* (London, 1723).

26. René Descartes, *Principia philosophiae* (Paris, 1644). According to Descartes, there could be no vacuum, and all space was filled with elemental matter. Since motion occurred, however, this matter must be broken up, and hence arose his three "elements," which are particles differing only in shape. In inverse order these are: the third element, consisting of angular, irregular, polyhedral fragments; the second, consisting of particles derived from these by their continual friction and impact against each other and hence more or less rounded in form; and the first, the very fine subtle matter left from this abrasion process and which is apparently infinitely divisible. In the grand vortices throughout the universe these particles move and collect differently. The metals are formed under the pressures deep in the earth by combination with the principles of sulfur and mercury (borrowed from the alchemists),

Descartes explained the hardening of steel by suggesting that the clumps or clusters of particles became more uniformly distributed at higher temperatures. Rohault clearly recognized (as had Hooke before him) that rapid cooling had an effect in preventing relaxation and gave a non-equilibrium structure at room temperature, which, because it was strained, would have increased hardness. He saw too that it was only in iron among the common metals that heat produced some drastic change below the melting point. Réaumur extended this picture to cover the

---

and the resulting metallic parts rise through crevices in rock until they get stuck to form veins of ore.

Descartes explains the properties of various kinds of matter in terms of the shapes and aggregation of their main "parts," for they can be arranged with more or less order and with more or less space between them for circulation of the first element or of salty particles. The manner of stacking determines crystal shape and influences the fluidity, ductility, diffusion, and cohesion. One Cartesian *traité de physique* carries the explanation of properties in terms of the fitting-together of polyhedral fragments to an extreme that could have occurred only to one who had supervised stonemasons at work: it was written in 1680 by none other than Claude Perrault, the famous architect of the Louvre, brother of the more famous teller of Mother Goose stories.

Descartes clearly perceived that the parts must be in motion because evaporation and diffusion occur, even in solids. Brittle bodies have such a degree of stiffness that the outer parts on fracturing transfer stresses progressively to the inner parts. Metals are ductile because the particles are longish and lie upon one another with a large shared surface, so that, as they are deformed, the parts slide along each other and transfer bonds without separating. Steel is hardened by quenching because the subtle matter escapes (causing the water to boil in so doing), leaving the pores contracted; but, because they are changing position very fast, the parts lose some bonds and thus become brittle.

Descartes's "parts," whether spherical or angular, were material, but they were not aggregates of indivisible atoms. Opposed to his viewpoint were the neo-Democriteans of the seventeenth century—particularly Gassendi and his followers—who believed in atoms as the smallest recognizable part of a substance. Boyle, Hooke, and Newton all took for granted the existence of some kind of particles as the basis of the properties of matter but were much more restrained than the contemporary philosophers in using them to explain everything. The essential crystallinity of materials was not appreciated, and there was much confusion between properties which are chiefly attributable to molecular structure and those due to microcrystalline aggregates. Nevertheless, seventeenth-century philosophy is shot through with concepts of parts which attract each other, which have spaces between them into which both particles of heat and other matter can diffuse, and by variation of whose packing and natural contact all the properties of hardness, strength, and

migration of interstitial components by diffusion and the freezing of them in non-equilibrium positions by rapid cooling.
Above all, he used his theory of the constitution of matter to
plan his experiments.

It is unfortunate that, with the rejection of most of Cartesian
physics, attention was withdrawn from the molecular and microcrystalline aspects of nature. Réaumur's concepts of the nature of liquids and gases, the nature of steel, the effects of high
temperature on diffusion, and the reasons for the hardness and
softness of materials are all more in keeping with present-day
thinking than the quasi-chemical ideas ignoring structure that
persisted through most of the eighteenth and nineteenth centuries. It is true that Réaumur was vague as to the nature of his
"parts," but he clearly understood that, to explain the properties of matter, it was necessary to have parts with varying
geometries and attachments to each other and that different
materials could diffuse into each other and aggregate or dis-
perse, depending upon the temperature. There was no doubt in
his mind that beneath the grains that are visible on the fracture
of a piece of steel there is another level of structure and, beneath
that, more. Experimentally, he was, of course, quite unable to
realize anything equivalent to the modern atom, but he clearly

---

ductility can be qualitatively explained. The existence of a hierarchy of structures, of parts built of smaller parts, or, as Steno puts it, of the solid within
a solid, is implicit in most of this discussion, yet no one properly related
various kinds of property to the appropriate levels of structure. The confusion
among the atom, the microcrystal, and the cell made it impossible for the
seventeenth-century structural ideas to blossom immediately into useful solid-
state physics. By the beginning of the nineteenth century they had given rise
to chemical atomism and mathematical crystallography, for the two extremes
of the dimensional scale lent themselves most easily to mathematical treatment. The intermediate microcrystalline aspect of matter was almost ignored
by eighteenth- and nineteenth-century physicists, though they unconsciously
depended upon it to make good in practice the assumption of isotropic uniformity of solids that underlay the successful development of mechanics and
elasticity. Of all structural elements, it is microcrystals that seem best to
match the "parts" which the seventeenth-century philosophers had in mind
when they explained the mechanical properties of matter. The science of materials would have developed much earlier had the pregnant ideas on structure not been discarded along with the magnificent but misleading vortices
when Cartesian cosmology was vanquished by the Newtonian.

perceived that all the facts relating to the formation and heat treatment of steel could be explained in terms of chemical solution and segregation on a scale below that which could be perceived on the fracture with a lens. He says specifically (p. 109) that the "arrangement and shape of the visible parts are usually the effect of certain natural tendencies and qualities of the invisible parts," and he clearly recognized that visible changes in structure are directly related to change in properties. He says that changes in the properties of steel on heat treatment occur because "salts and sulfurs" are absorbed into parts or molecules or are rejected into the voids between them. If heated sufficiently hot, the salts and sulfurs may be rejected even from the voids between the molecules and be forced outside the steel. The changes of hardness are a direct result of the number of points of contact of the parts and of the degree to which they are cemented together by interstitial materials.

Réaumur's interest in diffusion may have started with his study of the flow of air through moistened membranes (*Mém. Acad. Sci.*, 1714, p. 55). The progress of the reaction rim was observed on the fracture of successive samples withdrawn during either steelmaking or malleabilization. He suggested that diffusion could produce tiny voids and that porous solids would become more dense on prolonged annealing by a process akin to fusion.

The drawings which Réaumur gives to represent the microstructure of steel (Pl. 10, Figs. 5 and 6) are of great interest to the metallographer, for they are among the earliest attempts to depict in any way the structure of metal. Except for some symbolic illustrations in alchemical works, they are preceded only by Robert Hooke's drawing, in his *Micrographia* (1665), of polishing scratches and a corrosion pit on the surface of a razor and by Leeuwenhoek's sketch[27] of growing dendrites in a silver tree.

27. A. van Leeuwenhoek, *Philosophical Transactions*, XXIII (1703), 1430. This famous microscopist had recorded in another paper his observations on the fine particles of metals, which, he says, are inconceivably small. "One may indeed by the help of a good microscope just discover the exceeding small particles of gold and silver but one cannot perceive what figure they are; and who can tell of what multitude of parts these little particles which we see by the help of a microscope are again composed." And again: "[In steel] we can

Nevertheless, the writer is inclined to believe that Réaumur's sketches are not meant to represent the structure of steel as seen under the microscope. They are, more likely, simply a schematic representation of contiguous parts and interstitial voids. They could easily have been inspired by the purely symbolic drawings in Descartes's *Principia*, which illustrate the passage of light particles through matter. Although there is a suggestive similarity between Réaumur's drawings and the ferrite-plus-pearlite structure of a medium-carbon steel in the normalized condition, such structure can be seen only after polishing and etching; it would not have been distinguishable on the fractured surfaces that Réaumur studied, and he nowhere mentions more elaborate specimen preparation. It was, in fact, not until the 1860's that etched samples were systematically used for microexamination, although the use of etching for distinguishing gross features is as old as the Merovingian pattern-welded blades.

A fracture is much too irregular in structure to repay study at a magnification greater than that provided by a hand lens, and all that Réaumur could have seen would have been the plane transcrystalline facets or curved intergranular fractures, mixed with confused tearing. The highly significant detail of twentieth-century fractography would have been quite beyond his reach. He does, however, make very good use of the study of fractures at low magnifications, and the many plates in which he shows realistically the fractures of different kinds of iron and steel are of great interest to the metallographer. Naked-eye examination of fractures had, of course, been used to control processes from the very beginning of metallurgical art.

---

only discover the broken gaps or notches of a razor, for instance, and the coarser the parts are of which these metals are composed, as we may see in cast iron, the less valuable are the said metals; but the finer the particles are, the more valuable in my opinion will be the steel and iron which they compose.'' Forged metals, he says, ''consolidated by strokes and pressure of the smith's hammer that they seem to us to be but one body, though they do consist of a great many small particles, the coarsest of which are always obvious when we come to break the metals: and how often so ever you melt any of these metals and break them again after they are cold, you will always be able to discover the grainy particles thereof; but you will find them so strongly joined and riveted to one another that they appear to be one body'' (*ibid.*, XXVI [1709], 493–98).

Introduction

In a later paper (*Mém. Acad. Sci.*, 1724, pp. 307–16) Réaumur returns to the question of grain shape and intergranular fracture. He describes and illustrates the difference between the transcrystalline cleavage fracture in a solidified ingot of antimony and the intergranular fracture obtained when metals like lead, tin, zinc, and copper are broken at a temperature slightly below their melting points.

CHEMICAL CONCEPTS

The chemical background of Réaumur's ideas on metals is difficult to trace. He regarded chemical change essentially as a physical one, and he expressed the opinion that rates of reaction depend on temperature, on the concentration of the reacting particles, and on the strength of their bond to the matrix. He had the genius to realize, unlike most before him, that wrought iron was the purest ferrous material and that it was the admixture of some other substance that was responsible for the formation of steel and cast iron. This material he calls "sulfurs and salts," words which he nowhere defines, and in the use of which he seems not to follow any previous writer. The terms are, of course, closely related to the salt, sulfur, and mercury of Paracelsus and to the principle of inflammability that came to play so large a part in eighteenth-century chemistry as the phlogiston theory.[28] From his use of the words, it is apparent that Réaumur thought of a single inseparable mixture, a material substance composed of parts that are finer and more mobile than the parts of which iron is composed, between which it can penetrate if urged by heat, and into which it can enter. This material was, indeed, carbon, diffusing among microcrystals of iron; but clear concepts of atoms, elements, and crystals all lay in the future.

French chemical theory in relation to this matter at the time

28. See Hélène Metzger, *Les Doctrines chimiques en France du début du 17ᵐᵉ siècle à la fin du 18ᵐᵉ* (Paris, 1926) and *Newton, Stahl, Boerhaave et la doctrine chimique* (Paris, 1930); cf. also J. R. Partington and D. McKie, "Historical Studies on the Phlogiston Theory," *Annals of Science*, II (1937), 361–424; *ibid.*, III (1938), 1–58 and 337–71.

is perhaps best reflected in a paper by Homberg.[29] He supposed that the sulfur principle could form various kinds of "sulfury" matter, depending on whether it was associated with earthy, watery, or mercurial matter, which combination gave rise, respectively, to substances like charcoal, common sulfur, fats, or metals. The principle (like the modern valence electron) could be transferred from one material to another, as when charcoal is heated with a metallic ore. Although the French chemists at this time did not use the term "phlogiston," the concept is essentially that of Stahl. Réaumur differs from Homberg and other chemists in that he seems to regard his sulfurs and salts as material particles rather than as principles. He knew that iron became steel by picking up some matter from environments which he called "sulfurous" and which we now know to contain carbon. His invariable association of sulfurs with salts derived from his experimental observation that steel cementation proceeds much more rapidly in the presence of salts of various kinds than in charcoal alone; and perhaps also the harsher quality of steel in the craftsman's hands suggested the presence in it of something more than unctuous matter. Today we know that the qualities of salts, sulfur, and mercury are due to three different types of electron wave functions that are responsible for interatomic bonding.

Cast iron is a complicated material, and it is not surprising that Réaumur's ideas on its nature are considerably less clear than his understanding of steel. The formation of graphite either in primary flakes or in the form of temper carbon on annealing is extremely sensitive to minor elements in the composition, and it is understandable that Réaumur was not able to produce a consistent theory to explain all the effects that he observed. He knew that the manner of operation of the blast furnace would control the kind of iron that came from it and that he should

29. G. Homberg, "Observations sur les matières sulphureuses," *Mém. Acad. Sci.*, 1710, pp. 225–34. There is a good discussion of the relation of sulfur to the inflammable principle and to the element carbon by T. A. Wertime in *Osiris*, XI (1954), 211–22. The writer is indebted also to Mr. Wertime for the loan of an unpublished manuscript in which the contributions of metallurgists to the solution of the problem are pointed out.

start with a hard white iron if he wished to obtain a ductile material after malleabilization. From carefully observing the amount of slag formed during the refining operation in making wrought iron, he knew that a gray cast iron contained more earthy material—in modern terms, silicon—than a white one. He observed that thin parts of castings were often white, and before 1726 he had correctly described the role of cooling rate in determining fracture type, as well as the strong effect of small additions of sulfur.[30]

Although Réaumur knew that hot iron would scale in contact with air (and he added charcoal to his packing compound to prevent this), he seems not to have understood the role of decarburization or that he was producing two different kinds of malleable material under various conditions. He says that annealing in iron scale would give excellent results, and he seems actually to prefer the use of a mixture of bone ash and charcoal, although this would not now be expected to give the wholly white fracture that he desired. The product would indeed correspond more to modern American "blackheart" malleable than to the European "whiteheart" malleable that is generally associated with Réaumur's name. That he obtained superficial decarburization can be deduced from his description of hollow shells of unmeltable iron, which remained after a preliminary soaking anneal followed by raising the temperature to a point where the inside would melt and run out. He believed that malleabilization should be done at a temperature just below the melting point, and, curiously, he seemed to regard cooling rate as relatively unimportant. In the additional notes published in the 1762 edition he had retrogressed to the point where almost any anneal seemed to be acceptable as long as the product could be filed.

Réaumur reports that he started his work in ferrous metallurgy with the aim of producing castings with the quality of wrought iron. After some not very successful preliminary trials his interest turned to making steel, a change stimulated by a combination of the economic demand for the material (since all

30. See remarks on the 1762 edition in Appendix B, p. 374.

good steel was imported into France at the time) and the relative simplicity of the problem. The deviation enabled Réaumur to develop ideas on the nature of iron and steel which, in turn, suggested experiments that gave the solution of the initial cast-iron problem. It is a fine example of the unpredictability of the rewards of research and of the value of intellectual curiosity as a guide even in work with a practical aim.

Continued chemical advance occurred during the eighteenth century, and many new metallurgical reactions were discovered. Mostly, however, it was the period of increase in the scale of operation and of devices to cheapen production. In the field covered by Réaumur the exciting development of course was the identification toward the end of the century of the element carbon as the material to which, under the name "sulfurs and salts," Réaumur had attributed responsibility for the change in properties of iron as it was converted into steel or cast iron.

Réaumur's work was quoted with respect by most authors who wrote subsequently on iron and steel. Works were built to profit from his malleablizing process, yet oddly enough his most important contribution—his approach to metallurgy—had few imitators. The great metallurgical books of the eighteenth century tended on the whole to develop the older tradition of describing furnaces and practical operations, with relatively little consideration of the reasons behind them. Even the admirable books on assaying by Cramer and Gellert, though they bring chemical theory to bear on metallurgical problems, make no effort to combine this with physics. The mechanical and structural aspects of metallurgy made relatively little progress in the century and a half after Réaumur opened them up.

* * *

It has been said that the historian of science has no need of English translations of works in French, for the original alone can be the basis of his interpretation. Yet the present work of Réaumur is surely one which justifies the labor of translation in order that it may be made accessible to a wider circle of readers. It is not only a technical landmark but a document that reflects a fascinating period of history. There was a new spirit abroad in

France. The scientific elite were joined with literary men and civil servants in an interest in arts and crafts, and there was an aggressive curiosity that was eventually to lead to both social and chemical revolutions. The metallurgist, particularly the iron and steel man, will alternately scorn and admire Réaumur's experiments and conclusions; but, reading about them, he cannot help but gain a deeper understanding of his profession and its relation to other aspects of human endeavor.

C. S. S.

London, England
October 1, 1955

L'ART

DE
CONVERTIR LE FER
FORGE'
EN ACIER,
ET
L'ART
D'ADOUCIR LE FER FONDU,

Ou de faire des Ouvrages de fer fondu auſſi finis
que de fer forgé.

Par Monſieur de R E A U M U R,
de l'Academie Royale des Sciences.

A PARIS,

Chez M I C H E L B R U N E T, Grand'Salle du Palais, au
Mercure Galant.

————————————

M. DCC. XXII.
AVEC APPROBATION ET PRIVILEGE DU ROY.

THE ART
of Converting
Wrought Iron into Steel

&

THE ART
of Making Cast Iron Malleable

Or of Producing Cast-Iron Work with
the Finish of Wrought Iron

By Monsieur de RÉAUMUR

OF THE ROYAL ACADEMY OF SCIENCES

PRINTED AT PARIS

BY MICHEL BRUNET, GRAND'SALLE DU PALAIS
AU MERCURE GALANT

M. DCC. XXII

WITH APPROVAL AND PRIVILEGES BY THE KING

To His Royal Highness
My Lord
The Duke d'Orléans

My Lord,

The investigations which are the subject of this work have been favorably considered by Your Royal Highness from their inception. Your Highness has requested an accurate account of their progress, has patiently listened to the presentation of one entire Memoir, although it was a long one, and has been pleased to reward in a brilliant way my wish to serve the public interest and my efforts to succeed in this endeavor. These are ample reasons for my boldness in presenting my work to Your Royal Highness. The same reasons make me regret that it is not more worthy of such presentation. I am hoping, however, partly to supplement what is lacking by continuing my labors, by pursuing other investigations already in progress, in which Your Royal Highness is interested because they are of interest to the public. This is the only way in which I can try to express the extent of my gratitude, my unlimited devotion, and the profound respect with which I am,

> My Lord,
> Your Royal Highness's
> most humble and most
> obedient servant
> RÉAUMUR.

Preface

I HAVE PRESERVED for the different lectures combined in this volume the name and the form of memoirs, which I had given them when they were to be read before the Academy of Sciences. They were written as part of a more comprehensive work, to be incorporated in the *History or General Description of the Arts*, with the preparation of which it has been my privilege to be charged.* Here, one might say, they are out of their element. Some parts may seem insufficiently explicit or even obscure, which perhaps would not have given that impression if the discussions of the conversion of iron into steel and of the softening of cast iron had been preceded by chapters on the working of iron ores and the methods of smelting them, refining the metal obtained, and making it malleable. The usefulness of these memoirs would also have been more apparent if they had been followed at once by a description of the arts that utilize iron and steel. At present they stand by themselves, which was not the original intention. However, since once assembled they provide information on two subjects which are important to the

---

* The *Histoire ou description générale des arts et métiers* was an important collection of monographs produced under the general direction of the Académie Royale des Sciences in response to the order given by the great Colbert in 1675 as part of his plan to improve the industrial and economic state of France. Réaumur was editor of the series for most of his active life, and there is little doubt that his association with it provided the incentive for the present work. Although a number of the manuscripts were read before the Academy from 1711 on, and a few of them were published in the *Mémoires*, the series itself was not published until after his death, when they were issued under the more active editorship of Duhamel du Monceau. They include articles by Réaumur on the manufacture of needles and on anchors and his *Nouvel art d'adoucir le fer fondu*, which is a slightly modified reprint of the second part of the present work. The series is an important one in technological history and includes a number of monographs of metallurgical interest which are of particular value for the fine illustrations. Both the text and the illustrations provided the basis for similar parts of Diderot's *Encyclopédie*, and the project had much influence on the encyclopedist movement.

[5]

public and in which, moreover, it seems to be interested—and since there is enough information to be applied in actual production—it seemed better to have the memoirs appear as early as possible than to present them in a somewhat more favorable form.

They are divided into two parts; those of the first part deal at length with the conversion of iron into steel and with the more essential facts that should be known about steel. I have called this first part "The Art of Converting Wrought Iron into Steel," and the memoirs of the second part "The Art of Making Cast Iron Malleable, or of Producing Cast-Iron Work with the Finish of Wrought Iron"; for the goal I have set myself is to show how these arts can be mastered.

Authors who deal with the fundamentals of an art usually write somewhat more dogmatically than I have done. Furthermore, I shall not use quite the same method when I describe in my *General History* arts that are applied and known. In many cases, all I shall have to do then is to describe practices that are used every day. Proof of what I shall have to say can be had by anybody who will go and watch the artisans at their work. But since the rules which I shall have to give [in this book] are in fact either completely new or, what amounts to the same thing, are being kept secret, I must not only give them; I must at the same time prove their validity.

I might of course have started by giving the rules and then have proceeded to prove them valid by the experiments which I have performed. Instead I have started almost throughout by describing the experiments in scrupulous detail. I doubt if the former method is the better one for matters pertaining to the physical sciences. One sees more clearly how well founded conclusions are if they immediately follow the experiments from which they are drawn. In this way, the investigator plainly shows all he has done; he does not assess the strength of the proof; he avoids being suspected of not telling the whole story, which may give rise to the belief that he has neglected to prove something that would have been easy. If at the outset certain propositions are treated as facts, the reader is inclined to believe that the author has taken them for granted without having tried the experiments which in reality have been performed to give them support. Surely there is a great difference, as far as their forcefulness as proof is concerned, between experiments from which a conclusion has been drawn, which seem to have led to it as a necessary development, and experiments that have been made afterward to prove the proposition. Not that the latter kind of experiment cannot be excellent and that there are not many circumstances under which they should be performed; but it is much better if this is done to confirm conclusions drawn from the other kind.

In order to become familiar with a new art, it is hardly less necessary to learn what to avoid than what to practice; and this kind of information is provided when the author simply describes all the different roads he has traveled in order to reach his goal. There is nothing to prevent one from retracing one's steps from this goal on a straighter line. Finally, since we are concerned with new research, with discoveries, it is necessary to enable the reader to judge if everything that should have been tried has been tried. He must be saved useless trials but must also be given a hint of what might still be tried; he must even be shown the road toward further developments. Today the people want ideas; and, if they are satisfied with what we give them, we may hope that they will be indulgent about how we present it to them.

Those who wish to acquire only a rough idea of the arts of converting iron into steel and of making cast iron malleable will undoubtedly find in these memoirs some tiresome details. I do not know, for example, if in such a case perusal of the fourth memoir, which deals with the furnaces to be used, would be of any interest to the reader, and, as a matter of fact, I do not advise him to try it. I have had in mind mainly those who have the wish to do the work; and nobody who has not tried it would believe how many difficulties arise in the execution of the simplest tasks and how much trouble can be caused by difficulties which seem very minor. Perhaps the wish to eliminate them and to be lucid has made me write too voluminously. However, the time spent on books that point the way to practice must not be measured solely by the time it takes to peruse them. What they save during the execution of the work must also be taken into account. In books of this kind nothing must be left to guesswork; the author must not be afraid of presenting ideas that have been too far developed. The readers to whom they are the most useful do not ask for something on which they can exercise their intellectual powers. What they want is to have the processes clearly and fully explained.

But even scientific reasoning may seem superfluous to those who wish to learn only practices. Let them be aware, however, that such reasoning is the basis for principles which, if well understood, may enable them to overcome difficulties which the author may not have sufficiently explained or not even foreseen. If one takes as a case in point the discoveries that will be described, it will be noted that they are based on just such reasoning, which also may open the doors to further developments. Such reasoning should therefore not be regarded as aiming at something of merely scientific interest. Often, there is too little hesitation when knowledge is divided into facts that are interesting and those that are useful. This division is not as easy to make nor as clear cut as one might think, especially in this field. The useful, if looked at carefully, always contains something of theoretical interest, and it is rare if the theoretically interesting, when pursued, does not lead to the practically useful.

I admit, however, and how could I help admitting it, that most of the observations and reflections in these memoirs cannot benefit the ordinary artisan. They are almost exclusively for those who are capable of managing a business enterprise, who can put artisans to work, just as artisans can put their tools to work. To put it briefly, it is not necessary that everybody make steel or cast-iron products; but it is necessary to enable those who are capable of seeing it through to build the establishments in which this is done, and I dare say that my memoirs are sufficient for that. I am even more confident in my claims because a number of workshops have already been started in the Kingdom as a consequence of the oral presentation of some of these memoirs before the public assemblies of the Academy and the explanations which were given to those who asked for them. After being published, these memoirs will obviously increase this number.

But, no matter how fast these new establishments will be founded, it will always be slow measured by the natural impatience of the Nation. Since I have read before the public assemblies the memoirs describing the principles of our art, there has been a clamoring for a selection of fine domestic steels; and the people would have liked to see all the shops filled with the most perfect cast-iron products. However, you cannot progress so fast in the execution of something that requires a certain amount of planning, that requires assembling a certain number of workers and training them. Even if a job is ever so simple, the workers will not become accomplished in a day. In order to make iron castings, it is necessary to start by having patterns made, and it takes time to finish such patterns, and the expenses involved are considerable.

Objections of a quite different kind, which I am proud to have provoked, are those that have been raised after the meetings of the Academy I just mentioned. There were people who found it strange that I had published secrets which [they thought] should not have been revealed. Others would have liked it if these secrets had been confided to companies which could have made use of them and which, in working for their own profit, would also have worked for the general good of the Kingdom. The attitude indicated by the first school of thought lacks high-mindedness to such a degree that one may be proud of having an exactly opposite view. Does it not offend natural justice? Can we be quite sure that our discoveries belong to us so exclusively that the public has no claim on them, that they do not belong to the public in some way? It is the foremost duty of all of us to work for the general good of society. He who fails to do so if he can contribute to it in any way, he who fails to do so when it would cost him nothing but to speak up, fails in a fundamental duty and under most heinous circumstances. If this principle is accepted, are there very many situations where we are the absolute masters of our discoveries?

It is true that for some time there have been complaints about the small returns received from the public—that it does not even show its appreciation by praise after it has once been given some information. As long as a secret is not revealed, it is considered something marvelous; after it has been divulged, the people say, "Is that all?" They try to show that they had knowledge of it before; the slightest hint, the least resemblance, is considered proof thereof. This has been used as an excuse by several scientists for keeping their knowledge to themselves and by others for disguising what they seemed to divulge in such a way as to make the pleasure of acquiring such knowledge very expensive. If these complaints were well founded and the supposed unfairness of the public as established and as general as some authors assert, would we therefore be justified in keeping to ourselves what could be useful to the public? Would the physician be entitled in case of urgent danger to refuse help to sick people from whom he could not expect any remuneration or to those whose ingratitude might already be known to him? Are these people less interested in spiritual than in material benefits? Is not knowledge for which one is given fair credit the most real wealth? I shall add that not to publish one's researches as clearly as possible, to reveal only part of the findings, to plan to leave the rest to guesswork, means, in my opinion, to be responsible for the time one causes one's readers to lose. I wish man would not admire those who seem to work harder at making themselves being admired than at being useful.

I will admit though, I am perfectly willing to give the impression of going out of my way to admit, that it is fair to reward the labors of those who have made profitable discoveries. However, the public should owe them nothing but praise, which is not the least flattering reward to those who have been touched by real fame. It is up to those who hold the reins of government to deal out rewards of a different kind. But have there ever been circumstances here in the Kingdom where we have had more reason [than we have today] to hope that investigations which further the common good will be supported by the latter kind of reward? I should be afraid to see a comparison made between my work and the rewards by which His Royal Highness has been good enough to encourage my efforts. Do I dare take the opportunity myself by making public the extent of them? Gratitude obliges me to do it, and the interest of the public requires that I apprise the people of what can be expected by those who are capable of working with greater success. Hardly had I read my first memoir on steel before the Academy, when His Royal Highness, the Duke d'Orléans, expressed the wish that I be supplied with new means to continue my investigations; this lecture was followed by gifts which were considerable in themselves, but even much more so by the kindness, I dare say, the eagerness, with which he has been interested in making these gifts sound and lasting. So that they would forever be of benefit to the sciences, the Duke has thought of having them pass on after me to the Academy, to take care of part of the funds needed for the famous and useful work done by this body. (By decree and letters patent His Majesty has bestowed upon me a pension of 12,000 *livres* payable by the Ferme des Postes. By the same decree and the same letters patent this pension will pass to the Royal Academy of Sciences after my death.) I am not afraid that I may be suspected of being influenced by gratitude when I say that the sciences may expect much from a prince whose lively and enlightened interest in them cannot be denied even by his enemies. New discoveries, new inventions, always receive from him a ready welcome, and in most cases, when they are presented to him, his opinions contribute toward their improvement. Since scientists are constitutionally timid, he has charged a man whom they themselves would have chosen with making access to him easier for them. I am referring to the famous Abbot Bignon,* who is more eager and more capable to bring out the value of a good piece of work than the scientists are themselves.

Everything seems to assure the sciences, especially the practical sciences, most favorable conditions in the Kingdom. His

---

* J.-Paul Bignon (1662–1743) was *prédicateur et bibliothécaire du roi*, the king's spiritual and intellectual adviser. This position was always held by a member of the clergy, whose function it was to preach before the king and to answer all questions concerning religion, the arts, and the sciences that might be addressed to him. Abbot Bignon was a man of exceptional learning; he was a member of the Académie Française, honorary president of the Académie des Sciences, etc., and a contributor to the *Journal des savants;* he also was a personal friend of Réaumur.

Majesty* already demonstrates for them a liking that is surprising in one of his age, and this liking will increase if cultivated by studies (under the Archbishop of Fréjus) which, without doubt, have been responsible for its awakening.

But to come back to the second objection of which I have spoken—there are people who do not believe that the discoveries which are the subject matter of these memoirs should have been published. They would have wished that they had been restricted to the Kingdom; that we had imitated the examples of being mysterious given by some of our neighbors, which in my mind have little to recommend them. Our first obligation is to our country; but we are also under obligation to the rest of the world. Those who strive toward making the sciences and the arts more perfect should consider themselves citizens of the entire world. After all, if the research reported in these memoirs will have the result which I had in mind when I undertook it, there is no country which could derive as much profit therefrom as the Kingdom. In the future we shall be able to get along without the fine steels which at present are bought from foreign countries. This will be especially true if it may be assumed that we will not neglect—as we do only too often—to make the best of what we have and if it is assumed that we will not abandon our establishments as easily as we construct them.

Considering cast-iron products, they could have remained for some time a specialty of France but will [now that the secret has been told] be shared with those other countries which wish to manufacture them. The abundance of our iron ores and their favorable location give us advantages in this kind of work which are found in few other places. There is still another factor in our favor, as far as this kind of product is concerned, which will make it hard for those countries where otherwise the same facilities or even greater ones may exist. What counts most in this kind of product is the artwork. We should not bother with casting simple pieces which require no intricate pattern work. Other countries easily grant that we have what is called "taste," which is what counts in everything that has to do with fancy work. We will prove to have greater artistic feeling for

* Louis XV, aged twelve in 1722.

variations than anybody else; we are ahead in everything that has to do with fashionable novelties. These will be bought from us [when produced in cast iron] just as they are bought from us in many another branch of industry. It may not even be bad if cast-iron products are made in other countries, for it will make us work more carefully. We rather like to do what we see done elsewhere; often we rather add to the inventions of others than perfect our own.

There were two ways between which to choose in making these arts useful to the Kingdom, especially the art of making cast iron malleable—either to grant privileges to companies which, like the one making panes of glass,* would have had the exclusive right to manufacture this class of goods or to give all craftsmen the permission to go to work at it. The first might have led to the appearance of great establishments, and the public might have been able sooner to select products of this kind. Since the permission has been granted generally, it will be the artisans who do the work. But as their limited funds do not permit them to make the necessary outlay to produce a large quantity of castings and castings of a great variety—for the first patterns are expensive—the number of products available will grow much more slowly. The companies which could build larger enterprises will perhaps not risk it for fear of soon seeing their products copied by all the small shops. But added to the fact that love of liberty makes one wish that it be permitted to the people to do that to which one man has naturally as much right as the next one is the consideration that, if the workshops thus develop more slowly, in a less spectacular way, they will develop in a way more useful to the public. How can one make sure that a company is not overeager to make money? That is the great disadvantage of privileges which in addition tie the hands of those who have not been granted them and who might have been able to make better use of them, who might have had greater ability to perfect the new inventions. Not that individuals are not just as eager to make a profit as the companies are.

* The casting of large panes of glass was invented in 1676 by Abraham Thévart, who founded the works of Saint Gobain in 1691. It is to be assumed that Réaumur refers to a monopoly by this firm.

But the fear that their neighbor might sell more than they and the ambition to attract the buyer force them to sell at a lower price. I have proof of this need for increasing the demand. I had allowed certain artisans who worked under my supervision in the laboratory of the Academy to produce some cast-iron articles; against my wish they wanted to keep the price excessively high. When they offered at 200 *livres* a piece made of cast iron, which when made of wrought iron would have cost from 1,200 to 1,500, they thought they were being fair, although they ought to have offered it at 4–5 *pistoles* [i.e., 40–50 *livres*]. There is, therefore, no other way of making things cheap than to force the artisans to sell at competitive prices.

Finally, if the reader does not find here all the explanations which I would have wished to give, and which perhaps I could have given if I had thought of them, I shall gladly add as much as I can. Let him come to me with the difficulties that hold him up, and he will always find me ready to try to remove them.

It has been necessary rather frequently to employ expressions which cannot be familiar to all those who will read my memoirs. In general, I have defined such expressions. But, since it is possible to forget these definitions and there may be a question where to find them, I have—in order to save the reader the trouble of having to consult dictionaries—appended at the end of this volume a glossary of the terms which I thought might cause difficulties.

Extract from the Records
of the Royal Academy of Sciences
for 1720, 1721, and 1722

M. de Réaumur having read during the years 1720, 1721, and 1722 different Memoirs concerning the "Art of Converting Iron into Steel" and the "Art of Producing Cast-Iron Work with the Finish of Wrought Iron," the Academy has ruled that these Memoirs merit being set in print. In accordance therewith I have affixed my signature to the present document.

Paris, the 28th day of August, 1722.

FONTENELLE
Permanent Secretary,
Royal Academy of Sciences

[This is followed by two pages of a reprint of the *Privileges of the King*.]

PART I

The Art of Converting Wrought Iron into Steel

The First Memoir, Wherein, after a General Description of the Different Methods of Making Steel, an Investigation Is Made To Determine Which Materials Are Suitable for the Conversion of Wrought Iron into Steel and How These Materials Must Be Mixed in Order To Obtain the Finest Steel of the Highest Quality

IRON ORES consist of ferruginous parts, earthy parts, and parts containing sulfur and salts, of which sufficient proof will be given elsewhere, so that I believe I am justified in making this assumption at present. The art has discovered the means of separating the metallic [2] or ferruginous parts from the extraneous matters with which they are mixed, of collecting the scattered parts, and of obtaining from them masses which are then adapted to very many different uses. Liquefaction is the principal method employed to reach this goal.

The smelted ores form two liquids of different gravity; the one composed of the metallic parts goes to the bottom, while the other one, which is made up of the extraneous matters, floats on top and is nothing but a sort of glass. In most of the furnaces in which iron ores are smelted, after a certain quantity of ore has been liquefied, the liquid metal is allowed to run out and is usually conducted into big molds, where it assumes the shape of long prisms with a triangular base which sometimes weigh up to 2,000 pounds.* These are called "pigs." It is possible to give this material any other shape; chimney backs, kettles, pots and

* For a note on the weights used by Réaumur see Appendix A, p. 369.

pans, etc., when made of iron, are nothing but iron resulting from this first smelting. It is an impure iron, which has not yet been sufficiently separated from all the extraneous matter with which it was mixed in the ore. In this state it is called "cast iron." It is much harder and more brittle than wrought iron and cannot be hammered either hot or cold.

In order to make pig iron, or cast iron, malleable, it is refined, which means that it is remelted. Subsequently it is placed under a heavy [3] hammer which is moved by water power and weighs at least 1,000 pounds. The iron is given terrible blows and is then removed to be heated once more almost to the melting stage. It is then again put under the hammer, and all this is repeated several times. By means of being heated and hammered, the [originally] brittle material is thus changed into forgeable bars. Among the bars coming from the same pig iron, some may be wrought iron and others steel if different procedures are followed in refining different parts of this same pig iron. I do not intend to explain here in what the methods differ; I shall do that in great detail in the *History of the Arts*. At present I only wish to give a general idea of the different ways of making steel, which can be reduced to three.

The first and most common one is to make steel from pig iron or from cast iron, which, like pig iron, has been tapped from a furnace. Steel is made from this kind of iron in several provinces of the Kingdom: in Champagne, Nivernais, Franche-Comté, Dauphiné, Limousin, Périgord, Normandy, etc. Often this is a coarse kind of steel, which at certain places is called "agricultural steel," because it is hardly suitable for anything but tools to till the earth. However, if these irons are worked [i.e., refined] with certain precautions, fine steels are obtained. At Rives and at Vienne in Dauphiné very passable steels are produced from these irons, steels that are suitable for many articles of cutlery. Rather fine ones are obtained [4] from the irons of Limousin. There are certain places in foreign countries where they pay special attention to refining these irons properly and where good steels are successfully made from them.

The second method of making steel still makes use of iron obtained directly from the ore, but this is an iron which has never run out of a furnace. There is no steel that owes less to art. If there are ores that can be called "steel ores," they are the ones from which it is produced; for, by employing exactly identical processes, wrought iron, as well as steel, is obtained. A certain part of the iron smelted from these ores yields wrought iron, and another part yields steel. Around Foderberg in Styria there are large numbers of furnaces in which such ores are smelted and where the iron obtained is allowed to collect in the furnaces themselves without being tapped.

There are cases of this method of making steel here in the Kingdom, but the furnaces used are much smaller than those in Germany. It is in Roussillon and especially in Foix where we have ores which after being smelted are not tapped. After the ore has been smelted, the iron obtained is made to collect; it becomes a mass that takes shape on the bottom of the furnace itself; it looks like a cake or flattened ball. This is called a "bloom." After this bloom or mass has been pulled out of the furnace, it is cut into five or six parts along lines parallel to one of its large diameters. Each of these pieces [5] is then heated and forged until it has been drawn out into a bar. One part of each bar is steel, and the rest is iron. The remarkable thing, for which a rather likely explanation will be found hereafter, is that the part of each bar which is steel comes principally from the iron that was at the edges or close to the edges of the bloom; the rest gives wrought iron. Thus, the steel obtained from these irons is only one-fifth or one-fourth of the quantity obtained as wrought iron. These steels, which we obtain almost naturally from the ores of our Kingdom, are coarse, which may be as much our fault as that of the ores. Those yielded by the ores from around Foderberg, where basically identical processes are used, are fine.

These two general methods of making steel, either from iron that has run out of the furnace or from iron that has not been tapped, could be subdivided into many special methods if all the different practices employed by the artisans of different countries were outlined.

Finally, the third method of making steel consists of using wrought-iron bars for the conversion, which is the kind of iron that is employed for all ordinary purposes. The steels obtained from wrought iron are fine steels, and to a certain extent we are able to make them as fine and hard as we wish them to be; we always can prevent the presence of either vein or grain of iron in these steels. This is not true of those which are obtained directly from pig iron. Our artisans [6] know only too well that it is common to find the steels imported from Germany full of iron. They are sold to them in barrels, and this defect is the reason why a large part of the steel of each barrel that is bought is a complete loss to them. I shall not tarry here in order to praise the steels made from wrought iron, to elevate them above the others, or to compare the characteristics of the different kinds of steel; the time for that has not yet come. It is enough to know that in many countries all the fine steels used are made from wrought iron. England uses no others for her best products. They make this sort of steel there, although they are forced to import from Sweden the wrought iron suitable for the purpose. In Italy and various parts of Germany steel is likewise made from wrought iron. Finally, although there are many countries where wrought iron is not converted into steel, there is hardly one where it has not been tried, obviously because steels made from wrought iron have always been considered to be the best and the kind of whose quality and fineness one can most easily be assured.

The Kingdom, which has enough and to spare of ordinary steels, has none of these. Considerable sums are spent each year to import fine steels; furthermore, there is nothing that has been tried more often than the establishment of workshops in which our wrought irons could be converted into steel; but this is an art that is being kept secret in those countries in which it is practiced.

The Court, however, has been overrun—especially [7] within the last three or four years—by Frenchmen and foreigners of all nationalities who, hoping to make a fortune, have presented themselves as knowing the real secret of turning wrought iron into steel. But since neither their work nor the favors conferred on several of them has borne any visible fruit, those who promise to change the irons of the Kingdom into excellent steels have come to be considered almost as seekers after the philosopher's stone. The public considers as impossible something that has been tried in vain a great number of times; it does not wish or is not in a position to examine the reason for the failure of the experiments.

In spite of the deep-rooted prejudices against the conversion of our wrought irons into steel, the process seemed too important to me not at least to find out once and for all what one's attitude toward it should be; and, furthermore, I deplored that the Kingdom, although it is perhaps richer in iron ores than any other country in the world, had to spend such large sums each year on steel and steel tools which are imported from foreign countries.

It was not necessary to prove the possibility of converting wrought iron into steel; it had been demonstrated more than enough by the success with which this conversion is practiced in England, Germany, Italy, etc. All we needed to know was therefore if by the secret method employed in foreign countries we could from our wrought irons make steels which would equal those they make from theirs or if we should after all have to resort [8] in France to the practice of converting foreign irons into steel as they do in England. There they make excellent steels from Swedish iron, which at Paris at certain times costs hardly more than the wrought irons of the Kingdom and which at our ports is sometimes as cheap as the iron produced from our own ores. But my examination of the irons of the Kingdom— which I had an opportunity to do thoroughly when I described our different iron-smelting furnaces and ironworking forges and all the arts which utilize this metal—this examination, I said, had shown me that we had irons of so many different qualities that there seemed no doubt that we must have some suitable to become excellent steels, whatever the characteristics are which steel requires. I even knew that at one or two works at Béarn some official had given orders actually to convert the irons of that province into steels, which I had found good although a little inferior to those of Germany.

I supposed then, and I believed to be justified in supposing, that the proper iron to be converted into steel had already been found and that all that remained to be done was to find the processes suitable to convert it, except for then trying them on all our kinds of iron. But these processes are a secret kept as such by those who practice them. The books of secrets* do not fail to give this one among others, and, when one searches, one even finds enough there to choose from, all tested and reliable [9] in the eyes of those who do not try them. The number of these presumed secrets reported by different authors is so great that, if the real secret were one of them, one would do just as well to seek it anew as to attempt finding it among the false secrets with which it is mixed up.

What has helped me more in this search than the books is an observation I made about the processes in wide use by the artisans who must give great hardness to certain pieces of iron. Those who make large files use only iron for the purpose, but they nevertheless make them as hard as steel files. Gunsmiths give a similar hardness to many a pan cover of flintlocks made of pure iron, and that by means of pack-hardening. This means, as I shall explain in more detail elsewhere, that, after these artisans have given their iron pieces a suitable shape, they inclose them in sheet-iron boxes with a mixture of different agents. They coat these boxes with clay and then put them in a furnace, where they expose them to fire for periods of different lengths, depending on the thickness of the inclosed pieces. After having removed these pieces from the fire, they quench them, quite red, in cold water. There they become hard as steel. Now, why does this treatment render the iron capable of taking on such hardness? When I tried to discover this, I recognized as the reason that it converts the outer layers of iron into steel. Thus, the iron files [10] act like those made of steel; their teeth are steel. Experiments, which it is useless to describe here, have plainly convinced me of the change of this part of the iron into steel, a change of which the artisans are not aware; they really use steel tools but believe they are iron tools.

* Réaumur is referring to the books of miscellaneous craftsmen's recipes which were first printed early in the sixteenth century and continued to be reprinted with many emendations and additions throughout the seventeenth century and, for that matter, even today. He later (p. 42) refers specifically to the *Secrets concernant les arts*, a four-volume work published in Paris in 1716. This was mostly concerned with materials and tricks of the artist's trade, but it does include a few notes on the hardening of steel.

The conclusion I have drawn from this observation is that the substances employed in pack-hardening could form the basis of the compounds suitable for converting iron into steel and that, if those who pack-harden would heat their pieces longer, they would turn them into steel to the center. This would be quite unnecessary with the tools I have mentioned, which need hardness only in the outer layers; but the observation was important to me who sought to change iron bars entirely into steel.

The basic materials in the compounds used in pack-hardening are powdered charcoal, ashes, and soot, which are seasoned with salts and mixed with divers matters, either vegetable, animal, or mineral. Rather often the secret formulas for converting iron into steel are fundamentally nothing but these compounds. But each artisan has his favorite ingredients which he adds thereto and uses special amounts of which he makes a mystery. However, even if every artisan of Germany, England, or other countries had given me the recipe for his compound, I still would have had to resort [11] to the experiments which I shall describe in the following; it would not have saved me a single one. Regardless of the interest of this matter to the Kingdom, it was important enough in itself to merit a thorough examination. It was necessary to make sure if the ingredients used are the best ones or if one could use others instead whose effect might be more reliable or faster; to make sure, for instance, if certain salts deserve the preference allotted to them; if any have been overlooked which might be employed with greater success; if, perhaps, substances are included in these compounds which should be discarded as harmful or at least as useless. It was necessary to succeed in determining the right amounts of each substance, to find if there was any means by which one could make something better out of steel than what it is today, and to see how far the perfection of steel could be carried. Finally, it was necessary to find rules for the method of converting iron into steel, to make of it a mastered art, one easy for the artisan to practice. But the art had to be invented before it could be described. This could be achieved only by a number of experiments which necessarily seemed prodigious. I have dared to undertake them, and I shall be very satisfied with the work I had to do in this connection if the public profits from it.

In order to discuss the experiments I have performed and the observations they have furnished me in a way that is instructive, I shall distribute them [12] over several memoirs, which deal with as many parts of our art. The first part, or this first memoir, makes the reader acquainted with the road I have followed to discover the most suitable compounds for the conversion of iron into steel. It then tells which are these compounds; it reveals the mysterious part of our art. The second memoir contains only general observations which show how to regulate the fire properly and which are necessary to prepare the reader for the third and fourth memoirs. Of these, one gives instructions on how to make trial steels on a small scale, and the other explains the construction of the furnace and what is connected therewith. In the fifth an attempt has been made to classify the different kinds of iron according to their natural responsiveness to being converted into steel. The sixth contains observations on the changes taking place in the iron during its conversion into steel and a summing-up of the costs of the operation. The knowledge acquired from these observations will be useful in defining the characteristics which distinguish iron from steel more clearly than it has been possible so far. An attempt has been made to base this definition on [the phenomena accompanying] the conversion of iron into steel and the reconversion of steel into iron and on the analogies between the different methods of making steel directly from pig iron and those of making it from wrought iron. The seventh, eighth, and ninth memoirs are devoted to these subjects; they [13] also include instructions which will be found useful in practicing our art. The tenth memoir describes the means of judging the quality of the different steels and how they can be compared. In the last two memoirs an attempt has been made to explain the effect of hardening. The different kinds of hardening and softening are examined, and as many rules as possible are formulated concerning this very important chapter in the practical execution of our art. Let us now start with the first part.

As said before, the subject of this first memoir is restricted to a description of the experiments that have shown which substances, and how much of them, make up the compounds which, in my judgment, can be relied upon most confidently to convert iron into excellent steel. Although this is the secret part of our art, it does not mean that it is the most interesting; it is merely a recital of different trials, the detailed description of which I should have liked to avoid, if the recital had seemed less essential to me. A large part of the experiments that I shall describe have accomplished nothing; but I did not believe that it was less necessary to mention them than to mention those with which I succeeded best; they will save others the trouble of repeating them, or at least they will indicate what result one may expect from them. It is almost as important to know the substances and the amounts of substances that are to be rejected as it is to know those that should be [14] used. I could easily describe all at once the compounds that have seemed best to me and state that I am making this claim for them only after an infinite number of experiments. But why should I be believed if I do not make known what experiments I have performed? In the end it is only these experiments as a whole that can justify my preference for certain compounds. They will show the route I have followed and consequently will make it evident whether it is reasonably probable that I have tried all that could have been done toward the perfection of steel, toward carrying this perfection as far as possible. Furthermore, if I have omitted experiments which somebody might think should not have been neglected, they can be undertaken with so much more assurance that so far there is nothing definite that speaks against their success.

I must not start without giving a rough idea of the manner in which the substances necessary to effect the conversion of iron into steel are being used. Ordinarily, the artisans have boxes or large square crucibles in which they put the wrought-iron bars that are to be changed into steel. Some make these boxes or crucibles of sheet iron, others of cast iron, and still others use only earthenware crucibles. Instead of boxes some use specially constructed furnaces into which they can place long bars. Whichever it is, after [15] having cut these bars into lengths that correspond to the length of the vessel into which they are intended to be put, they arrange them in layers which they separate from each other by other layers made of the compound suitable for changing them into steel. When the crucibles are filled, they are covered, luted, and exposed to a violent fire for different lengths of time, depending on the construction of the furnace and the quantity and thickness of the iron in the crucibles. This will be explained in the other memoirs. What has been said is enough for the present.

It was necessary to undertake experiments that would reveal the effect on wrought iron of different substances used separately or mixed together in different proportions when they surround this iron while it is being heated by a fire of suitable force for a suitable length of time. To do this, I started with a large number of small, square or oblong crucibles made of clay. All the crucibles for one furnace charge were of the same size and shape; in each one I inclosed pieces of iron of the same quality, of equal weight, and alike in all dimensions. I kept the heat as constant as possible. I packed the iron of each crucible in a different substance or in a mixture of different substances, so that the difference in the change effected in the iron had to be attributed solely to the difference in the substances, since otherwise everything else was the same. [16] I often used crucibles that could hold only half a pound or even a quarter of a pound of iron with the compound in which it had to be packed. Thus it was easy to dispose of thirty or forty tests in a single charge in a rather small furnace. If I had wished to start with experiments on a large scale, the funds of a great state would hardly have been sufficient for all those I needed. And so I shall say in passing that the majority of those who have tried to convert the irons of the Kingdom into steel have failed because they wished to start their work on too large a scale. It seems to me as if some of them were in possession of the fundamentals of the secret, but before they understood what they had to add or what they had to cut out on account of the nature of the irons to which they had to apply them, or on account of the construction of the furnaces which they were forced to use, they always wanted to start immediately by converting a large quantity of iron. Their first ex-

periments were so expensive that, before they were able to perform all those which it was necessary to undertake in order to
adjust the amounts used in their compounds, they had exhausted
their small capital and all the resources of those who had become their associates.

I started by trying out eight different compounds. Pack-hardening had suggested some of them; I added others which I had
found in print and one which [17] M. d'Angervilliers, having
the good of the Kingdom in mind, had brought me from Germany, which his position as intendant of Strasbourg enabled
him to reach. The result of this first experiment was at least as
good as I had expected it to be. The irons of all my boxes, after
having been exposed to the fire for fifty-nine hours, were more
than half-changed into steel; after having been put back in the
fire a second time, for the same duration, they were all steel.
True, they were not the kind of steel I wanted; some were too
coarse, others were scarcely harder than iron, some were fine
and hard but broke under the hammer; it would have been impossible to work them. However, it was enough to show me
that I was on the right road but that I had to discover what was
missing in some of my compounds and of what others contained
too much; in short, that it was necessary to take each one apart
in order to learn the effect of each of its components and that
then I should have to combine these different components in
different proportions.

To leave nothing undone and to go back as far as it was possible to go, I thought I should start by investigating if iron that
has been heated for a long time, and violently, without being
exposed to the direct action of the flame, might not acquire the
qualities of steel through this effect alone; that is, if the prolonged heating itself might not produce part of the changes I
observed. In order to clarify this point, I inclosed pieces of iron
[18] in several crucibles where I packed them only in inert or
almost inert substances. Some were surrounded by potter's clay
like that of which the crucible was made, some were packed in
ordinary lime, some in plaster [of Paris], some in powdered calcined bones, some in different kinds of sand, some in leached
ashes, and still others in ground glass. All these experiments

showed me that heat was not able to make steel out of an iron packed only in excessively earthy and almost inert substances. Several of these substances, however, produced other effects in the iron which seemed to me worth noticing and which may have their usefulness.

Ordinary lime, for instance, and bone ash (i.e., calcined bones), far from imparting to the iron any tendency to become steel, only made of it an iron that could be more easily filed and hammered. This is an observation of which I shall subsequently make practical applications which are perhaps as important as the conversion of iron into steel.

But a second observation, which the foregoing makes even more peculiar, is that plaster of Paris, which itself is nothing but the calcine of a particular kind of soft stone and from which one ought to have expected rather similar effects as from ordinary lime, produced very different ones. Indeed, it did not change the iron into steel; but who would have suspected that it is one of the most effective [19] fluxes of iron? When the crucibles in which I had put plaster were exposed to a heat of the same intensity as that used on the other crucibles, I found the iron bars reduced to a round mass, or one a little flattened; in short, as a mass which had been formed on the bottom of the box.* When the heat was less intense, so that the iron had not melted, it was completely broken up into scales which came loose at a mere touch. Only at the center of each bar there remained a few fibers of a very soft iron; but the scale was friable as all iron scale is. Sometimes I opened the crucibles containing plaster when this iron started to get hot, and I observed a peculiar phenomenon—the plaster gushed out of the crucible bubbling as a liquid would but much higher.† There were real bubbles, real spurts of a fine powder, for the plaster had remained as powdery as it was put in. Furthermore, the crucible in

* This effect is due to the formation of fusible iron sulfide by reaction with $CaSO_4$.

† Robert Hooke (*Micrographia* [1665]) had previously observed this liquid-like behavior of heated gypsum powder. It occurs only when gas, in this case water vapor, is being rapidly evolved or when gas is forced through the powder bed, as in a modern fluidized catalytic reactor.

which I put plaster almost always broke before having sustained great heat. After this experiment I tried if ordinary lime and bone ash would not also help in melting the iron, but I did not get the impression that they made it easier.

Iron packed in sand such as the kind from Fontenay-aux-Roses, which is held in great esteem by the foundrymen of Paris, seemed only softer after having been taken from the crucible. It did not regain its old [20] hardness until after it had been quenched in cold water. This experiment proves that the smiths should not be afraid of throwing sand of the nature of the afore-mentioned on iron which they wish to protect against burning in the forge and that they have no reason at all to fear that by this treatment it might become less manageable under the hammer or the file.

Although in this experiment the iron showed no tendency to become steel, it is still noteworthy that in this one and in some others there was a kind of change in which the heat may have played the principal part. I mean that the iron bars which had a fibrous fracture [see Mem. 5] lost their fibers, and the iron bars which had platelets were afterward found to have much smaller ones.

The pieces of iron packed in soft potter's earth or clay which was molded over their contour also remained pure iron. However, they seemed to resist the file more than those that had been packed in the other substances.

Leached ashes had at most as much effect as potter's clay.

Glass rather closely resembles the nature of sand; however, it contains more salts, which render it more fusible; but it keeps those it has seized. The iron in some boxes was packed in ground glass which had been passed through a very fine sieve. This iron acquired some hardness without becoming steel in any [21] way. What made this experiment remarkable is that the bars which were put in the crucibles black, dirty, perhaps a little rusty, emerged very white. The most easily descalable steel is never so white even at the spots where it has been quenched the hottest. The glass had melted; it had wetted and, one might say, washed the pieces of iron. It had taken away from it all the dirt without removing any scale, at least the volume of the iron had not been noticeably diminished. Several arts require a perfectly clean iron. Sheets of iron that are to be tin-coated are *pickled* or cleaned in sharp liquids. Perhaps there are circumstances under which one could substitute for these liquids the expedient with which the preceding experiment has provided us. If successful, this method would save long and tiring work, as illustrated by the art of tin-coating iron or of making white-iron sheets.*

The result of the preceding experiments that concerns the subject under investigation is that iron cannot be converted into steel by the heat of fire alone; that this heat is not sufficiently aided by substances that are inert, too earthy, and too devoid of oils or salts; and that these earthy substances are not in themselves capable of furthering the conversion of iron into steel.

The makers of pack-hardening compounds recommend the juice of some plants for the hardening of iron; many of them particularly use much garlic in [22] their compounds. The most piquant sauces were never seasoned with so much juice of this plant as the inert substances in which I packed the irons of some of my crucibles. But this seasoning did not yield a very active compound; it did not change the condition of the iron.

I then tried what effect fats and oily substances alone would have on iron. I copiously soaked with different fats such as ordinary tallow and different oils, especially linseed oil, the earthy materials and calcines which I had found in the foregoing to be incapable of producing any effects by themselves. Of these saturated earthy matters or calcines I made a kind of paste in which I packed the irons of different crucibles. I learned from these experiments that oils alone were not capable of acting on the iron in such a way as to convert it into steel. I came to the realization that these oils burn more than is desirable; but, although, in order to prevent them from burning fast, I often luted the crucibles with great care, I did not notice that they produced any change in the iron in the direction toward becoming steel.

In the same way I tried the effect of salts either by packing

---

* Réaumur continued to be interested in the subject and published his conclusions as a *Memoir* of the Academy of Sciences in 1725 under the title, "Principes de l'art de faire de fer blanc."

flat pieces of iron in nothing but different kinds of salt or by mixing a considerable quantity of these salts with earthy and inert matters. These experiments added the information that salts alone could not impart to iron a tendency [23] to become steel. All they did was to break up the fibers of soft iron without converting it into a state where it would become granular and could be hardened by quenching.

But I observed that this effect, which could not be produced either by fire alone, or by oils or fats alone, or by salts alone, could be obtained by oils and salts mixed in certain proportions. It is known that soap is really nothing but an oil thickened by alkaline salts until it has become a solid body. I mixed soap in different amounts with purely earthy matters. Iron imbedded in this mixture was half-changed into steel. I mean that the lower part of the bars took on the qualities of steel, while the upper part remained iron. If the conversion was not accomplished over the entire bar, this was not the fault of a lack of activity on the part of the soap but because it melted and afterward occupied only the lower part of the crucible and could act only upon the iron that was there. The iron which had changed its nature was really very bad steel, but, such as it was, it at least proved that the conversion of iron into steel must be expected from a mixture of oily parts and saline parts.

I then proceeded at once to try substances that naturally contain oils and salts. First I tried these materials alone without any admixture. In some of my crucibles I put charcoal which had been reduced to powder; in others [24] mineral coal; in others unleached ashes of green wood; in others soot, either as it comes out of chimneys or after having been burned; in others horn which had been burned enough to have turned into charcoal but not into ashes; I had this powdered and then passed through a sieve. In other crucibles I put [pieces] of an old shoe burned to the same point as the horn and prepared the same way. I also tried the excrements of several animals, such as horses, chickens, and pigeons, either without burning them or after having them burned. I found that each of these substances had the power to change the iron into steel, which was to be expected from the oily and saline ingredients with which they are impregnated. However, not all these materials are equally effective. Only charcoal, soot, and burned leather can change the iron into fine, hard steels, although these are usually hard to work and remain full of tears and cracks after forging; in addition, they require somewhat lengthy heating. However, the effect of soot and that of old leather is more prompt than that of charcoal. Horn, which is so greatly extolled by the makers of steel, seemed to me to have no advantage over soot; it even had much less effect. Ashes do not render the iron difficult to work, but they do not make much of a steel out of it; they make of it at best a very coarse steel which actually does not deserve the name of steel. Pigeon dung yields fine steels [25] but intractable ones—that means steels which go to pieces under the blows of the hammer when they are hot forged. Horse droppings and chicken manure hardly did more than ordinary ashes. Mineral coal, which had been powdered and sifted, had a very prompt effect. It much reduced the volume of the iron, it corroded it, and it made of it a hard, fine steel which was, however, intractable.

The over-all result of the last experiments seemed to be that several of the above materials could be used in the compounds that are suitable for the conversion of iron into steel; that some of them had to be abandoned or their effects moderated, such as those which render the steel intractable; that, conversely, it was necessary to try to intensify the activity of those which seemed to act too feebly or too slowly; and for this purpose to try if the addition of certain salts would not condition them so that they would act more effectively.

I then investigated what assistance one might give these materials by trying to discover from which salts it should be expected. The more complex experiments become, the more difficult it is to draw conclusions and even to decide whether the results permit conclusions. Thus it was more difficult to decide about the effect of each salt than about that of the other substances I had tried. Salts, as we have seen before, have no effect in converting iron into steel when they are used alone or mixed with [26] substances which are excessively earthy. Other experiments had shown the extent of the effect of charcoal alone. I used it as a base and investigated how much more it would accomplish owing to the different kind of salt with which it was combined. Thus, I believed, I should first have to prove the effect of the different kinds of salt. I took an equal amount by weight of each and mixed it with an amount of charcoal which was much greater by weight than that of the salt, but the same in each crucible, and which throughout surrounded a piece of iron of the same size. I then made similar tests with the same salts by giving them as a base, as a carrier, a mixture of soot, ash, and charcoal the proportions of which will be given elsewhere [see pp. 38 ff.].

The effects of the salts tested by these two methods seemed to be pretty much alike; the most important conclusions that could be drawn from these experiments after they had been repeated several times were as follows:

It seemed to me that the fixed [non-volatilizable] alkalies accelerated the conversion of iron into steel but that they almost always made of it a steel that was difficult to forge, full of cracks, one that could be neither hammer-welded nor doubled. This became evident when I employed different kinds of soda such as soda from Cartagena, Alicante soda, potashes, etc. Egyptian soda, which also seems to contain alkaline salts, and which some chemists cite as an example of alkalies that are not the work of the artificer, Egyptian soda, I want to say, also gave me a steel that was difficult to forge.

Other [27] salts seemed to arrest rather than aid the effect of charcoal. This was the case with borax. I also was in doubt if alum and green vitriol had contributed anything toward furthering the conversion of iron. I was not sure that they had done anything until I had used them in considerably larger amounts than the other salts.

A more peculiar effect of some salts is that the steel which they produce does not last. Steel which had a beautiful fine grain after being forged and quenched once had no grain or almost none after being forged and quenched a second time. However, this peculiar effect was not consistently produced by the same salts. I mean that, when I wanted to produce again with these salts steels of little durability, I was not always successful.

The salts which sometimes yielded steels of such low stability do not belong to the same class, which renders this phenomenon more difficult to explain. They are sal ammoniac, the salt called "glass salt,"* vitriol, and saltpeter concentrated by tartar (i.e., the salt that is obtained after a mixture of two parts of tartar and one of saltpeter has been ignited together).† The last-named salt, like all the alkaline salts, produced a steel that was difficult to process.

Steels made from wrought iron have been accused of losing their fineness in the measure with which they are worked. But this defect is not common to all of them; it is peculiar to those which owe part of their [28] conversion to salts like those of which I have just spoken. Steels made from wrought iron stand up about as well as those obtained directly from pig iron if the proper ingredients are used in making them.

Finally, the most important conclusion I have drawn from the experiments with the salts is that they have demonstrated that, of all the salts, sea salt is the one most suitable to change iron into a fine, hard, easily forgeable steel which does not become weaker by being forged. Rock salt and the salt taken [as a by-product] from the boilers in which saltpeter is refined, although belonging to the same class, still have never given me such good results as salt obtained from sea water. I do not wish to say that I believe that salt coming from the mines or from saltpeter [works] cannot be substituted for salt obtained from sea water, but I am reporting scrupulously what my impression was when I say that I have had better results with sea salt.

In order to make the experiments with salts more all-inclusive, I wished, after having investigated the effect of dry salts, to make some experiments with liquid salts, with "spirits of salts."‡ I soaked the charcoal with which I wished to fill a

* *Sel de verre.* This is crude sodium carbonate from the ashes of the saltwort plant, often called "sal alkali."

† This material is the well-known reducing "black flux" used extensively in assaying. It would be composed principally of potassium hydroxide and carbonate with some nitrite and with considerable amount of free carbon.

‡ *Esprits de sels.* "Spirit of salt" is the old name for hydrochloric acid, "spirit of vitriol" for sulfuric acid; so that "spirits of salts" are acids in general.

crucible in aqua fortis until it had been reduced to a soft paste. The iron that was packed in this paste became a steel which lasted only until after the first quench; after being forged and quenched a second time, it had again become iron. If I had not forbidden myself all theorizing in this first memoir, this experiment would give me an opportunity to explain why steels [29] made with certain salts are not durable as they would be if they were made with charcoal alone. I did not consider it necessary to continue the experiments with the spirits of salts. It would be inconvenient in practice if one had to resort to them; the cost might thereby be increased too much. It is to be feared that steel produced with any kind of spirits would not stand up in the fire like those which are made with dry salts. In addition, evaporation of the spirits inclosed in the crucibles would be very considerable.

After the salts, I thought I should try whether various mineral substances, which are great fluxes of iron and which consequently might be suspected of being capable of changing its texture,* might not be successfully employed; some of these same materials are said to be excellent for use in certain pack-hardening compounds, as, for instance, antimony, arsenic, common sulfur, and verdigris. But, in spite of combining the first three of these substances in all possible ways, I found that all they accomplished was to spoil the iron or steel. As far as the verdigris is concerned, it seemed to me that, when it was used in small amounts, like the salts, its effects were not as bad as one might have expected. The steel could still be hammer-welded, which is quite contrary to the prejudice of the artisans who believe that everything which contains a little copper renders iron intractable.

The texture of the iron that had been packed in powdered charcoal [30] mixed with antimony was changed, without, however, having become that of steel. It no longer had either brilliant platelets or fibers like ordinary iron [see Mem. 5], but neither had it grains like steel; the molecules had assumed an intermediate shape; they were flatter than grains of steel and

* That is, its fracture, which was the principal means of controlling the process. See Mem. 5.

more raised than the platelets of iron; they were dull, whereas the platelets of iron are brilliant.

Common sulfur used in the same amount and with an equal amount of charcoal as the preceding substances changed a soft iron into an intractable one and kept the charcoal from converting it into steel. But when I mixed the same amount of charcoal with an amount by weight of sulfuric acid equal to that of the sulfur which I had used in the other mixture, the iron did change into a coarse steel which hammer-welded only with difficulty.

After I had tested all the substances which I believed capable of acting on the iron, after I had recognized which were entirely to be rejected and which could be used with some success, it remained to find out what result the effective substances would produce if different ones of them were combined together and if they were combined in different proportions, and which of these combinations would be the best. After all this had been tried, it did not seem possible that the most favorable compounds for converting iron into steel could have eluded me. Indeed, the number of the combinations that presented themselves was great, but it was not [31] as immense as it might seem. It is not necessary to proceed by almost imperceptible differences when it is desired to produce perceptible effects. There is a rather great latitude in the precision of natural philosophy.

I would say that after all these experiments the compounds that seem best to me require only powdered charcoal, ashes, chimney soot, and sea salt. But, by mixing these substances in different proportions, one can make different compounds, of which the one which I consider the most suitable for changing iron into a very fine and very hard steel consists of two parts of soot, one part of powdered charcoal, one part of ashes, and three-quarters of one part (or a little less) of sea salt. This means that, if 16 pounds of soot were used, one should use 8 of charcoal, 8 of ashes, and 6 pounds (or only 5) of sea salt.

I give this compound preferred rating if it is desired to make steel out of those irons which are most suitable for the purpose (a different chapter of the *Art* deals with the characteristics of these irons); but this same compound is not the one which best suits certain other irons. It would make of them steels which are too difficult to forge, which would give trouble in hammer-welding or doubling, and which, after having been worked, would be left full of cracks. These irons require a less active compound. The one to be used is as follows: Take two parts of [32] ashes, one part of soot, one part of charcoal, and three-quarters of one part of sea salt, or almost that, as in the first recipe.

Like the first one, this second compound can be successfully used on the irons best suited to become steels. Like the other one, it will convert them into good steels, but it acts more slowly. When one makes use of this compound, the operation is completed only after much longer exposure to fire of the same intensity. For this reason alone the first compound should deserve preference; and another reason may be that it gives the steel some additional degrees of fineness.

It will be shown elsewhere that it can even be used without fear on various kinds of iron which it may convert into steels that are a little difficult to handle. This is possible because I shall also give remedies to correct the bad effects it may produce; and these remedies will hardly cost the equivalent of the time and charcoal required additionally by the weaker-acting compound.

It is only too common that an air of mystery surrounds everything that is called a recipe or compound. Something the givers of secrets seldom fail to do is at least to make the prescriptions call for amounts from which no deviation is permitted. I would imitate them, as I have no intention of doing, if I failed to tell that, between the two compounds which I have just given, there is an infinite number of intermediate ones which can be successfully used. [33] I have fixed the amounts for the two preceding ones so exactly only because it is necessary to give the majority of artisans something definite on which they can rely; but what I can and must emphasize is that the amounts given for these two compounds indicate the limits within which it is advisable to be contained. One cannot go much beyond these limits without running the risk of producing steel which is too difficult to forge or steel which is too coarse, which also would require an excessively long treatment. If the amount of ashes

were decreased in the first compound, or if it were eliminated altogether, it would be very hard to find irons which it would
change into easily workable steels. If, conversely, the amount of
ashes were increased too much, if they alone were made to occupy three parts of the compound, and if the remaining part
were divided between charcoal and soot, one would need a fire
of much longer duration in order to make steel out of the iron, a
much larger quantity of compound would have to be used, and
often only coarse steel would be obtained. But using amounts
intermediate between the two limits which I have indicated is
possible without doing any harm. For example, one-third part
of soot, one-third of ashes, and one-third of charcoal with the
amount of salt of one of the compounds will give a mixture
with which one will succeed. But with iron with all the qualities requisite to becoming good steel, the first compound [34] is
better for the reasons I have outlined. With iron that lacks some
of these qualities it is safer to make use of the second than of the
first one. This is enough for all practical purposes; I shall add
only, as a rule, that, the more oily substances there are in the
compound, the greater is the risk of producing a steel with
cracks, a steel which is difficult to forge; but the steel is also the
more promptly obtained. It is principally the soot and the charcoal that contain the oily matters, and the quantity present is,
therefore, decreased if the amount of these two substances is reduced and that of ashes increased, the ashes being principally
employed to moderate the effect of the other two. They also
have an effect through their alkaline salts, of which, however,
they do not contain sufficient to produce the bad effect of which
I spoke in my discussion of the action of the different salts.

In order to convince myself still more of the bad effect of an
excessive quantity of oily constituents, I soaked the substances
of the first compound in linseed oil. The resulting steel was very
hard to forge under circumstances under which this would not
have been the case if oil had not been added to the compound.

Neither is the amount of sea salt which I have suggested so
important that it cannot be varied; it even could be completely
eliminated, but the process would take longer. The salt contributes a great deal to its acceleration and also contributes to

the hardness [35] and to the fineness of the steel. If the sea salt were eliminated, a larger quantity of compound would be needed for the same quantity of iron. It is possible to increase the amount of salt, but, if it is increased beyond a certain limit, it is harmful. If it is doubled, for instance, it is to be feared that it will produce a steel that cracks. Perhaps the salt itself has this effect; perhaps it makes it easier for the oily constituents to penetrate into the iron. However, increasing the sea salt never has seemed to me to produce as bad effects as increasing the oily substances.

Into one crucible I put powdered charcoal all by itself—that means without salt and without any other matter; but I used a large quantity for the amount by weight of iron. This iron was changed into fine steel, but this was accomplished only after almost twice the time required by the first compound to produce the same result; and, after being forged, this steel was full of cracks.

When I wished to include in my compounds inert or almost inert matters, such as potter's clay, sand, or lime, I arrested or weakened the effect of the active matters, depending on whether I used larger or smaller amounts of the inert matters. This is indeed the effect one should expect. However, if steel must be made of those irons which are too inclined to become steels that are difficult to forge, some of them could be made tractable by moderating [36] the effect of the active materials by some absorbent substance. To our weak compound, namely, two parts of ashes, one part of charcoal, one part of soot, and three-quarters of one part of salt, to this compound, I said, add one part of ordinary lime—or better still one part of bone ash (i.e., one part of bones that were burned and reduced to ashes). There are irons which I was never able to change into anything but steels that could not be hammer-forged, except when I used this compound; and, by using it, I obtained easily forgeable steels. One can go even farther with the amount of inert matters. I have sometimes induced iron to change into steel after mixing two parts of bone ash with one part of [wood] ashes, one of charcoal, one of soot, and the usual amount of salt. But, taking everything into consideration, it is better not to try to make steel out of irons that require the introduction of these correctives into the compounds; if too much of them is introduced, they completely prevent the success of the operation. For instance, I have tried a process described in a book of *Secrets concerning the Arts,** which was printed at Paris by Jombert in 1716 (Volume I, page 12), with which I have not been successful, the reason being, I believe, that it uses quicklime in an amount too large for the rest of it. This process requires that one take one part of soot, three-quarters of one part of oakwood ashes, and one-quarter of one part of crushed alliums;† that one boil all this in twelve parts of water until these twelve parts have been [37] reduced to four; that one quench the iron billets in it and arrange them in layers separated by the compound made of three parts of charcoal, three parts of quicklime, one of soot, and one-quarter of one part of decrepitated salt. This beautiful process has left my iron very soft, which I attribute to the excessively large amount of quicklime.

I have sometimes added one-eighth of one part of lime to my usual compositions. In such a small amount it has done no harm; it even has had a good effect, which was to diminish certain blisters, of which I shall speak later, which sometimes rise on the surface of the iron. A quantity of plaster of Paris smaller than that of lime, that is, approximately one-twelfth of one part, is still more effective in preventing them.

Crushed glass, which some people use in their compounds, also has hardly any other use than to decrease these blisters; but it does not do it any better than lime and plaster, and it would hold up matters in the shops if enough glass for crushing would have to be collected there. Furthermore, the trouble it remedies is such a minor one that one should not worry about it at all. In large-scale operation it is above all necessary to keep in mind using only those materials that are easily available.

The same book of which I spoke above gives (on page 31) another compound, one of the ingredients of which it would, for instance, be difficult to obtain for work on a large scale. [38] It consists of twelve parts of beechwood charcoal quenched

* See note, p. 24.

† *Allium sativum* is garlic.

in urine, ten parts of horn, three parts of ashes of green wood, and three parts of powdered pomegranate peel. Where would a shop obtain its supply of the last-named powder, which, in addition, I consider more harmful here than useful?

But to come back to the two compounds which, I believe, ought to be given preference; they fortunately require only agents which are easy to collect everywhere and which with the exception of sea salt are cheaply bought everywhere. The necessary preparations do not involve any large expense. With the soot, all it amounts to is to make it pass through a coarse sieve or a kind of screen. If it is reduced to finer parts, this will be so much better. It is by no means necessary to have it burned, which I have learned by using it burned and not burned. As far as the ashes are concerned, in spite of all that has been said on how they should be chosen, provided they are of green wood, regardless of the kind of wood, I have always found them good. They are passed through a moderately fine sieve. The charcoal is passed through a similar sieve after it has been reduced to powder by means of a pestle. Any charcoal may be used. Although that made of oakwood is a little more active, it has not seemed to me as if the charcoal made of soft wood had made any noticeable difference in the results. Beechwood charcoal, which has a position between oak and soft-wood charcoal, perhaps deserves [39] to be preferred. But, to be frank, these are differences that are difficult to distinguish by the most exact experiments, and such fine differences are of little importance in practice.

The sea salt also must be reduced to a fine powder, and, in order to powder it more easily, it must first be decrepitated in a crucible—that means it is held for some time in a crucible which is heated red-hot over the fire. At the end all that is left is to mix the different amounts of these materials as exactly as possible.

If the work is to be done on a large scale, there are ways of doing all these little jobs which will prove to be considerable short cuts. It is so easy to think of such ways that it may be rather unnecessary to indicate any; and they can be varied at will by those who are in need of resorting to them.

In the factories the charcoal could be powdered by stamps

that are moved by water power; and in ordinary forges one would only have to make some slight additions to the crushers in order to adapt them for this service. Instead of having these stamps fall on slabs sprinkled with water, as is done when they are used to crush hammer scale, one could make them fall into wooden troughs or into a kind of mortar. Then one could crush the charcoal in the mortars, as it is crushed in powder mills. Sea salt could be crushed in the same mortars. For the purpose of passing the charcoal and the salt [40] through a sieve, one could use sieves, similar to those of the bakers, inclosed in a kind of cabinet; nothing prevents the owners of the factories from having them moved by water power by conducting water over a wheel which has been connected with the drive shaft of the mill. As for the soot, it is passed through fine screens. All this does not require much time in a well-regulated shop.

The compound is, so to say, much better made, much better prepared, to the extent to which the different materials are more perfectly mixed. It can be done by hand if the necessary time is taken. One knows that the mixture is well made when the material seems of the same color wherever one looks at it. [On the other hand,] any machine fit to toss, or to mix, could be used here; a kind of drum could be employed for the purpose.

In some of my experiments I dissolved the salt in water in order to mix it more perfectly. I then sprinkled the other, already well-mixed materials with this water; but I do not have the feeling that anything was gained by this method. In addition to forcing one to allow for some time in which the compound can dry, it has seemed to me to render it less active. It may be that the salt escapes from it more easily. I have also found it more inconvenient than helpful to moisten these agents with urine, as one moistens those used in pack-hardening and as it is prescribed, as I have shown [see p. 43], for [41] some compounds used in making steel. Moist compounds in the form of pastes may be suitable for pack-hardening, although they are not suitable for making steel. The reason will become evident when pack-hardening is discussed.

Just as it is necessary that the materials which go into the compounds are present in certain proportions, so is it necessary to use a certain quantity of compound for a certain quantity of iron. If the compound is not sufficiently carefully rationed, the steel may be spoiled; too much compound makes it crack; and, if one uses too little, it is not strong enough to act effectively and leaves it iron. As with the rest, however, one is given rather much leeway. Differences in the crucibles or boxes in which the iron is placed, differences in the furnaces in which it is heated, lead to the use of larger or smaller amounts of compound. It is sufficient to know that in general only $2\frac{3}{8}$ ounces of compound is required for each pound of iron; this means 1 ounce of soot, $\frac{1}{2}$ ounce of ashes, $\frac{1}{2}$ ounce of charcoal, and $\frac{3}{8}$ ounce at most of salt. For work on a large scale one takes for each quintal [200 pounds] of iron approximately 7 pounds of soot, $3\frac{1}{2}$ pounds of powdered charcoal, $3\frac{1}{2}$ pounds of ashes, and $2\frac{1}{2}$ pounds (or 3 pounds at the most) of sea salt. If the iron that is to be converted into steel is of excellent quality, the amount of this compound may be increased. This will only accelerate the operation, and the steel itself will [42] be improved as far as its properties are concerned. Conversely, if the iron is not very suitable to be made into steel, it will be safest to decrease the aforenamed amount. Besides, the price of the materials that go into the compound must not influence one to economize with it. No matter what amount is used, even if it is excessive, the sum by which these materials increase the price of steel over that of iron is no object worthy of consideration. It will be shown in later memoirs how high the other expenses are. It will also be explained how the compound is arranged layer by layer with the iron. But I shall add here that, when the steel is taken from the furnace, the compound should not be considered useless. It has become less by weight and by volume, but what remains is in perfect condition to act on more iron. One does not have to be afraid of mixing this old compound with the new; the effect of the latter will not be too much weakened provided one has been careful to use certain precautions in preserving it, which I shall not forget to describe elsewhere.

The Second Memoir, Containing General Observations Helpful in the Proper Regulation of the Fire

T IS NOT enough to have found the most effective compounds and to understand how to adjust the amounts used in relation to the quantity as well as the quality of the iron. It is also necessary to understand how to portion out, one might say, the duration and the intensity of the fire, and it is especially important to prevent the flame from entering the crucibles or similar containers in which the iron is inclosed.

The fire of the furnace must never act directly on the iron or the compound. Instead, its action must be communicated to both only through the walls which contain them. If a sizable crack develops in these walls, it will be useless to urge the fire, to increase its intensity and duration; for the iron bars or at least those parts of the bars which are near the cracks will always remain iron. Iron becomes steel only with the help of the compound, and, when the fire penetrates into the container which holds it, it destroys this compound. It changes its nature—first it reduces it to ashes and then to a hard, half-vitrified mass which can no longer provide [44] the iron with the oily and saline parts* necessary to produce in it the changes which they should effect.

The crucibles or similar containers must be placed in a way that permits one to check from time to time whether such dangerous cracks have formed. Even if they are ever so small, it is easy to recognize them, for a blue flame never fails to appear all along a crack. This flame lasts until the soot and the charcoal have been reduced to ashes. If this happens and if the cracks are large and the operation has not yet gone far, it is better to extin-

* For a discussion of Réaumur's "parts" see note, p. 142.

guish the fire and to remove the bars than to continue a project which would waste time, charcoal, the compound used, and part of the iron. But if the cracks are fine, if they extend only over part of the width or the height of the crucible, and if the operation will be finished after only a little additional firing, the heating may be continued, because it takes time for the compound opposite the little openings to be reduced to ashes, and that part of the compound which is a little farther removed from the openings will not burn.

Thus it is essential that the containers in which the bars and the compound are placed be tightly closed. If they have a lid, this lid must be luted on with clay which has some tendency to soften, for those kinds of clay which are more resistant to fire are subject to cracking. If the lid closes [45] imperfectly, the compound near it burns, and there is furthermore a sublimation of salts which is sometimes so considerable that all the openings of the cover or the arched roof of the furnace become white with deposited salts. I have never found them to taste of anything but sea salt, but I have never collected enough for an assay other than by tasting. The compound will have become weaker because of all the salts it has lost in this way; and the further loss of oily parts is no less considerable for being less noticeable.

It is astonishing, however, how long this compound conserves its strength if no air is admitted to the box. Even if the fire has been urged to great violence for several days, layers of compound are found between those of iron, and their condition after several days of firing is almost the same as after some hours. They still have their original color, and what they have lost of thickness is not even one-quarter. However, when I have weighed all the matter that had been exposed to the fire, I have found that its weight had decreased by approximately one-half. It is probable that most of this decrease is attributable to the watery parts which were removed, since the volume is not reduced in the same proportion as the weight. One thing is certain—this matter seems as inflammable as it was at the beginning, and consequently the oily part has not been consumed, although it has burned [46] so long. This fact, although it appears strange, is nevertheless in accord with the rules of plain physics.

Fire consumes bodies only as long as it can remove their parts. In this instance it cannot remove those of our compounds. Lighted charcoal, well covered with ashes, is on fire for a long time before it is entirely consumed.* The walls of a crucible have a much stronger effect than ashes as an obstacle to evaporation. The inclosed matter would not continue to burn unless it were constantly rekindled, one might say, by the fire.

It is advisable not to fill the crucible all the way but to leave about 1 inch,† or $\frac{1}{2}$ inch, of empty space at the top, depending on the size of the crucible, for the compound, which expands during the first moments, might distend the walls and cause them to crack unless it found a void into which it could go.

After a bar has been withdrawn from the crucible, the first glance will tell whether the whole bar, or part of it, has been near a place where there was enough air to harm the bar. When the crucible was tightly closed, and when the compound surrounding the bar was not burned, the color of the bar is dull brown; but, when the compound surrounding it has been reduced to ashes, the bar is slate-colored and has brilliant white spots. In that case the bar is covered with a scale which can easily be detached by hammer blows; the iron becomes burned when the compound is burned.

After the [47] amount of suitable compound nothing is as decisively important to the perfection of the steel produced as the right degree of heating. If the exposure to the fire is either too short or too long, the steel will be defective. It is easily understandable that a fire of insufficient duration will leave the bars iron or partly iron; and this defect is easy to recognize in the first tests. After the bar has been forged and quenched, one recognizes without being very skilful if a vein of iron is still present. But steel that has not been exposed sufficiently long to the fire sometimes fails in another respect. There is nothing that has disconcerted me more frequently during my investigations of

* What a pity Réaumur did not speculate more on this. He was very near to seeing the importance of atmospheric oxygen in combustion. He clearly realized that air must be excluded if the compound was not to be burned and the iron ruined.

† For the measures used by Réaumur see Appendix A, p. 369.

steels than the imperfection of which I wish to speak. I sometimes withdrew from the furnace steels which could be worked
admirably, which upon quenching acquired the most beautiful
grain. Nevertheless, when it came to trying them out, I found
them soft, and [the edges of] cold chisels made from these steels
turned back at the first blow. I did not know what to make of
it, for this happened with the same irons with which I had been
completely successful in other charges when I had used the same
amounts of compound. Sometimes I blamed it on air which had
entered the crucibles and sometimes on something else which
had just as little to do with it. Since my iron had become steel to
the center, it did not occur to me to suspect that it was still in
need of being acted upon by the fire; but that was of what I had
to become convinced. When I began to think that perhaps [48]
the fire had not finished its task when it had broken up the fibers
of the iron and had conditioned it to acquire a fine grain on
quenching, and that it still had to induce the sulfurs and the
salts to act in such a way as to give the steel all the hardness one
expects of it—when, I said, I had conceived this latter idea, I
put my soft steels into the fire for a second time after having surrounded them with compound. When I withdrew them, I found
that they had all the hardness I could wish for. This is an experiment which I have later repeated a great number of times,
always with the same result, so that, if steels are too soft, in
spite of the compound which I have recommended, the fault lies
in their premature removal from the fire. The remedy consists in
putting them back in again.

It is necessary to be careful, however, not to apply too drastic
a remedy; for just as steel, when not exposed sufficiently long to
the fire, becomes insufficiently hard steel, steel that has been
exposed to the fire up to a certain point fails in other respects.
I mean that it is too difficult to work—that it tends to go to
pieces under the hammer. There is considerable waste in forging, and any billets or bars that are finally forged from it remain
full of tears and cracks, and their edges will be sort of nicked.
Such steels are therefore not suitable for fine work.

The memoir on hardening will give me an opportunity to report some peculiar facts about the nature of [49] these steels.

However, I shall say here what I have said before at a different occasion—that the difference between too much and too little is no indivisible quantity. It is large enough to be easily recognized. The fire must be continued for an additional one-sixth or one-fifth of the ordinary time in order to ruin the steel. Furthermore, I would not recommend that in steelworks every charge be given a fire of the same duration. By this expedient alone steels of different qualities would be obtained which would be suitable for different products. The artisans to whom they would be sold as such would use one kind for products in which great hardness is not essential but which must be very well finished, very smooth, and free from laps and cracks. The others would be employed for tools in which hardness is of prime importance.

If I were asked in approximately how many hours of heating iron bars of a definite thickness can be changed into good steel, I should have to answer that this is a problem which cannot be solved without knowledge of the shape and the capacity of the furnace used, and of the quantity of bars placed in it, and that the nature of the irons and the compounds employed add further variables. There are furnaces which would make it necessary to have the fire burning for twelve to fifteen days; but I have sometimes made steel—in very small quantities to be sure—in less than one hour. To give [50] a clear idea of the reasons for this difference, I shall tell of an observation which has led me to look for and find furnaces capable, it seems to me, of shortening the process as much as possible.

We have seen in our exploratory investigations that the fire alone is unable to effect the conversion of iron into steel. It accomplishes this only after the introduction of saline and sulfurous parts [into the iron]. However, in order to enable these parts to penetrate to the center of the iron so that they can be effective there, passages have to be opened, which means that the iron must be heated to the utmost and in a way softened. Consequently, the more rapidly iron is heated in the furnace and the higher the degree of heat which it acquires there, the more rapid will be the conversion into steel. It does not start until the iron begins to become soft, but, when it has reached this point,

the conversion is accomplished rather promptly. A great number of experiments have demonstrated this to me. I arranged my
iron bars so that I could withdraw some of them in order to
judge the stage at which the others had arrived and whether it
was time to discontinue the fire. It has happened that I tested a
bar which had been exposed for ten or twelve hours without
finding any considerable change. Two or three hours later, I
took out a bar that was among those closest to the one I had
taken out earlier, and often the latter was completely converted
into steel. The first ten or twelve hours [51] had not effected as
much change in the iron as the last two or three hours, the reason being that the fire does not work successfully until the iron
has arrived at a certain degree of heat, just as the smith cannot
easily shape his iron under the hammer until it is hot. I have
tested this further by another, more conclusive method which I
am glad to describe, because there is some indication that the
experiments which I have performed on a small scale might
prove useful on a large scale. I filled a small crucible with compound, covered it, and put it in the fire without having placed
pieces of iron inside; but, when it came close to being white, I
ordered iron bars to be heated in an ordinary forge until they
were almost melting. Then I opened the crucible, placed the
pieces of iron in it, and reclosed it at once. I was careful to have
a lid prepared for it which closed tightly but could easily be
taken off and put on again. Without giving the crucible and the
iron time to cool, I then continued to heat the crucible, and I
found that the iron which it contained had been converted into
steel much sooner than it would have been if I had put it in the
crucible simultaneously with the compound. This means that
the duration of the fire—if one begins to count from the moment when the crucible containing only compound is put in the
fire up to the time when the iron has been converted—that this
duration of the fire was shorter than it would have been if I had
inclosed the iron [52] in the crucible right at the beginning. The
difference would be still more considerable in large-scale than in
small-scale operation. The reasons will be shown later.

It must be said of the intensity of the fire, however, what has
been said of its duration—that it can be excessive. Although

iron is not considered to be a fusible metal when it is alone, I have sometimes given such violent fire to the crucibles that the bars melted. The material which then trickled down from them formed little flat pieces. In this case the melting was assisted by the sulfurs and salts of the compound. It is known that common sulfur can make iron liquid in a moment. However, any iron that melts in the crucibles is wasted iron; it becomes cast iron;* it is rarely possible to shape it under the hammer, and, if so, there is too much discard.

If it happens that the iron partly melts in the crucible and the compound surrounding the bars that have dripped has not been consumed or reduced to ashes, whatever remains of these bars is steel, which has all the hardness imaginable but is also very difficult to work and almost always stays full of cracks. I have sometimes found, however, that two neighboring bars had softened to the point where they touched and stuck together at one end and thus took on a shape entirely different from the one they would have had if they had merely been lying close enough together to touch each other. Consequently, [53] the iron had been molten there. But these same ends forged with hardly any more difficulty than steel that had been heated a little too long—they were very hard steel. The ends of these bars had therefore always been surrounded by compound, and they were of excellent iron. After being forged, this steel had no extraordinary number of cracks, and sometimes it was less cracked than steel obtained from bars which I had given a more moderate fire but one twice or three times as long.

However, the iron cannot be heated either too rapidly or too violently provided it is not heated until it melts. In order to be

* If iron is heated to above 1,130° C. in the presence of sufficient carbon, it will form a molten carbon-rich eutectic—actually, as Réaumur says, a cast iron. If a limited amount of carbon were present and if the temperature is high enough, the liquid could be a true steel, as Réaumur seems to suggest in the next paragraph. Ludwig Beck (*Geschichte des Eisens*, Vol. III) believed that Réaumur was near to the invention of cast steel. It seems, however, highly unlikely that the furnaces used by Réaumur could achieve the necessary temperature of over 1,400° C., and more probably the welding-together of the bars was a result of the formation of a high-carbon cast iron which was subsequently partially decarburized.

able to prove this proposition, I shall add that I have made steels with very gentle and very slow fire. For this purpose I put the crucibles in which the iron was contained in a furnace like those in which ores are assayed for their metal content and metals for their fineness. The heat in these furnaces is not lively; it is maintained only by air which enters freely through holes which permit more or less of it to pass, depending on how wide the registers are open. The operation took a long time; but the iron which had been heated so slowly, which had been processed little by little, became no more perfect steel than iron treated more abruptly. Steel obtained from iron of the same quality and size, which was the product of only a few hours of heating, seemed to me in no way inferior to steel on which the fire had acted for several days. I have [54] often observed that steel which is the product of more violent and faster heating has larger and more numerous surface blisters (of which later) than when the iron is handled more gently. But these blisters have no effect on the quality of the steel.

When I have found that long exposure to fire gave steel bad qualities, this has been most often the case when the steel was put back in the fire several times with fresh compound like the one used when it was still entirely iron. Thus, repeatedly exposed to the action of fresh compound, it is in the same condition as if one had started by packing it in too much compound or in compound which was too strong. Long-continued firing will seldom do harm (unless one goes to an extreme) if the iron is not transferred from the crucible and put back with fresh compound. These observations give us a rule—that is, never to put the iron back in the fire with a compound as active as that used the first time. It should be packed either in compound which has served before or in compound which, though fresh, is weak.

When I have given a steel fresh compound and put it back in the fire several times, this was done mainly in order to find out to what point of fineness and hardness it could be brought and whether its hardness and fineness would increase every time it was put back [55] or what limit there was to this increase. This seemed to me one of the most important experiments to be performed. I learned in fact that, the more often the steel is put back in the fire, the more hardness and fineness of grain it acquires; but it must never be given more than what it can acquire of these two properties with twice the amount of compound and twice the duration of firing that are ordinary; and still there are few irons that can stand this second ordeal. If one goes beyond this, this steel which has been made finer and harder will nevertheless be less so than another in practical application. It will be impossible to hammer-weld parts of it together and especially to hammer-weld it upon iron unless it has been heated to the melting stage several times. However, each heating to the melting stage weakens a steel, whatever its quality. The repeated heating necessary with this hard-to-work steel will cause it to lose more of its good qualities than it has gained by the continuation of the operation of the furnace. Finally, it will always be difficult to obtain very neat, well-finished products with this steel, because it will have many cracks; but it can be employed between two pieces of iron or two pieces of mediocre steel. This shows that there is a limit beyond which the perfection of the steel cannot be pushed whatever one may try, for it cannot be made finer and harder without becoming more difficult to work.

Whatever [56] the shape of the furnace, whatever the shape of the crucibles, it is almost impossible that all the crucibles heat equally. It is not even possible that all the bars in a large crucible share equally in the action of the fire. This remark indicates that the crucibles and the different parts of the crucibles should be filled with bars of different thicknesses because the thinner bars require a shorter time or less forceful heating to become steel. It is unnecessary, however, to go so far as to reduce the thicknesses precisely in the same proportion in which the degrees of heat decrease. This would be too great a task and a useless one. Bars of three or four different thicknesses will be enough for any furnace. In the following I shall give a few examples, which would not have seemed necessary if experience had not taught me how careless are those who work without attention to principles. Together with M. Geofroy and M. de la Hire, the Younger, since deceased, I was appointed a few years ago to examine the experiments which a foreigner aspired to perform. I was much surprised to see that of two crucibles, which he was to place side by side and which had to heat as equally as it is possible in one and the same furnace, one was filled with iron in the form of quite large square bars and the other with iron which he had ordered to be made almost as thin as sheet iron. He claimed, however, that all this iron would become [57] steel in the same time, because, he said, he had given a stronger compound to the former than to the latter.

A very important remark must be made here—namely, that it not only requires more time to convert thicker bars into steel but the time necessary to effect the conversion does not increase in the same proportion as their thickness. I mean that, if iron bars 3 lines thick become steel in twelve hours of firing in a particular furnace, twenty-four hours of the same firing will not make steel out of bars 6 lines thick. Even if they are of the same width as the former, they will require more than thirty-six hours of the same firing.* Repeated experiments with bars of different thicknesses have made me realize this.

It follows from this observation that it will be profitable to use thin bars if possible, because it saves time and charcoal. It is true that thin bars have required more of both in order to have reached this state and that in proportion to their weight it takes longer to forge them when they are withdrawn from the furnace than it would take to forge thicker bars; but one saves with interest in the furnace the amount spent additionally in the forge. There is an added advantage in the use of thin bars if one assumes everything else to be the same, for they become more perfect steel. The observations that follow will show [58] the reasons. Even the ordinary workmen who use fine steels prefer the little bars to others because they save them the labor of drawing them out and flattening them by forging.

Several factors may concur in preventing the effect of the fire from being proportional to the thickness of the bar. Two pieces of iron which together equal a third in thickness, while each of them alone has the same height and length as the third, equal

* The fact that Réaumur's times do not vary as the square of the thickness (as in an ideal diffusion experiment) is due to the fact that much time is taken in reaching a steady temperature.

the third in volume but considerably surpass it in surface. It follows that this third bar must require more than twice the time to be heated than each of the thin pieces needs. It is true that the parts of the fire have to cover only twice the distance to reach its center, but, since its surface is not twice that of the thin piece, there are not twice as many parts of fire that act on its surface as in the case of the small piece. For the same reason, the amounts of sulfurous and saline parts supplied by the compound to the two [different] pieces are not proportional to their volume. In each instant the thin piece can receive more of them relative to its mass. When I said [see p. 47] that the compound is not burned in long heating, I only wished to make it understood that it is not reduced to ashes. It certainly becomes weaker every moment, every moment a portion of its oily matter [59] is consumed and a portion of its salts is removed; but this reduction in the strength of the compound is not proportional to the firing time. I mean that, for instance, much more sulfur is burned during the first hour than during the second one, more during the second hour than during the third. Iron which has been exposed to the action of this compound for twelve hours will therefore have been exposed, one might say, to an action more than twice [*sic*]* as vigorous or to the action of a compound more than twice as effective as iron that has been exposed to this action for twenty-four hours, since the compound that was fired during the last twelve hours does not have the same activity as that which was fired during the first twelve hours. The effect of the difference in activity of the compound cannot be compensated for by increasing the quantity of this compound. Furthermore, there are limits which must not be exceeded, for if two quantities of combustible material (whether wood, sulfur, or whatever), one being twice as large as the other, are simultaneously placed in identical fires, the larger one will be burned in less than twice the time.

Another rule obtained from the preceding observations is that it is always better to fill the furnace with flat iron than with square iron and that, of two bars of equal length and equal

---

* The "twice" on this and the following line is obviously an error for "half."

weight or volume, the thinner one becomes steel in less time than the [60] thicker bar. For instance, if, of two bars, both of which are 1 foot long, one is 1 inch wide and 3 lines thick and the other one has been forged into a square 6 lines wide on each side, they are of equal volume and weight; but the flat bar will be converted into steel much more promptly than the thick bar.

The Third Memoir, Containing Instructions
on How To Make Trials
on a Small Scale

HE FIRST application of the observations made in the preceding memoir will be to serve as a guide in trials on a small scale. Such exploratory tests may seem attractive to anybody who likes to experiment or wishes to contribute to the improvement of our art; but they are, in addition, absolutely necessary for those who wish to undertake the conversion of iron into steel on a large scale. What has been said about the compounds has made it clear that they must be put together differently and also used in different amounts with irons of different quality. This will be reconfirmed and further explained in the memoir in which the different kinds of iron will be examined with regard to their tendency to become steel. Indeed, it will be attempted in the same memoir to determine the characteristics of each kind of iron and what can be expected from it. However, the rules which will then be given cannot be relied upon to such an extent that we can dispense with trials. Exploratory tests are the surest way of discovering how to treat any particular kind of iron that is to be converted into steel. A few [62] days suffice to perform all the experiments necessary to make everything sufficiently clear, and such experiments may save much unnecessary expense and place one in a position where one is certain of what one is doing thereafter.

It is left to everybody's choice on how small a scale he will make his trials. If several kinds of iron are to be investigated, the tests can hardly be made on too small a scale in the beginning. It always results in more saving, as the size of the crucibles varies in proportion to the quantity of iron which is to be inclosed in them.

Crucibles of any shape may be used; but there are some that are more suitable than others, depending on the circumstances under which they are to be employed. If a great number of trials is to be made at once, there are none more convenient than oblong crucibles of little depth (Pl. 1, *A B C D*). I could not say how many of these I have used that were only about 3 inches long, 1 inch wide, and hardly more than 1 inch deep. They will easily take two or three pieces of iron (Pl. 1, *R*) which are thin and yet thick and long enough to be worked after they have been converted into steel.

The advantage of crucibles of this shape is that they can be placed side by side and one on top of another (Pl. 2, *G*). Several of them can be luted together, so that they form a stack, and they can then all be exposed to the fire at once as if [63] a single, large crucible were exposed. Before arranging the crucibles so as to make up this pile, they should be carefully numbered, which is easy. Then one writes down the order in which they have been arranged and writes down at the same time the kind of iron and the amount of the compound contained in each numbered crucible. To rely only on one's memory is not safe enough in deciding what causes the differences in the outcome of the experiments.

Square crucibles (Pl. 1, *F L M*)* may be used as well as the oblong kind, but they are less suitable for the smallest trials. Large square crucibles of little depth can be used in place of several oblong crucibles, which is done by dividing them into several parts by partitions made of clay or sheet iron (*N OO PP QQ*).

There are cases where round, deep crucibles can be used, but it is rarely done except when only one test is to be made at a time, or else when the fire in which they are to be placed makes it possible for the crucibles to be laid down. The reason for this will be given later.

The crucibles must have covers of the same clay of which they are made. These could be shaped like the tops of boxes (*C2*), but this would take longer. There are two other suitable ways of making them fit well even though they are left flat: either by

---

* The numerous typographical errors in letters and numerals referring to the illustrations have been corrected by the translator.

carving a guideway all around the upper rim of the crucible [64] before it is fired—the labor spent on this guideway does not take long, nor is it difficult (*I K*)—or by cutting a rabbet around the rim of the crucible (*D F*) and a similar one around the rim of the cover (*E G*). Both ways are good, but the guideways are better than simple rabbets. Round crucibles should have covers or, rather, stoppers like bottles, but it is best to leave on these stoppers something that overhangs the rim of the crucible (*e f*).

Even if the cover fits ever so accurately on the crucible, it would be difficult not to leave any gaps, and the joints must therefore always be luted (*V X X*). If the whole crucible were covered with lute, it would simply become that much tighter. Lute always protects the compound from possible accidents because of a crack which may form in the wall. The lute covers such cracks, and, even if it melts, it runs into the cracks and sometimes closes them quite well.

The lute that is needed is nothing but simple, sandy clay; it is unnecessary to mix it with ground glass, salt, and iron filings, which is the practice on various other occasions. If it seems difficult to get an idea of the degree to which this clay must be sandy, take the kind in which the brass or iron founders cast their products [65] and which they call "molding sand." It is an unctuous sand—a sand whose grains hold together because of the clay with which they are mixed. The driest sand mixed with clay would be suitable for making such lute. Concerning the manner of using it, all it amounts to is to temper this sandy clay with water to the consistence of paste and to spread it over the places that are to be luted.

Nothing shall be said here about the proper clay for the crucibles. Those who wish to learn which clay is suitable for them will find instructions in the next memoir.

The potters will make them for you in any shape you wish. If there is no potter handy and if you wish to make them yourself, it will be easy. You need a mold. The mold required here is nothing but a piece of wood, which must have the shape that the cavity of the crucible is intended to have (*S T c g*) and which has a handle by which it is held while it is covered with the prepared clay and the clay is tamped down. The job is so simple

that you can do it without waiting until my résumé of this subject in *The Art of the Potter* has appeared in print.

Before the iron is placed in the crucibles, these must be fired.
This is something a potter does without fail. Before the crucibles are fired, they must be thoroughly dried; but this warning
still [66] concerns only those who will make their own. If there
is no furnace available which would be suitable for firing them,
they should be covered with unlit charcoal which is lit gradually. Long firing cannot spoil anything, and, if they were only
moderately fired, they would still be good. In case of an emer-
gency any vessel made of fire-resistant clay can be used instead of
crucibles. Our stoneware pots, for example, still known in the
Kingdom under the name of butter pots, are suitable provided
they are well luted and heated gradually. After they have once
become hot, they can withstand the greatest heat. A rounded
fragment of a tile put on the pot and well luted will take the
place of a cover.

In trials on a very small scale, the recommendations given in
the first memoir concerning the amount of compound should be
disregarded. The smaller the trials, the greater should be the
ratio of compound to iron, because the compound near the walls
of a crucible is in a position to be burned; and, since small crucibles have more surface than the large ones in proportion to
what they contain, there is more compound to burn.

After the crucibles have been chosen and the compounds prepared, a layer of compound is put on the bottom of the crucible,
and then the layer of compound is followed by a layer of iron
consisting of several pieces or a single piece, depending on the
width of the crucible. [67] Even if the space between the pieces
of iron in the same layer is small, it is enough; but they must not
be quite so close to the walls of the crucible. A second layer of
compound is put on this layer of iron (*Y Z*), and, if the height of
the crucible permits it, this is followed by a second layer of iron
and then by a third layer of compound.

Regardless of the number of layers of iron, one always starts
and ends with a layer of compound. These two, and especially
the top layer, must always be thicker than the others, for they
are closer to the walls, and the top one is more exposed to [leak-

age of] air. When the layers of compound between the layers of iron are about 2 lines thick after they have been well pressed down, it will be sufficient. An empty space, even though very small, should be left between the cover and the last layer. After the cover has been put on, it is luted, and, when the lute is dry, the crucible is ready to be transferred to the fire.

The advantages of using thin iron were pointed out in the previous memoir. When only small trials are considered, the pieces of iron that are to be tested should be drawn out into flat sections which are at the most 2 or 3 lines thick and 5 or 6 lines wide.

Round crucibles are inconvenient, because they do not permit the iron to be put down in layers. The pieces of iron would have to be too short unless these crucibles [68] had an extraordinarily large diameter, and, in addition, there would be many places that could not be filled. If this kind of crucible is to be used, it must therefore first be partly filled with compound, and small bars or flat sections of iron (*a b*) must then be introduced into the compound. These bars or flat pieces are in a vertical position when the crucible is upright, so that, if the crucible does not heat evenly over its entire height, one and the same piece, one and the same bar, will be found to have become steel of a different quality at different places. This happens much more seldom with a bar placed horizontally, for a crucible heats up nearly evenly everywhere at a particular height.

Thus, if trials are to be made on a somewhat larger scale—for instance, on 8 or 10 pounds of iron—oblong crucibles should always be used or square ones of a height in proportion to the furnace and to the quantity of iron that is to be tried out.

It would be easy to make these exploratory tests wherever there are kilns for firing brick, pottery, faïence, lime, plaster, etc. After being well luted—either each separately or luted together to form a stack if that seems better—the crucibles are placed into those parts of the kilns where the heat is the strongest. If the crucibles have no accident, if they do not melt, and if they have been filled with very thin pieces of iron, [69] these can be converted into steel during the time necessary to fire the clay objects or to calcine the rocks with which the kilns have been charged. If they are not entirely steel, they must be put back into the same fire a second time.

Kilns like these are not found everywhere, but forges are, belonging to locksmiths, cutlers, toolmakers, farriers, and others working in iron. Any forge of this kind can be adapted for the trials, and it can also be prepared very quickly for the purpose by making a kind of furnace out of it. All one needs is a baffle similar in a way to those the silversmiths place in their forges when they wish to melt silver. The baffle that is needed here (Pl. 1, *k;* Pl. 2, *A B*) is a piece of fired earthenware shaped like an arc, or, better still, a three-sided piece of earthenware, two sides of which would stand perpendicular on the third if the angles joining them were not rounded. In this case one of the sides, the one that must be in front in the forge, is shorter than the others (Pl. 2, *B*). The size and height of this baffle are determined by the number of tests that are to be made at one time. By putting several baffles one on top of another, it is also possible to build a kind of furnace (*O P*).

If one is caught unprepared, it is possible to build in any forge something equivalent to a baffle if [70] moderately heat-resistant paving stones are available. Brick and pieces of fired earthenware arranged one on top of another could also take their place. The crucibles are put in the middle of this kind of small furnace on a brick or a fragment of a tile which is a little higher than the tuyère. All the empty space between the wall of the forge and the side walls of the baffle is filled with charcoal, and then the bellows is started to work—first comparatively slowly and finally as fast as desired. Care should be taken continuously to arrange it so that a fair amount of charcoal always lies between the tuyère and the crucibles. If the blast were directed immediately at the crucibles, it would cool them; but, if it were to find only a small amount of charcoal in its way and the flame were to be hurled directly at the crucibles without being broken, it would melt them unless they were made of an excellent clay. It is also advisable to leave some empty space all around the [inside of the] baffle so that the blast can circulate; and, in order to make it more inclined to do so, an opening may be left at that side of the baffle which is parallel to the wall of the forge.

This method of heating is very convenient if only a few tests are to be made at a time, and, if only one is to be made, it is the fastest of all possible methods. Further, for just one trial it is not even necessary to rig up the baffle. A few bricks or stones suffice to hold the charcoal, or one could even do [71] without them. In this case, for a single trial made in the forge, I prefer the round crucible. I use one in the form of a true hollow cylinder (Pl. 1, *d*), which everywhere between its walls has a diameter of about 2 inches and is 7–8 inches long. After some compound has been put in this crucible, two or three pieces of thin, or flat, iron are pushed in. It is then filled up with compound and stoppered, and the stopper is luted in, after which the crucible is laid down in the forge and covered with live charcoal. The operator, who pulls the chain of the bellows with one hand (Fig. *h*), must hold in the other a pair of tongs with which he turns the crucible from time to time. (It is in order to make this turning easier that it is advisable to use a round crucible.) The blast of the bellows may then be forced a little more, for the spot where the flame has its greatest effect, and which might be inclined to melt if it were continually exposed to this greater heat, is heated a little less intensely when the crucible is turned. This method permits finishing the test in two or three hours at the most, and sometimes in one hour.

In this case it is even permissible to use mineral coal instead of charcoal, which will only accelerate the process.

If desirable, the crucible may stand upright instead of being laid down. Although it has little to stand on, [72] it is easy to hold it upright with charcoal; but, when it is standing, it is not as easy to turn it as when it is lying.

For the purpose of making trials on a somewhat larger scale, as of 8–10 pounds of iron at a time, and in order to make these trials fast, the most suitable furnace is that of the ordinary brass founders, those who cast all the small products made of this metal. It will be necessary more than once to speak of this furnace, and it might just as well be described now as later. Its walls inclose a cavity (Pl. 2, *a a b c d d e*) the section through which, taken at any height, is about 7 inches square. The depth of this cavity usually is 25–26 inches. This depth, or, what

amounts to the same thing, the height, of the furnace is divided
into two unequal parts by a plate of iron (*d d k k*) which first was
forged as a square of a size equal to the horizontal section
through the cavity of the furnace, after which its four corners
have been cut away (*o*). The part of the furnace that is over
[*sic*]* the plate (*e*) is the ashpit, and the height of this part is
always the one that is arbitrary. The plate actually is the bottom of the furnace. From this plate to the upper rim it is about
17 inches. It is on this plate that one places the crucible with the
metal that is to be melted [73] or heated. Charcoal surrounds
this crucible almost evenly on all sides. The charcoal is fired by
the blast of a double bellows.† A pipe conducts the blast of the
bellows into the part I have called the "ashpit," and from there
it quickly passes into the furnace through the four holes left by
the cutouts at each corner of the iron plate. Everywhere else the
plate touches the walls of the furnace; the cutouts are arcs of
circles.

The furnace is closed with a flat cover, which is fitted as well
as possible on the upper rim of the cavity. The open spaces remaining where it does not fit perfectly serve as a way of escape
for the air.

The walls of this kind of furnace are made of bricks laid flat
one on top of another; but, in order to protect these walls, in
order not to be forced to demolish them because the fire has
weakened them, they are faced with tiles which are as wide as
the faces of the cavity. These tiles are called the "lining" of the
furnace. When the furnace has to be repaired, all that has to be
done is to give it a new lining. In order to be able to make this
furnace wider or narrower at will, a layer of fire-resistant clay is
put between the brick and the lining. Any reduction of the
thickness of this layer made when the lining is changed is an
addition to the width of the furnace.

The iron plate is supported by two small [74] iron bars which
can be taken out and replaced. This also makes it easy to remove
the iron plate under certain circumstances when the founder

* *Dessus;* obviously a misprint for *dessous* ("under").

† Note that this furnace uses blast; it is not the usual brass founder's
natural-draft furnace.

finds it necessary, but they are not concerned with the use to which we wish to put the furnace at present.

It is possible to make in these furnaces exploratory tests on steels in crucibles like those used by the founders. As I said before, this has the disadvantage that the iron has to stand upright or that the pieces must be very short. It is better, therefore, to have oblong crucibles (*l i*) made. They can safely be made as long as one of the sides of the furnace is long, but their width must be such that the crucible does not reach the edges of the holes through which the blast enters.

If you do not wish to make use of a foundry furnace that is ready, if you wish to build one, this furnace should be made larger in one direction than in the other, so that the crucible that could be placed in it would not have to be as narrow as those which the ordinary furnaces can accommodate.

This crucible is not surrounded by charcoal on all sides as the round crucibles are, but it will nevertheless heat satisfactorily. One must even be careful not to heat it as strongly as possible, not to work the bellows too fast, or the iron might melt. When the crucible walls have become white, an attempt should be made to keep them at this color [75] and to prevent them from becoming red again; only enough heat should be supplied to maintain this condition.

Even if only one crucible is placed in the furnace, several irons can be tried out at one time and also several compounds if desired. If several irons are to be tried, they are first forged to the desired thickness and cut to pieces of a convenient length, and each iron is then marked with a letter or some other sign. If there are three irons, one is marked *A*, the other *B*, and the third *C*. If the width of the crucible permits placing all these pieces in every layer, their order should be changed when new layers are made. If in the first the order is *A*, *B*, *C*, it should be *A*, *C*, *B* in the second and *B*, *A*, *C* in the third layer.

If several compounds are to be tried out with the same iron or irons, a large crucible will take the place of several small ones. For this purpose one needs plates of sheet iron or of fired earthenware, which must not be too thin. One of these plates is put down horizontally each time it is desired to change the compound. A little clay thinned to the consistence of paste and spread over the last layer of the compound used will also serve satisfactorily to separate this one from the new compound that is to be tried.

If a special [76] trial furnace is to be constructed, purely for experimental purposes, I would not advise, however, to build one like those of the founders. It should be similar on a small scale to those which will be described for work on a large scale. The following memoirs will show to what tests the steels obtained in these exploratory experiments must be subjected in order to ascertain that they have all the proper qualities.

The Fourth Memoir, Dealing with the Design of a New Furnace Which Is Considered To Be the One Best Suited for the Conversion of Iron into Steel, and Containing Some General Observations on Other Furnaces

I N ORDER to make steel on a small scale, any furnace is all right, as long as only exploratory tests are to be made. This is not true for work on a large scale, which must be done at the lowest possible cost. I am not aware that the public has been given descriptions or designs of furnaces in which the conversion of iron into steel is accomplished on a large scale. In the countries where this work is done they are apparently no more inclined to share the dimensions of furnaces than to reveal the compounds used to effect this conversion. The artisans are more concerned with their little profits than with the general welfare and make a mystery of everything. I know of other types of furnaces of which they are jealous and which they make every effort not to show to others. What is said by Jousse* and some other authors [82] about the small furnaces into which crucibles with iron bars and suitable compounds are placed cannot be called "information."

All those who have attempted to convert the irons of the

---

* Mathurin Jousse, *La fidelle ouverture de l'art de serrurier ... ensemble un petit traicté de diverses trempes* (La Flèche, 1627). The author was an ironworker and carpenter who worked on the construction of the Jesuit college at La Flèche. He has several chapters describing the recognition of various kinds of iron and steel from the characteristics of their fracture, though, as Réaumur rightly says, he has little enough on the manufacture of steel. (See also note, p. 178.)

Kingdom into steel had large furnaces constructed which re-
sembled in part either the kilns of pottery works or those of
glassworks. For a few years we had two of these, built by Eng-
lishmen, which they claimed were like those used in England
for the same purpose. One was at Harfleur, and the enterprise
was backed by M. Law.* The other was at Saint-Germain-en-
Laye. They had benches on which to put the crucibles containing the iron, similar in a way to the benches of the kilns at glassworks on which the pots are placed. I personally have seen the
second of these furnaces, to the cost of which the Duke de
Noailles contributed, hoping to obtain a plant which would be
of use to the public.

Whatever furnaces may have been employed for our operation,
there is no doubt that the best are those in which a given effect
can be produced with the least consumption of wood or charcoal. As it is easier to heat a small furnace and its contents than
a large one, the operation is in general more rapidly completed
in the small furnaces. [83] In the smaller ones the conversion of
the iron takes place faster, and in the larger ones more iron is
converted at one time. But if these two favorable factors approximately outbalance each other, then the small furnaces
seem to deserve preference. I mean that if in a small furnace a
given quantity of iron is converted by starting the process over
again several times, and if in a large furnace of a different shape
during the same number of days and with the same quantity of
wood only the same quantity of iron is converted into steel as in

---

* John Law (1671–1729), Scottish financier, whom Philippe d'Orléans had
hired to refill the coffers of France (and his own) left depleted by Louis XIV.
Law based his scheme of refinancing on an exploitation of France's colonial
possessions. He established what amounted to a state bank in 1716, whose
notes for a time were regarded as more stable in value than coin, and played
an important role in promoting trade and industry in the provinces. The success of the bank enabled Law to float, with government indorsement, a great
scheme for the exploitation of Louisiana and other French colonial possessions. After a period of wild speculation and vast inflation, the "Mississippi
Bubble" collapsed in the spring of 1720, but somehow the British did not
learn from the spectacle, for the explosive growth and even more calamitous
collapse of the South Sea Bubble occurred later in the same year. The lack of
derogatory adjectives suggests that Réaumur wrote this reference to Law
before 1720.

the small furnace, then the small furnace is to be preferred. If, for instance, a large furnace accommodates 5,000 pounds of iron at a time but these can there be converted into steel in not less than ten days of continuous heating; and if a small furnace can hold only 500 pounds of iron at a time but they become steel in twenty-four hours including the time used to load and unload the furnace, and the consumption of wood is the same, then the small furnace deserves preference. It costs less to build, the risks are not so great, since there is less iron in the furnace at a time, and it is more agreeable and more convenient for many reasons to complete the operation in a short time.

It was shown in the second memoir that steel made very rapidly was in no way inferior to one made slowly. [84] Now then, since nothing is gained by operating slowly, there is no reason not to choose the fastest way; for it saves time as well as fuel. The effect produced by a hotter fire outweighs by far the additional consumption of wood and charcoal caused by this increase in heat. A thick iron bar surrounded by a very small fire, regardless of how long this fire is maintained, would never arrive at the point where it takes on a whitish-red color, while, if part of the charcoal which [in the former case] would be thrown on bit by bit were burned all at once, it would promptly give the bar this degree of heat.

But the most important of the means of increasing the activity of the fire is to have it urged by the blast. This is another increase in force that far outweighs the additional fuel cost. The enameler's lamp* furnishes proof of both of these propositions.

* The enameler's blowpipe is an interesting antecedent to the modern welding torch and to the blowpipe used so extensively by chemists and mineralogists for dry assay. Blowpipe analysis seems to have been started by the Swedish metallurgist Andreas Swab in 1738, but it was his countrymen Cronstedt, Bergman, and Berzelius who were principally responsible for its development. The Egyptians used mouth blowpipes in smelting and crucible-melting operations. The sixteenth-century authors Cellini and Biringuccio do not mention the use of the blowpipe for either soldering or enameling but laid the work directly on charcoal or bran fires, sometimes urged by bellows. It was, of course, but a small step from the latter to the use of an oil-lamp flame urged by an air jet. Kunckel (*Ars vitrariae experimentalis* [Amsterdam, 1679]) de-

By means of the enameler's blast the flame of his lamp softens the glaze in an instant, but the consumption of oil does therefore not become much greater. Ten times, one hundred times, as much oil burned in the same time without urging the flame through the blast would not have as much effect.

The preceding reflections are partly responsible for my determination to try to make steel in furnaces in which the heat of the fire is stimulated by bellows. [85] In this kind of furnace we are able to make it as hot as we wish merely by forcing more air into the furnace, and we can also decrease the heat by using less air. In the beginning I made use of the foundry furnace described in the previous memoir (Pl. 2). I was very successful in trials with 10 or 15 pounds of iron, and, in order to ascertain whether it was possible to work in this furnace on a large scale with the same success, I first had one built into which approximately 300 pounds of iron could be placed. When it came to trying this new furnace out, I encountered many obstacles which I had not expected. I shall report them, for they will show the necessity for the changes I have made, and they will give support to my belief that this type of furnace has been abandoned by others because they did not try hard enough to overcome these obstacles and that now furnaces have been chosen in which the operation takes much longer and is much more expensive.

I shall not again discuss at length that these furnaces are heated with wood charcoal. In order to take advantage of all the heat that this charcoal is capable of giving in this furnace, the iron should not be inclosed in boxes made of sheet iron or cast iron. The sheet iron would soon be burned, and the cast iron would soon be melting. To experiment, I once placed my bars into a cast-iron pot of ordinary thickness, and, although I was careful not to give the fire all the activity I could have given it,

---

scribed a little blast lamp for laboratory glass-blowing and mentions that it can be used for trying metal ores on a hollowed charcoal. Boyle (*Essay on the Great Effects of Even Languid and Unheeded Motion* [London, 1685]) remarks that he was able to melt not only the more fusible metals but even copper itself with a lamp or candle urged with "a small crooked pipe of metal or glass such as tradesmen . . . call a blowpipe."

[71]

the pot did not last one hour. [86] It melted and had holes in it at several places. Sheet iron, even though thick, would give no more reliable service.

We thus have to content ourselves with earthenware crucibles or something similar. Round crucibles will not do. You may recall the reasons given in the previous memoir. I had oblong crucibles made whose greatest dimension would just fit the whole width of the furnace. Their capacity was such that they could hold 75 pounds of iron with the ingredients necessary for their conversion. I was afraid that if I made them larger they would become difficult to handle—it would be difficult to put them in the furnace and, especially, to take them out again. In order to take advantage of the entire height of this furnace, I had four identical crucibles stacked one on top of another. This can be visualized if one assumes that the furnace marked *kk* on Plate 2 is built on a larger scale and that instead of the crucible (*i*) it contains several. The dotted lines [?] in this figure mark the separation of these crucibles from each other. But here is the great disadvantage of such an arrangement—the crucible at the bottom is loaded with the weight of the three others. This load, which can easily be borne by the cold crucible, is too much for it when it has become softened by violent heat. Its walls crack and sometimes collapse. Sometimes the crucible is entirely flattened, everything is thrown into confusion, [87] and one is fortunate if one loses only the crucibles, the charcoal, and the compound; for often part of the iron is burned. I have had several such experiences, even under circumstances where the lower crucible was not by far as heavily loaded as I just assumed [i.e., by three crucibles]. If the iron were contained in only two crucibles, the lower one would still carry too much of a load. One must concentrate therefore on taking advantage of the depth of these furnaces if the work in them is to be profitable.

A split crucible belongs to the type of accident that happens even in furnaces in which the heat is more moderate and the operation takes longer. The crucible is filled with substances which rarefy when they start to get hot. The lower layers of these substances are pressed down by the weight of the bars above them; but, when they expand, they lift these bars a little.

They exert a similar strain on the walls and the bottom of the crucible. In addition, the walls are necessarily under stress as they are being heated and tend to expand. They do not expand at the same rate on all sides, and the side which expands the most separates from its neighbor, and a rent is formed.

Finally, when crucibles are put one on top of another, it necessarily involves a loss of space—namely, of all the space occupied by the cover and the bottom [respectively] of the two crucibles that touch each other and any empty space between them.

A crucible [88] which alone would contain the iron which so far we have distributed over several would be less likely to have some of the disadvantages described in the foregoing, but it would have others. As said before, it would be difficult to place it in the furnace, at least unless it were put in place while empty, and it would always be difficult to take it out. Finally, if crucibles were satisfactory, they would be a considerable item of expense; for one would not dare trust them sufficiently to put them into the fire a second time.

However, one of my greatest objections to the use of foundry furnaces is that the holes through which the wind enters are inclined to stop up frequently. As long as it is only a question of keeping the fire burning for two or three hours, as for melting brass or silver, it is not difficult to open these holes. One knocks with a poker upon the hole and forces the stuff that covers it to fall into the ashpit. But, when the furnace is large and when the fire has been going for a long time, the walls of the furnace and those of the crucibles produce much vitrified matter which drops down from all sides, runs toward the holes, and stops them up in such a way that it is difficult to open them. Furthermore, they then stay open only for an instant, for new stuff will soon close them again. Each time they are reopened, the furnace gets cold, which causes considerable loss of time and charcoal.

Two expedients [89] which, it seems to me, come very easily to mind completely eliminate the trouble caused by either the use of crucibles or the vitrified matter which stops up the holes through which the wind must enter. In order to avoid the clogging, I have replaced the four holes that are flush with the bottom of the ordinary furnace by four tuyères like those of the forges of the locksmiths, toolmakers, etc. I have placed these tuyères vertically on the bottom of my furnace and so that their upper openings are about $2\frac{1}{2}$ inches or 3 inches above the bottom. I also have made them stand free, so that they do not touch the walls anywhere.

When the wind enters the furnace through openings that are 3 inches above the bottom, there is no reason to fear that these will become stopped up. Regardless of the amount of vitrified matter which collects in the furnace, there will never be enough to rise 3 inches over the entire width of the furnace.

If these tuyères are chosen to be as strong as those of the ordinary forges—in other words, if they have the shape and the dimensions of those in the sketch (Pl. 3, Figs. 7, 8), they will be satisfactory even if they are made of nothing but cast iron; but, if thin tuyères are used, they will not last. This was proved to me in my first tryout. I had been content with tuyères made of [90] flat bars about 2 lines thick, and they melted. Their openings became closed by their own material, which will never happen if the tuyères are as thick as those of the common forges.

In the following, I shall propose a solution for the trouble with the crucibles which will considerably decrease the cost of their manufacture, avoid loading them with the weight of the bars they inclose, avoid stacking them up one on top of another, reduce the risk of having them split, and make them last longer: I will not give up the use of clay. If it is well chosen, it is the best material of which they can be made, but I substitute square-cut plates of fired earthenware for the ordinary crucibles. Only two plates will contain the iron that would require several crucibles, and they will protect it better against the immediate action of the fire. These two plates suffice to hold 300 or 400 pounds of iron and more if desired.

In order to understand how two almost square plates can take the place of a very large and very solid crucible or of several smaller ones, it is necessary to know the principal changes I have made in the ordinary furnace and how my new furnace differs from it. Its size is not definitely fixed; but, in order to describe it more easily, I shall restrict myself to one which I had built and which is only just capable of holding 550 or 600 pounds of iron [91] comfortably but into which still more can be placed if the iron is thick. It will be shown later that on the same principle furnaces of any desired size can be constructed.

The inside of this furnace which is meant to make only 550 or 600 pounds of steel at a time has a square base or one almost square. Two of the sides that are parallel to each other (Pl. 3, Fig. 1, *ef ef*) are each 23–24 inches long, and the other two (*ee ff*) are 21–22 inches. The furnace keeps the same dimensions over its entire height, which is about 32 inches measured from its upper rim to its true bottom (Fig. 2, *gn*). Its true bottom is the place where it is separated from the ashpit (Figs. 2–5, *A*).

When I just said that the interior of this furnace is square over its entire height, I meant to give only a rough idea. The principal artifice of its design consists in eight guideways or slots for which I make allowance from top to bottom when the furnace is being built. They are grooves in two of the faces or walls which are parallel to each other. One of the faces has four of these guideways, and the other face has the other four (Pl. 3, Figs. 1–4, *g h i k;* Pl. 4, *D E E D*); they are identically placed on the two faces. I shall call two of the guideways of each wall the center guides (Pl. 3, *h i*) and the other two of the same wall the end guides (*g k*). The center guides are about 8 inches apart from each other, and both are at an equal distance from the middle of the face into which they are carved. [92] The end guides are each almost 3 inches from the end nearest them. Each guideway is approximately 2 inches or $2\frac{1}{2}$ inches deep and over 1 inch wide.

It is by means of these guideways that the plates of earthenware take the place of crucibles. Four plates together with the faces of the furnace make three crucibles which are only a few inches shorter than the height of the furnace itself. The two guideways placed opposite each other (Fig. 1, *h h i i*) receive one plate and hold it upright (*m*). The two center guides together with those parts of the faces and the bottom of the furnace which are between them form the largest of the crucibles (Pl. 3, Figs. 1–4, *m m;* Pl. 4, *A*). Each layer of iron in this crucible can consist of three bars, each bar being more than 2 inches wide, and the iron of all these bars weighs up to 300 or 350 pounds. This crucible alone requires two plates; each end plate forms another crucible with the face of the furnace parallel and nearest to it (Pl. 3, Figs. 1–4, *l l;* Pl. 4, *B*). The layers of iron in these crucibles can consist of only one bar of the same width as those of which there are three in each layer of the center crucible; or, if two bars are placed in each layer of these small crucibles, they must together not be much wider than one of the bars of the large crucible. The space between each center plate and the end plate nearest to it is the space where the charcoal is burned (Pl. 3, Fig. 1, *n n;* Pl. 4, *C C*). That part [93] of the bottom of the furnace corresponding to this space is where the tuyères (Pl. 3, Figs. 1–4, *n n*) are. Each tuyère is placed at the same distance from the plates, but they are closer by some inches to the walls of the furnace than to the center.

Although the guideways overlap the edges of the plates, these crucibles would not completely bar all entry to the flame unless the joints were carefully luted after the plates have been put in place. From what was said in the previous memoirs it is now known that the lute can be made of any sandy clay moistened to the consistence of paste. This lute, which easily enters the joints, stands up admirably, especially that which has been made to enter the part of the guideway located inside the crucible. When the guideways have been closed up with this clay, there is no reason to fear that the flame will penetrate into the crucible through the joints, and there is no other part of the plate that is as completely tight. In fact, instead of using a clay that vitrifies to stop up the guideways, I prefer to use lime which has been moistened a little. If it is put well inside the guideway, it sufficiently bars all passage to the flame, and it also has another favorable effect—that is, when the furnace run is finished and the plates must be taken out again, they can be loosened without effort. They do not adhere to the guideways, while it sometimes happens that the guideways become chipped when the empty spaces remaining [94] between them and the plates are closed up with a clay that vitrifies too easily.

The width of the plates must be such that they reach into the guideways on both sides without, however, extending all the way in to the back. This last requirement is the basis for one of the advantages of this arrangement over ordinary crucibles.

Every plate made of clay, every material in fact, expands as it is heated. The increase of volume is also rather considerable in a clay crucible heated to the point where it becomes white. Now then, whenever some part expands while it is bonded to others which do not expand at the same rate, the latter do it violence— they force it to bend and sometimes to break loose or to split. This is the effect produced by the junction of the sides of the crucibles; but it is different with our plates. When the fire makes them expand, they can advance into the guideways. There is nothing to buttress them, since the lute which we use does not fill the space between the edge of the plate and the back of the guideway; this space is always empty. I repeat—the lute only serves to close any empty space between the plate and that part of the guideway which overlaps this plate.

Although it is so easy for the plates to expand, it would still be difficult to prevent them from warping a little unless another simple precaution were also taken. By this I mean that they should not be made completely flat but should be given some curvature, [95] and care must be taken that the convex side forms the inside of the crucible and that the concave side is consequently turned toward the charcoal. All the concavity required is only 4 or 5 lines where it must be the greatest—that is, at the middle. As the result of this precaution one sometimes finds at the end of a furnace run that the plates are as straight, or as flat, as they would be if they had been expressly made that way. Fire tends to give convexity to the surface upon which it acts. It therefore straightens the plate as it heats it, for a body expands as it becomes hot and expands the more the hotter it becomes. The fire distends its parts. The surface of the plate which is outside of the crucible must therefore expand more than the one inside, a fact which necessarily results in a change of curvature that tends to straighten the plate. If the plate became more and more concave on the outside, the inner surface would have to expand more than the outside. The opposite happens and must happen if this concavity becomes smaller; then the length of the concave surface gradually becomes more nearly the same as the length of the convex surface.

No piece of fired earthenware is more easily made than my

plates; if they are more difficult to make than brick or four-faced tiles, it is only because they are larger. After the clay has been kneaded and [96] softened to the extent it should be, one takes a piece large enough to make a plate and transfers it to a wooden table without legs put, if convenient, right on the floor. This table is of the same size and shape that the earthenware plate is meant to have (Pl. 5, Fig. 2, *p*) and will first have been carefully dusted with clay reduced to a fine powder, or with fine sand or ashes, so that the moistened clay will not stick to it. This mass of clay is beaten either with mallets or with wooden paddles, or even with a flat bar of iron, for here almost any tool will serve. By this beating the clay is forced to stretch to the edges of the wooden table, and, in order to give it exactly the size and the shape of the table, all the clay that extends over the edges is then cut off with a knife (*y z*). Care must be taken not to beat so hard that the clay tears here and there, and to add new clay at spots that are too thin. If too much clay has been used, if the plate is thicker than it is meant to be, it can be made thinner by additional beating—by forcing more clay to extend beyond the table and again removing this clay with a knife. Anybody who has tried to make three or four plates will know more about it than he can here be told.

Since all clay shrinks in drying, it is advisable to give the plates larger [97] dimensions in all directions than they are meant to have after they are fired. The softer the clay is, the more it shrinks in drying, but generally it is enough if the plate is made 1 inch or $1\frac{1}{2}$ inches larger in all directions than the furnace requires. If one errs here by too much or too little, it is easy to do better the next time.

It is really necessary to have several wooden tables suitable for the making of plates, for it is better at least to allow a plate to stiffen for several hours on the table on which it was made, as this reduces the risk of breaking it when it is lifted off. Furthermore, a very even floor is needed on which to lay the plates as they are made and where they are allowed to dry as it suits them, little by little; for, when they dry rapidly, they warp. If they seem to be inclined to do that, they should be weighted down somehow, as, for instance, by iron bars. They must be turned over as soon as the top side begins to get hard.

When they are dry, they are fired; but this should be done only when they are thoroughly dry. The safest way of having them fired is to put them in a potter's kiln for earthenware. If such a kiln is not available, they could be put in an ordinary oven, which must be heated little by little and as slowly as possible. If they are fired abruptly, there is the risk of having them burst or split.

When I have [98] had no oven, I sometimes had them fired between two plates of iron, above and below which I put charcoal, with the plates lying down flat. Or I had them fired in a different way (*r s t u*)—that is, I put them upright into an iron framework made of two horizontal frames supported by four uprights. On the lower frame were pieces of nailrod, which formed a grate on which the plates were stood upright with a space of at least 1 inch or $1\frac{1}{2}$ inches between them. On the upper frame there were more rods, perpendicular to those of the grate; these served to hold the plates, to prevent them from touching each other. The spaces between two plates were filled with small pieces of charcoal, which were also placed under the lower frame and over the plates. This is a pretty satisfactory method of firing but not as satisfactory as firing in kilns or ovens.

Considering everything, however, the most important thing in this connection is the choice of the material of which these plates must be made. People living near glassworks need no instructions; it suffices to tell them that the plates should be made of the same types of clay of which the glassmakers make their pots and, better still, to have them fashioned by the same men who make these pots. In this way, the mixture, which must always be compounded of clay that has previously been fired and clay that has not, will contain these ingredients in more proper proportions.

The ordinary [99] kinds of crucible clay may be used if the kinds employed for the pots used in glassworks are not available. The crucible clays are the same clays of which tiles and brick are made. But instead of mixing sand with these clays, as one does in making tiles and brick, in order to make crucibles and these plates, the clays must be mixed with at least one-third of grog made of butter pots or stoneware pots. This grog is nothing but such old pots smashed up and reduced to grains of the size of coarse grit, or almost like the grains of brick or of broken tile ground up for ordinary cement. One could even use brick, broken tile, or fragments of ground-up tiles, if the tile of the country where one finds oneself is excellent tile.

In large cities like Paris, the ragmen also collect broken stoneware pots to sell them to the makers of crucibles. In the country it would not be so easy to recover the fragments of such pots. It is then necessary to have small bricks made—either entirely of clay or those in which only a little sand is used. These bricks must be fired as much and more than ordinary brick and can be ground up and mixed with the fresh clay of which the plates are to be made.

There are types of clay that must be washed several times, which means that they must be repeatedly kneaded in water in order to be cleansed of their salts. [100] But the best is to have a clay that is known to be perfectly fire-resistant. In many glassworks it is necessary to bring this kind of clay in from very far, and the transport is the most expensive part about it. However, this is an expense which we must not hesitate to incur in connection with our steel furnaces.

The more fire-resistant the clay, the less need there is for making the plates thick. It is much better to have thin plates, for they and consequently the bars which they inclose heat much more rapidly. In order to take advantage of this fact, an effort must be made not to let oneself be forced to use plates that are an inch thick. If the clay is excellent, one can make plates no more than 7 or 8 lines thick. Crucibles made of the clay of Beauvais, although still thinner, are resistant for a long time to the most violent heat of the fire, and it is regrettable therefore that their resistance to cooling is so low. In short, we should apply ourselves to everything connected with the making of plates as to one of the most important aspects of our art.

Let us go back to the furnace and finish the discussion dealing with the arrangement of the plates, so that together with the walls they form very tight crucibles. On the bottom of the furnace where each plate is to rest there must be a guideway similar to those on the sides; or, better still, the spaces on the bottom of the furnace which are to become [101] the bottoms of the crucibles should be made to be at least 2 inches higher than the rest. The plates will then come down below these higher places. This arrangement can be seen on Plate 5 in Figures 2, 3, and 4. Lute put inside of each crucible against each plate will make the bottom joints very tight.

It remains to give each of our crucibles a cover. Again it is essential to have these covers close well to prevent the flame from penetrating inside and also to prevent considerable evaporation of salts, as said before, as the compound is weakened by everything that is lost by sublimation. After having tried different kinds of covers, I prefer the ones that are made to overhang like those of all boxes. The flanges of the covers go down by about an inch below the edges of the plates (Pl. 4, *Z Z2;* Pl. 3, Figs. 4, 5), and they terminate at some distance from the ends of the covers, because the covers are a little better made if they are a little longer than the crucibles on which they are placed. The extra length rests in slots cut into the end walls of the furnace (Pl. 4, *a*). Here, as elsewhere, lute will again close any possible gaps left by the joints.

Besides the effect which is the reason for putting the covers on, there is the additional very good one that their flanges hold the upper edges of the [102] plates down. They thus prevent these plates from warping upward, which is the direction in which they would warp the most. Instead of leaving the upper sides of the covers flat, they may be given a slope. The upper side of the cover of the center crucible will have the same slope on both sides; but the upper sides of the covers of the end crucibles will have only one slope—toward the fire. This design facilitates the falling of the pieces of charcoal (Pl. 4, *l m n;* Pl. 3, Fig. 3, *u x y*).

Still another cover is needed, much larger than the others, to close the opening of the furnace itself. If the furnace were left open above, much more fuel would be consumed and the crucibles would not be heated as much. This cover could, of course, be flat like those of the furnaces of the brass founders, but it is much better if it is arched into a low vaulted roof. I shall give no definite rules concerning the height which this arch should have but shall say only that the covers are not right if they are made flatter than the one I have shown (Pl. 4, *o p q r s* and *5*) and that, if they are raised much more, the furnace heats less well because the place that reverberates the flame would be farther away from the crucibles. There may be a thousand little variations in the construction of this cover, but I shall point out only what is more or less essential. It shall be several inches thick, made of good clay similar to the kind used for the plates. It can [103] be put on the furnace before it is fired but not before it is thoroughly dry. Tears which may form in it are not to be feared as much as those which may form in the plates. All that matters is that the parts of this cover hold together. It will last a very long time if it is made thick and of good clay and care is also taken to tie it in two or three places as shown in the figure (*o q*). The ties are frames made of four thin iron bars, two of which are pierced on both ends so that the ends of the other two can be slipped through. These have screw threads on which nuts are fastened which hold the assemblage together. Ties assembled any other way would not for long grip the cover, for, the more the cover is exposed to the fire, the more it shrinks in volume. By turning the nuts, it is easy to compress it as much as necessary to prevent the widening of the cracks which may appear in it.

The top of this cover has a round opening (*r*), a few inches in diameter, which is closed with a stopper (Pl. 4, 7) when desired. This is the opening by which the charcoal enters the furnace. The stopper itself has a hole in which a smaller stopper (Pl. 4, *9*) is set. This hole is opened when a little air is to be admitted to the furnace. For letting in more air when necessary there are still four more small holes [in the stopper] not far from the large one, each of which has its own stopper. The opening [104] in the middle [of the roof] is surrounded by four smaller ones (*r s*) which with their stoppers serve as registers. Finally, at least two or four other openings are needed; two of these are located so that they are approximately opposite the middle of the spaces in the furnace between the center crucible and one of the end crucibles—that is, the spaces where the charcoal must fall.

When the charcoal enters the furnace, it falls on top of the center crucible. The two openings of which I have just spoken make it possible to reach into the furnace with a little iron rod with which the burning charcoal is then guided to the space between the crucibles.

The last-mentioned openings will be kept closed unless there is reason for pushing the iron rod into the furnace. When it is necessary to create a draft in the furnace and to give the flame an outlet, it is better to give it this outlet through openings that are very close to the middle of the cover; for, in order to get there, the flame must pass over the center crucible and will heat it more.

The coals will not stay so long on the cover of the center crucible if this cover is given some convexity, which is simple, as previously indicated.

Although I have said that the large cover of the furnace is vaulted and that the vault is inside, there must be a flange (*q*) on the outside, a few inches high, which forms [105] a square whose sides are parallel to and half or three-quarters as long as those of the base. This flange can be made of sheet iron. It serves, as will be explained later, to hold pieces of charcoal which are set afire there before they are passed into the furnace.

Finally, it is advisable that the flange [*sic*]* of the furnace have a rabbet on which the cover can rest.

The cover is lifted only when the furnace is emptied or charged. If it is too cumbersome to be lifted by hand, this can be done either by a lever suspended over the furnace from a gallows-like support or by a pulley over which a chain passes. Whether the chain is connected with the lever or passes over the pulley, it will be attached to an iron grapple, and this grapple will be hooked to pins, also of iron, which are part of the ties around the furnace [see p. 84] or to some other spot that is considered more suitable. In this connection, everyone can choose the expedients that suit him best; the one illustrated on Plate 5, Figure 1, is satisfactory.

When steel has been made [repeatedly] in a furnace from iron bars of the same quality and the same thickness, one knows ap-

* *Rebord;* misprint for *bord* (''rim'').

proximately for how many hours such bars must be fired in order to be converted into good steel. But one never knows it accurately enough. There is no certainty that the air has blown with the same force [106] in different furnace runs or that the charcoal has burned with the same intensity; and dryness and moisture also cause differences. Further uncertainty is introduced by changing the irons or using iron of a different thickness. If one does not wish to work blindly, it is absolutely necessary to be able to withdraw from different locations in the furnace bars which after being tested permit one to judge the condition of the others. This is easy in our furnace by means of certain openings which have not yet been mentioned. They resemble windows which make it possible, if you wish, to see what goes on in each crucible (Pl. 3, Fig. 2, *q q2 q3;* Pl. 4, *F F2 F3*). In building the furnace, one leaves these openings. I would advise to allow for at least three in each crucible, at different levels, one over another, and to make them only 1 inch or 2 inches less wide than the crucible is when the plates are in position. They should be at least 5 inches high, and the discussion that follows seems to indicate that they should be higher. Whatever the size of these openings, each must have a plug of the same shape which must be as long as the furnace [wall] is thick. These plugs are made of the same clay as the plates and the covers. Each time they are put in place, the joints must be carefully reluted.

These openings [107] weaken the structural stability of the furnace somewhat, but this is more than counterbalanced by strengthening the furnace at four different levels by iron ties (Pl. 4, *K K K K*). These ties may be made of iron straps which are bent at right angles as often as necessary. The ends will be welded together so as to form a frame made of one piece and of the right size for the place where it will be located; but it would be still better to make the ties like those of which I spoke in describing the cover [i.e., the roof; see p. 82].

It is optional whether all the openings are located on the same side of the furnace or distributed over the two sides at different levels. Even if the stoppers fit ever so exactly, the iron may heat a little less near the openings than it would if the masonry were all one uniform block; but the amount by which the heat may be reduced cannot be considerable. If all the openings are to be on one side, all that is necessary is to give the tuyères on that side somewhat larger mouthpieces than the other tuyères have. Since the wind will then flow more freely on this side, it will maintain a greater heat.

Thus, instead of trying to reduce the openings we provide in the furnace, perhaps we should be tempted to experiment with leaving one side of each crucible practically open from top to bottom and to [108] have solid masonry only at those locations where the ties must be applied. Several favorable consequences seem to make this an attractive proposition; for, in addition to the possibility of withdrawing bars at any furnace height desired, there are other features that are rather important. There would be the convenience of charging and emptying the crucibles from the sides—a convenience which is of importance to those who wish to take advantage of all the heat the furnace has absorbed. If the furnace is charged or emptied from above, it is necessary to wait until it has become colder than when it is charged or emptied from the sides. The former method forces the operator to have his face directly over the upper openings of the crucibles and to plunge his arms rather deep into the crucibles, but there is no necessity at all for this in charging from the side.

The great advantage is, however, that one is constantly in a position to see what happens at every level of each crucible. There is no possibility of repairing accidents that happen to crucibles placed in ordinary furnaces, while the openings under consideration would make it easy to correct those which happen to the plates that take the place of crucibles and make it the easier the larger the openings are in the sides. If one of these plates develops a considerable crack or if a hole should form, this crack or hole can be stopped up with pieces of broken tile or with [109] pieces of fired earthenware in the form of plates which are thinner than the usual tile fragments. The tile fragment is rubbed with ground glass or with low-melting lute and is then introduced into the crucible between the layers of iron and the plates. In this way the largest holes can be closed. When a less important accident occurs, when only light cracks have formed which nevertheless would give access to a small flame which at long last would consume the compound and reduce it to ashes, fresh compound can be added to replace that which is burned; it can be pushed wherever desired with a small rod or a small, thin piece of iron.

When the fire has burned in the furnace for some time, everything sinks; for, by drying alone, the compound decreases in volume so that a large empty space is left in the upper part of the crucible. By means of plugs which can be taken out when desired, one makes use of this space by putting in it iron bars which are thinner than those put in at first, together with the compound that seems necessary. Since these bars are thinner, they become steel at the same time as the others.

Perhaps we shall learn through experience how to turn these openings to still greater advantage; perhaps experience will indicate that the crucibles should not be charged with anything but iron that is already heated to the degree necessary for it to become steel, which would save considerable time and charcoal. [110] Support of this theory may be found in some of the observations related in the second memoir. They indicated that a very great part of the time during which the fire, or the furnace, is active is spent in bringing the iron to the point where the compound can have its effect on it—that is, in heating the iron sufficiently to make it whitish-red. It would take only very little time until the same quantity of bars turned red or white in an open fire. The only difficulty remaining, and in connection with which some experimentation is needed, is to find out how the compound which is already in the crucible can be most easily distributed nearly evenly between the layers of bars which would be placed in it white-hot. Several expedients present themselves. One of the simplest might be to give each end of the bars, as well as the middle, two blows with the chisel and to leave the chips which the chisel has partly detached standing away from the rest. This would not much prolong the operation, and these small protruding parts would prevent the bars from touching each other and create between them spaces where the compound could go.

Another expedient would be to use pieces of iron wire as large in diameter as the layers must be thick. These would be placed crosswise over the bars of the bottom layer, and the bars of the following layer would be laid on the iron wires. As the points of contact between [111] the bars and the iron wire would be very small, the conversion of the bars into steel would not be noticeably slower at these points than elsewhere. It will be possible to think of many other ways of charging the furnace with hot iron if one looks for them. Perhaps the mere indication that here is a possibility to save money will make someone wish to investigate further.

The more open the furnace is to be, the greater will be the necessity for increasing the number of the ties of which I have spoken above, or at least for increasing their strength. This can be very easily arranged. As soon as bars of a certain thickness are used, the furnace will have all the strength that is needed. At the locations chosen for placing the ties little setbacks are carved out, which, if you wish, will be only as deep as the tie itself is thick; and it is these setbacks which hold the plugs [*sic*]* in place.

The plugs, or at least some of them, will be better if they themselves have an opening parallel to their length and reaching from one end to the other (Pl. 4, *O P Q R S*). A small plug of a size to fit this opening will close it. If all one wishes to see is how far the firing of the crucibles has progressed, all that is necessary is to pull out one of these small plugs.

In addition to all the openings of which I have spoken, it is advisable to provide for at least two more in each furnace; these will be opposite the middle of the spaces that receive the charcoal (*I I*). It is not necessary that they be very large, and each [112] will be closed by something like a little door. Their purpose is to make it possible to pass a small iron rod through them with which to stir up the charcoal when this seems advisable. Sometimes they are used to permit entry to a poker or a heavy iron bar, which is thrust horizontally into the opposite face of the furnace. This poker placed horizontally holds up the pieces of charcoal; it prevents them from coming down too fast, which must be done under certain circumstances—especially when the charcoal is too fine. These openings are also used when the bot-

* *Bouchons;* probably misprint for *bandes* ("ties").

tom of the furnace is to be cleaned, when the vitrified matter is to be removed.

This furnace is built of bricks, which are bonded together with a good, unadulterated clay or with clay prepared like crucible clay—or at least everything that is close to the interior of the furnace is thus constructed. Ordinary mortar made with lime and sand is not suitable for structures that must withstand violent heat; it may at best be used to build the outside and to coat the entire exterior of the furnace itself. The bricks, especially those which come close to the interior, must be of the kind that is fire-resistant. If such bricks are not available, they must be specially made either of the clay used for glassworks pots or at least of the clay used for ordinary crucibles mixed with grog made of stoneware. It is absolutely necessary to have some of these highly fire-resistant bricks, though not many. It is enough if they are used to build the four upright columns between the three crucibles.

Alternatively [113] each of these columns can be made of a single piece of prepared clay, a piece which must be as long as the furnace is high, as wide as the space that must be left between two plates, and about 7–8 inches thick. After these pieces have been allowed to dry well and have also been fired thoroughly, everything by which their thickness exceeds the amount needed for the guideways is inclosed in the masonry. Furthermore, to help keep these pieces in place and decrease the danger of warpage during the time when they are still soft, during the time when they are molded, three or four pieces of iron are inserted in each one at different levels. Each of these pieces is forked at both ends. When the clay columns are set in place, these iron cramps will be in a horizontal position, and where they protrude from the columns they are locked in the masonry.

Something that would be still better, however, would be to make at least these columns of stones like those of which the *hearths* of the furnaces are built in which iron ore is smelted. It cannot be difficult to find this kind of stone in most of those places which will be given preference in choosing a location for a steelworks—namely, a place near forges. If it comes to the worst, these stones could be brought in from afar as one is also sometimes forced to do for ore-smelting furnaces. If the whole interior of our steel furnace [114] were built of such stones, it would therefore only be more durable.

Now our furnace is built. I also assume that the plates are in their places and that the joints have been luted with all the care I have suggested. The next step is to charge it and to light the fire and maintain it. In order to charge it, we shall start by cutting the bars of iron which are to be changed into steel into pieces of equal length but each shorter than the crucibles by 1 or $1\frac{1}{2}$ inches. There is no furnace that heats evenly everywhere. Where ours is the least hot is near the bottom and near the top; and, as the thickness of the bars must at least to some extent be in proportion to the activity of the fire at the locations where they are placed, according to the general observations of our second memoir, the layers of iron near the bottom and near the top of the furnace will be made up of bars that are thinner by half or one-third than those of the layers near the middle. Thus we will need bars of at least two different thicknesses, and, if we had three thicknesses, it would be even better. We would start with layers of the thinnest iron, then take the iron of medium thickness, and after that make layers of the thickest iron; then we would again take iron of medium thickness and end up with layers of thin iron.

It is hardly [115] necessary to go any further. However, the spot where a furnace develops the greatest heat is not exactly in the middle, and the zone of the most intense heat also varies in different furnaces. If one wishes to know approximately where this zone is in order to be able to space the layers of iron of different thicknesses more intelligently, this information can be obtained after the first furnace run. All that is necessary is to place vertically into the furnace a bar which must be nearly of the same width and thickness everywhere. This bar is broken into a great number of pieces which are tested separately. One recognizes those which have been insufficiently converted into steel, those which have been overexposed, and those which are the best; and, as it is easy to judge at which level of the furnace each was located, it is also easy to be sure of the zones which heat the most and those which heat the least.

After the iron that is to be inclosed in the furnace has been cut into pieces and the compound has been prepared, the bars that are meant to make up each kind of layer are weighed so that the weights of every layer of the thinnest iron, every layer of medium iron, and every layer of thick iron will henceforth be known. The weight of one layer makes it possible to judge approximately how much other layers will weigh, and approximately is good enough here. One also weighs the quantity of compound which is needed for each layer of a different weight. This compound should be put in a vessel made of either clay, [116] wood, or metal. This will give three vessels of three different sizes, each of which is as good as a measure of the compound that must be spread between the layers of iron. All this is necessary only to save the time of weighing and continuously weighing again. The layer of compound which separates a layer of thick iron from a layer of thinner iron should be of medium thickness; the eye will be as accurate a judge as is necessary to decide what must be added to this layer or taken away from it.

Because of the design of our furnace, each side crucible can contain only about one-third of the iron contained in the center crucible. Although the total surface which these two crucibles together expose to the fire is about equal to the surfaces of the center crucible upon which the fire acts, the action of the fire upon the iron in these small crucibles is still not as powerful as upon the iron in the large one. The advantage derived from their lesser capacity does not quite compensate for the disadvantage caused by their location near the walls of the furnace, which, being thicker than the plates, are more difficult to heat and which are continuously cooled by the outside air. It is advisable, therefore, to fill these small crucibles with bars which are thinner by about one-third than those of the large crucible. Even so, it is not to be expected that these bars will turn entirely into steel the first time [117] the furnace is fired; but during a second and, still better, during a third furnace run the conversion of the iron into steel will be very satisfactory. The walls of the furnace have then had time to become hot, and they hold the heat they have soaked up.

If one would like to have a furnace which permits him to

place in the small crucibles iron of the same thickness as that in the large crucible, he would only have to make this center crucible still larger, which would be perfectly all right. In it the operation would take longer, but more iron would also be converted at one time.

Finally, after the crucibles have been loaded with iron and compound, the covers will be put on, they will be luted, and all that remains to be done is to light the fire, which must be undertaken with some care. Pieces of burning charcoal are first thrown into the spaces between the crucibles; one then fills these spaces with black charcoal and uses the bellows a few times to set this coal slightly on fire; after this the cover of the furnace is put on, and put on firmly. The blast is used continuously until all the charcoal is burning, and, when its amount becomes smaller, more is thrown on. I now assume that the fire burns well and that the furnace is starting to heat up. There are certain precautions to be observed in order to maintain the fire under the most favorable conditions possible. The discussion of two points will show wherein these precautions mainly consist. The first is to avoid having too large a quantity [118] of charcoal fall between the crucibles; it is not necessary that the spaces meant to hold it are filled up with it and still less necessary that the charcoal is packed there, one piece pressed against another. One might think, and the foundrymen seem to be convinced of it, that, the more burning charcoal there is between the crucibles, the faster and more intensely they ought to heat up. Experience has convinced me of the wrongness of this assumption. And as there is always a reason to explain facts after they have once become known, the reason that presents itself most naturally as an explanation here is that, when the charcoal is packed, the action of the wind falls almost entirely upon the coal and only little upon the plates. The wind cannot hurl the fire against them. The layers of charcoal provide, so to say, a shelter for the plates; moreover, the wind sets fire to a small quantity of charcoal which it finds in its way much more briskly than it would to a more considerable quantity.

The flanges of the covers of our crucibles have a favorable effect in this regard; as they extend over the spaces where the charcoal is, they make the openings of these spaces narrower, and the charcoal enters less easily. These overhanging parts produce still another excellent effect—that is, they deflect the wind on to the charcoal.

Even this restriction of the openings of the spaces [for the charcoal] has not always seemed sufficient to me, and then it has been necessary to add small bars here and there which served as a grating. I had these bars [119] made of clay like that used for the plates; one of their ends rested on the center crucible and the other on one of the side crucibles. I mentioned above two openings through which pokers are inserted which are thrust horizontally into the opposite wall; these pokers also have a similar function.

The second important point is never to allow unlit charcoal to fall between the crucibles, for it would moderate the heat which it is meant to maintain and increase. I should like it if the charcoal never entered the furnace unless it were almost red. It is incontestable that all charcoal that enters the furnace without having first acquired the degree of heat of the coal already there cools the rest. It is without doubt this consideration which has led to giving so much height to the ordinary furnaces in which iron ore is smelted. Before the charcoal that is thrown on black has reached the spot where the heat must be violent—the spot where the ore becomes liquid—it has had time to be set entirely aflame. In order to obtain the same effect in our small furnace, all that is necessary is never to permit unlit charcoal to enter it; and it is easy to have it lighted on the cover. I gave this cover a flange which serves to hold the charcoal that is thrown on it. When the flame which passes through the holes in the cover has turned this charcoal almost red, it is allowed to fall into the furnace, and more black coal [120] is put in its place. Most of the charcoal which has entered the furnace is stopped by the cover of the center crucible, where it is left for a moment until it has become white. It is then pulled from above the center crucible into the chambers, so that these are always filled with perfectly burning coal. If it is considered too much trouble to light the charcoal on top of the cover, if it seems preferable to throw it into the furnace completely black, the furnace must be made higher to allow for more space between its cover and those of the crucibles, so that the charcoal has more time to get hot before it descends between the crucibles.

During the first and second hours of firing the furnace the fire should not be urged too much, for the plates should have time to heat up little by little. If this is done, they will later stand up better, for they are less strained if the compound does not swell so suddenly. After this first period the heating should be very brisk.

I have pointed out the convenience and the necessity of the tuyères by which the wind enters the furnace. I shall add here, however, that it is absolutely necessary that they stand up very straight; if they leaned ever so little toward one of the plates, the wind would act too powerfully upon the spot toward which it is directed; it would weaken it little by little and pierce it at the end.

Thanks to the elevation at which the openings [121] of these tuyères are put above the bottom, there is no reason to fear that they will be stopped up by vitrified matter; but it may happen that a piece of charcoal falls into one of these openings in such a way that it is lodged there like a plug which the wind is not strong enough to lift out. Such a case is rare; but, when it happens, it would be a nuisance to be forced to take off the cover in order to pass a poker into the furnace, which would get cold during this maneuver. Such an accident is repaired by means of four doors provided in the ashpit opposite the tuyères (Pl. 4, *L L*). When necessary, the door opposite the tuyère which does not furnish enough air is opened, and a poker with a crooked end or a heavy iron wire as used by kettlemakers is passed through it into the ashpit; subsequently, the end of this poker is inserted in the tuyère, which is thus easily opened up.

If three or even more tuyères are built into each fire chamber instead of two, this can have no ill effect, provided they have the proper thickness to resist the fire. When the wind enters the furnace at more places, the flame will be hurled less violently against the spot opposite each place of entry; consequently, the plates will be less likely to melt. In order to protect them still better, I am suggesting a tuyère of a novel shape, which I have not yet tried out; but I see no reason to doubt its success. It is shown on Plate 3 in Figure 8. It alone is nearly as long as one of the fire chambers without being as [122] wide. It will be easy to have these tuyères cast in molds. Since the same quantity of air is admitted to the furnace, the same quantity of heat will there be maintained. But, since this air passes through a considerably larger opening, there is no longer any reason to fear that the flame will attack the plates so strongly that certain spots will be weakened too much. It will act more evenly upon the entire area of the plate.

I have been content to indicate that the heat of the fire of our furnace is spurred by a bellows of which so far I have given no dimensions. A double bellows such as used by the ordinary founders is all that is needed. The one I have used was $3\frac{1}{2}$ feet long from the end where it is the widest to the *headpiece*, or head—that is, the place where the upper board moves as on a hinge. The width of its upper board, and of the lower one as well, was 23 inches near the tail and $17\frac{1}{4}$ inches where the head, or headpiece, starts.

The job of the workman who is charged with keeping this bellows in motion consists in raising the wider end of the lower board. This board moves on the headpiece as on a hinge, and the weight with which it is loaded causes it to descend again as soon as the workman stops pulling it up. We say that the bellows has produced one full blast when this board has been raised and [123] has then fallen back by its own weight into the position from which it had been moved. A workman who is occupied exclusively with raising this board, who is only doing the one job which can easily be continued for several hours in succession, can comfortably pull the bellows five hundred to six hundred times every fifteen minutes and each time raise the end of the lower board 4 inches. Thus he will make the bellows produce five hundred or six hundred full blasts every quarter-hour. If this regular movement of the bellows is kept up, if it is interrupted only when more charcoal has to be put on or that which is in the furnace must be helped to come down, a job which the same workman who pulls the bellows can also do and which in a way will give him a rest; and, if the thickest iron in the furnace is only about 3 lines thick and about 20 wide, this iron can well be converted into steel in one day, or at the most in one and a half days, if the furnace has been operating the days before. The operation will take longer the first time the furnace is heated or, what amounts to the same thing as the first time, if it has stood for several days without fire, if it has completely cooled down.

The consumption of charcoal during one furnace run should not reach six barrows* or at the most seven. It will be necessary to remember this later in calculating the cost of converting iron into steel [Mem. 6, pp. 134 ff.].

As it is [124] very easy to increase the number of furnaces of the type I have just described, their small capacity does not prevent the establishment of plants of any desirable size. As soon as several furnaces are in operation, several times 500–600 pounds of steel can be produced in one or two days; but, if it seems preferable, furnaces can be constructed on the same principle, in which any desired amount of iron can be converted into steel in one batch and in as short a time.

Just one furnace can produce several thousand pounds of steel at a time if desired. All that is necessary is to make it longer than our small one in proportion to the amount by which its capacity is to be increased. I say "longer," for I do not consider it practicable to increase its other dimensions considerably. If it were made much wider, it would be difficult for the plates to stand up, at least unless they were made thicker. Later I shall report some observations to show why it is not advisable to make the furnace much higher. The problem is therefore reduced to increasing the number of the crucibles and the number of the chambers for the charcoal. If we wish to build a furnace capable of holding 1,250 pounds of iron, for instance, we assume that the center crucible of the small furnace will hold 350 of these pounds and give our new furnace the necessary length to have three crucibles like the one [125] in the middle of the old furnace. Whereas the other furnace had only one large crucible and the two side crucibles, this one will have the same side crucibles but three large ones (Pl. 5, Fig. 3, *F H G*), which will be separated

* *Voie de charbon*, now 1 hectoliter of wood charcoal (2.838 bu.).

from one another by the spaces meant to receive the charcoal (*L L*). These fire chambers will be as large as those of the short furnace, and each will have its two tuyères. As long as the same quantity of wind issuing from each of the tuyères of the short furnace also issues from each of those of the long furnace, we can be sure that the effects will be the same, since the design of the two furnaces is identical. All that remains to be done is, therefore, to supply each furnace with the quantity of wind it requires in proportion to its size; in a moment we shall compute how great this quantity must be, and we shall see that it will not be difficult to find bellows to supply it.

One might think it would be just as well to increase the number of the small furnaces as to build one that is as long as several of them together. However, on close consideration it will be realized that the long furnace has definite advantages over several small ones of the same total capacity. It has been shown that it cannot be helped that the side crucibles heat less well than the center ones. In increasing the number of the furnaces, we increase the number of these side crucibles. One man can watch one large furnace better than several small ones. The heat [126] will be more intense in the large furnace, for the center crucible of the short furnace will always suffer from being close to the side crucibles; and I have no doubt at all that we can make the center crucibles of the long furnace larger than the center crucible of the small furnace without having to increase the chambers for the charcoal.

As soon as the furnace is made longer, the number of the covers must be increased, but there is nothing objectionable about that. It is unnecessary to describe how these covers must be spaced and where the holes must be placed through which the charcoal falls down. Practice and my foregoing discussion will provide the needed information.

Instead of manpower one can—in fact, one must—have recourse to water power for working the one bellows or the several bellows for the long furnaces, if these are built in the country where watercourses are available. There is no need to use double bellows; simple bellows, entirely of wood like those of the furnaces in which iron ore is smelted, are practical in this case. The wind which these bellows drive into a common pipe (Fig. 3, *A*) is subsequently distributed into several smaller pipes (*B C D E*), which conduct it below the spaces where the tuyères are, and these admit the wind to the furnace. The wind will thus be distributed more uniformly than it would be [127] if a single pipe conducted it to just one place in the ashpit. I should like to see the smaller pipes made square and provided with a damper, by which I mean a small piece capable of restricting the flow of the wind. With this damper, the amount of wind conducted between the crucibles can be reduced as desired. If one crucible or even one of the plates of a crucible heats more than the others, the amount of air passing through the tuyères of such plates could be decreased. This damper would be nothing but a simple piece of flat wood covered with chamois leather. Each pipe would have a slot into which this piece would fit exactly.

This piece, when pushed in as far as possible, would bar all passage to the wind; [on the other hand,] the wind would flow much more freely or, what amounts to the same thing, would pass in greater amount through one pipe than through the others, depending on how far the damper would be pulled out.

The facts reported above enable us to compute rather accurately the amount of wind that must be furnished by the bellows to a furnace of any size. And if the bellows are already there, as they are in forges or iron-smelting furnaces, we can judge the size of the steelmaking furnaces for which these bellows would be adequate. The computation is simple for those who have the slightest knowledge of geometry. [128] I shall give some examples. Those who cannot follow the calculations, although they are ever so simple, can use the results to decide what size their bellows must have and also how fast they must move.

I first take a simple bellows like those used in iron-smelting furnaces or iron forges. They consist of two wooden boxes without leather, which is used only in their valves. I shall spend no time on the design of these bellows, which are so simple in appearance as to be ingenious; they will be described in great detail elsewhere. Without bothering about their exact dimensions, which are of no use to us at present, I assume that Figure 10 of Plate 3 represents the table, or board—that is, the top of the upper box—of one of these bellows, and that Figure 11 is a pro-file view, or section, through the two boxes. *E L, I H* is the lower box; *E F G* is the upper box, depressed; and *E K F* is the same, raised. Let us look at it first in the latter state; the volume of air that will be ejected from the bellows when *E K* is lowered to *E F* is equal to something like a wedge comprised between two planes which are parallel to each other and about equal to *B B C C;* one of them would pass through *E F* and the other through *E K.* I know, and I shall explain the reason why in another book, that the base of this wedge is part of a circle. This is shown here in the section, but I shall continue to con-sider it as being straight; greater precision would be useless for the present purpose of our calculation. In order to determine the quantity of air ejected [129] with each blast of the bellows, all that is needed, therefore, is to determine the volume of this wedge. Let *l* be the length *B D* of the bellows, *e* the width *B B* at the headpiece, and let *a* be *D C*, which is half of the difference between the width of the bellows at the headpiece and the width of the bellows near the tail, or, what amounts to the same thing, *e* + 2*a* shall be the expression for the greatest width *C C* of the upper table; *h*, line *K F*, shall be drawn from the middle of the upper table to the middle of the lower table at the moment when the upper table is raised as high as it will be raised for every blast; in short, *h* represents the greatest distance of the upper table. After these definitions, regardless of the di-mensions of the bellows, the general expression for the volume of air ejected with each blast, or of our sort of wedge, is easily found to be

$$\frac{eh}{2}\sqrt{l^2 - \tfrac{1}{4}h^2} + \tfrac{2}{3}ah\sqrt{l^2 - \tfrac{1}{4}h^2}.$$

This formula* can be used for the double bellows as well as for the simple bellows; it does not matter that in the double bellows *h* is the length of the farthest distance of the lower table of the bellows from the table in the middle and not from

---

* It is curious that, when Réaumur decided to ignore the circular path of the end of the bellows, he did not assume the base of the wedge and pyramid to be tangent to the circle instead of its chord. This simpler solution is actually nearer the truth: $2hl(e/4 + a/3)$.

the upper table. The double bellows ejects air while being in-
flated as well as while being compressed; but the quantity of air
ejected during these two periods is always equal to that which
is taken in while the lower table descends. With this same formula we can therefore determine the quantity of air ejected with
each full blast by the bellows we [130] have used heretofore,
and for which I have given the dimensions. The only thing that
would make a change in the formula is that it was found for
wooden bellows, which are boxes with almost flat side and end
walls, while our double bellows made of leather has pleats for
walls, which are never entirely distended when the bellows is
distended. It is possible to compute by how much these pleats
reduce the volume, but it is not absolutely necessary to make a
very precise computation. The time spent in being unnecessarily
exact is lost time. Later I shall instead supply an estimate that
comes sufficiently close to the amount that should be deducted
for the pleats.

Let us now substitute in our formula the dimensions of this
bellows I have described. I said before that it is $3\frac{1}{2}$ feet long;
consequently, $l = 42$ inches; but the pleats form isosceles tri-
angles at the end of the bellows, and the height of these tri-
angles, or the depth of the pleats, is 4 inches. Since the internal
pleats are almost equal in volume to the outside ones, it follows
that, by reducing our length by 2 inches, we will bring it down
to that of a bellows of the same capacity but without pleats, so
that $l = 40$ inches. The width e of the bellows at the head was
found to be $17\frac{1}{4}$ inches, but, because of the amount that must be
deducted for the pleats on both sides, which are however less
deep than at the end of the bellows, [131] we can estimate it at
15 inches; thus $e = 15$ inches. The width of the bellows near the
end, $e + 2a$, would be 23 inches; but, since the pleats, which
still are on both sides, are as deep as those at the end, 4 inches
must be deducted. Consequently, $e + 2a = 19$ inches; therefore, $a = 2$ inches. We also found 4 inches for the distance
which the lower board travels in descending, so that $b = 4$
inches. We now have $l = 40$ inches, $e = 15$ inches, $e + 2a = 19$
inches, $a = 2$ inches, $b = 4$ inches. $\sqrt{l^2 - \frac{1}{4}b^2}$ will still be

[99]

practically equal to 40 inches; it differs from l by less than 1. Let us, therefore, substitute these values in the formula

$$\frac{eb}{2}\sqrt{l^2 - \tfrac{1}{4}b^2} + \tfrac{2}{3}ab\sqrt{l^2 - \tfrac{1}{4}b^2}.$$

After all the substitutions and deductions have been made, we will have 1,213⅓* cubic inches for the quantity of air ejected with each full blast. Let us neglect the fraction and multiply this quantity by 500 or 600, which is the number of times a workman can easily pull the bellows every quarter-hour, and we have the total quantity of air which our bellows ejects every fifteen minutes. Leaving a choice whether the number 500 or 600 should be used shows sufficiently that we have been more than accurate enough in the rest of our calculations. If we use an intermediate value, say, 550, the quantity of air ejected every quarter-hour will be 667,150 cubic inches.

If presently we wish to build a furnace like that in Figure 3, Plate 5, with four fire chambers, [132] instead of the furnace for which we made the preceding calculations which had only two, it is enough if twice the quantity of air is admitted; and this doubled quantity of air will maintain a fire which will, for the reasons you may recall, convert more than twice as much iron into steel during the same time. In brief, if one triples, quadruples, etc., the quantity of air supplied every fifteen minutes, one can more than triple or quadruple the quantity of iron or the capacity of the steelmaking furnace. It is apparent, therefore, that bellows worked by water as we have them today will be suitable for furnaces of any size desired. The bellows of the small forges in which raw iron is refined to make it forgeable alone would supply enough air to furnaces capable of holding more than 6,000 pounds of iron at one time. As an example, let us consider the small forge at Imphy in the Province of Nivernais. Men whose exactitude I trust have assured me that every simple bellows of this forge produces 206 blasts every quarter-hour. I had asked them to keep an accurate record. The two bellows

* Actually 1,413⅓. Réaumur makes another error on p. 101 in computing the volume of the larger bellows. That these errors are arithmetical and not typographical is shown by the fact that the total volume of many blasts is in both cases correctly computed from the single-blast volume given.

together thus produce 412 blasts. The length (l) of each of these bellows is $7\frac{1}{2}$ feet, so that $l = 90$ inches; for each blast, the upper board is raised 14 inches, so that $h = 14$ inches; $l^2 - \frac{1}{4}h^2$ is nearer 90 than 89, but let us put it at 89 nevertheless, although this will have an unfavorable effect on our calculation; the width of these bellows near the headpiece, or e, equals 14 inches, and the width of the [133] bellows at the other end, or $e + 2a$, equals 42 inches; therefore, $a = 14$ inches. Substituted in the formula

$$\frac{eh}{2} \sqrt{l^2 - \tfrac{1}{4}h^2} + \tfrac{2}{3}ah \sqrt{l^2 - \tfrac{1}{4}h^2},$$

these values give $20,151\frac{1}{3}$ cubic inches for the volume of air ejected with every blast of the bellows. If this quantity is multiplied by 412, the number of blasts produced every quarter-hour, the total amount of air supplied during this time by our two bellows becomes $8,302,349\frac{1}{3}$ cubic inches. If we compare this sum with the quantity of air ejected during the same time by our double bellows, which we found above to be 667,150 cubic inches, it will be seen that the ratio is greater than 12 to 1, so that our last two bellows supply more than twelve times as much air, during the same time, as the double bellows of our short furnace. They would therefore supply more air than is necessary for a furnace which could hold 6,000–7,000 pounds of iron.

But the last bellows are still only small bellows; those used in smelting ore are of a very different size. Whatever the capacity one might dream of giving the steelmaking furnaces, such bellows would surely provide the wind one would need. A single one of these bellows ejects 98,280 cubic inches of air with each blast; and at a time when they were worked slowly I counted that each produced 120 blasts every quarter-hour, or the two together 240. Therefore, 23,587,200 cubic inches of air would be supplied [134] by these bellows during the time in which our double bellows supplies only 667,150, which means that these two bellows give more than thirty-five times as much air during the same time and would consequently be large enough for furnaces capable of holding 18,000–20,000 pounds of iron at a time, although it seems improbable that such sizes will be considered for this type of furnace.

Forge masters who may not like to bother with such calculations can at least conclude from our results that the bellows of their chaferies or refineries supply all the wind necessary for steelmaking furnaces holding 5,000–6,000 pounds of iron and that the bellows of the tall furnaces in which they smelt ore, the wooden bellows which are 13–14 feet long, supply more wind than is needed for furnaces holding 18,000–20,000 pounds of steel. In addition, they know that they can cut off from this quantity of wind whatever excess they may find they have. Let us leave these computations, however, and turn to a consideration of the design of our furnace and that of some others.

The thing that must be foremost in one's mind in connection with the design of a furnace is that the heat should be used as efficiently as possible, that as little as possible of the effect of the fire should be wasted; and yet this is a condition rarely found in most of the furnaces [135] that are being used. I am not going to examine, for example, whether the furnaces of the brass founders or those of glassworks could have more favorable shapes than they have now, but I can see that the greater part of the heat of these furnaces is not used to produce the desired effect. The general rule for determining the quantity of heat usefully employed is to take the sum of all the surfaces on which it acts and to find which portion of this total surface was planned to be heated when the furnace was designed. We can apply this rule to one of our examples. To obtain the sum of all the heated surfaces in the furnace of the artisans producing small castings (Pl. 2), we have to take the surfaces of the inner walls, the surface of the bottom, that of the cover of the furnace, and the surface of the crucible. It is only the surface of this crucible that is intended to be heated; and, to realize this intention, the design of the furnace makes it necessary to heat surfaces of which it obviously is only a small part. No calculations are needed to see this; it is enough to remember that in this case the crucible stands free. It is the same thing in the kilns of the glassworks where the pots containing the melting glass have a very small surface compared with that of the considerable volume of the furnace.

When the same rule is applied to our steel furnace, it will be seen how efficiently the fire acts here. With the exception of the cover, a very small [136] part of the bottom, and the upright columns between the crucibles, everything that is heated needs to be heated. There are almost no walls here on which the effect of the fire is wasted. There are even cases where the heat spent on the columns can be used profitably. This I shall discuss elsewhere, for the use of this furnace will not be restricted solely to the conversion of iron into steel.

In addition to the fuel wasted in heating the walls, there is in most furnaces still another case of ineffective fuel consumption. Happily, we have to make few changes in the dimensions of ours to guard against this condition. If the crucibles were spaced much farther apart than we have done it, if more space were left between them for the charcoal, it might be assumed that the heat of the furnace would be increased. [In reality,] the increase would be in charcoal consumption but not at all in the effect produced. When these chambers are given twice the space we have given them but the quantity of wind is not increased, the force that is effective in setting the charcoal on fire is only half as great as it was before, so that if the heat, if the activity of the charcoal, were strictly in proportion to the magnitude of the force that is applied to produce it, each particle of charcoal, each hot spot, would have only half [137] the activity; there would be twice as much fuel on fire, but the fuel would be only half as active.

Let us pursue this reasoning further: let *aa* and *bb* (Pl. 4) be the sections through two [fire chambers heating] crucibles of equal capacity; let there be inside *aa* a column of fire only half as large as the column inside *bb;* but let the fire of column *aa* be more active. The crucibles *a, a* will heat more than the crucibles *b, b;* the width of the column does not matter; the result depends on the activity of the parts that act upon the walls *a, a* and *b, b*. By increasing the wind, we could increase the activity of column *bb* and cause it to produce the same result as column *aa;* but then we would increase the consumption of fuel, which we might have saved by bringing the walls *b, b* closer together.

Most furnaces like those of glassmakers, potters, and china-

ware-makers, and the reverberatory furnaces or kilns which like
the former are heated with wood, need a big column of fire; but
this is because this column, after having risen, must divide in
order to heat the vast volume of these furnaces. In order to heat
their walls and their arches, all the air or empty space inside of
them must have at least the same degree of heat as the walls and
crucibles of the furnace are to have; and the heat employed to
warm these great empty spaces is another case of pure waste in
this [138] kind of furnace, of which there is almost no example
in ours.

I still must give the reason why I decided to make this furnace
longer rather than higher when I pondered about increasing its
capacity—why I did not believe I ought to add to it in height a
large part of what I did add to it in length. It might even seem
that a furnace twice as high as another would require only the
same quantity of wind, for the air which enters the furnace below leaves it above—so that the same quantity of air is active
over the entire height of the furnace regardless of which one of
the two it is. But the thing to be noticed is that this air does not
act with the same force everywhere, and I have not overlooked
that our furnace should heat as uniformly as possible at different
levels. The air has its great effect the first instant it enters the
furnace. It acts explosively upon the first pieces of charcoal it
encounters; it then has still all the velocity it has been imparted
by the compression of the bellows. After this first velocity is
checked by the first obstacles it encounters, it continues to rise
only because of its lightness and because more air wants to take
its place. Another phenomenon which one might more easily
fail to observe than the foregoing is that, when the air arrives at
the holes of the furnace, it is cold; it is condensed. After it has
entered the furnace, it becomes hot; it expands. There is an elevation [in the furnace] where the air has [139] acquired all the
heat and all the expansion which the hotness of the furnace can
communicate to it; then, above this elevation where the air has
expanded as much as it is possible, its effect is less strong than it
was before, although its volume is greater. This [statement]
seems to be supported by a most common observation—namely,
that the effect of air upon fire is the more successful the more

force there is behind the air, which is also constantly demonstrated by our bellows. When the air has just been admitted to
the furnace, it expands, and it expands the faster the hotter the
furnace. This expansion must occur quite suddenly, approximately as if a spring lets go. At that moment the rising air acts
upon the pieces of charcoal that are all around it not only in an
upward direction but in all directions, even downward. Since
this action is very sudden, I imagine that it must have a great
effect on the charcoal; it resembles in a way the action of the
same air when ejected by the bellows. The following instant—
that means after the air has expanded about as much as is possible—it rises rapidly because it is rarefied; but it no longer pos-
sesses this sort of impetuosity which is imparted to it the moment the expansion occurs; it acts precisely only upon the pieces
of charcoal which would impede its ascent. Thus there is something comparable between the height of the furnace and the
length of a cannon—if the cannon were much longer than required [140] by the time necessary for setting the powder aflame,
the force of the powder would start to diminish the moment it is
entirely aflame. Thus the force of our air must start to diminish
the moment it has completely expanded.*

The tall furnaces in which iron ore is smelted confirm these
observations. There the greatest heat is above the tuyère and
does not go higher by as much as 1 foot or at the most 2 feet.
In the 12–15 additional feet of height of this furnace, the heat
always continues to decrease, although this kind of furnace becomes narrower as it becomes higher and although the air is
much more compressed at the top than it is at the bottom.

Therefore, when I tried to increase the height of our steel
furnaces considerably, I could not work profitably. However, if
the upper part of the crucibles is filled with *thin* iron, these furnaces can be made higher; and, furthermore, if it should seem
preferable to light the charcoal inside the furnace rather than on
its cover, its height *must* be increased by the space needed to hold
the black charcoal.

The plates forming our crucibles are another great help in having a favorable fuel balance, if they can be made of excellent clay

* It is curious that the idea of chemical reaction did not occur to Réaumur.

which permits to keep them thin. But if the good types of clay are unavailable, the plates must be made [141] thicker. Under such circumstances one might even substitute walls of small bricks which would be only as wide as ordinary bricks are thick.

Finally, when it seems unimportant to finish the operation as fast as possible, or at least less important than the advantage of not having to bother with making clay plates, which does require very much care, it is possible to use cast-iron plates. I rejected this material at some other place in this memoir [p. 71], but this was done only because I assumed that we wished to give the furnace all the heat the bellows are capable of supplying. These plates will have to be made the thinner the more energetically the furnace is to be heated; but they must always be kept thicker than the clay plates if bellows are used. They warp at least as much as those made of clay. If they are badly warped after a furnace run, they must be turned around for the following heat—that means the surface which was outside the crucible must be placed inside.

The draft* that naturally enters the furnace can replace bellows, but it will not be powerful. If only this draft is to be used, its entry can be facilitated by considerably enlarging the openings in the ashpit, which were put there for a different purpose.

By making some slight changes in our furnace, it can be adapted to being heated [142] with wood and without bellows. This will be necessary when it is used for softening cast iron, which will be discussed later on; but it can also be so employed for the conversion of iron into steel, which will then take longer but be less bothersome. Under those circumstances we even have the convenience of being able to use cast-iron plates of the same thinness as the clay plates, which nevertheless will not fail to last for a long time.

In order to adapt this furnace to wood firing, it should be

* The use of a stack or chimney to obtain enhanced natural draft, though described by Glauber in 1651, was not applied to industrial furnaces for long after. However, furnaces with high wide bodies extending above the fire had long been used in brassmaking, and Gabriel Jars (1774) describes a furnace of this kind in use in Sheffield for the cementation of steel. Probably this was only a small improvement over that of Robert Heyden of Bromley, which was described by Robert Plot in his *Natural History of Staffordshire* (1686).

given at least one opening at the lower end of each of the fire-boxes. These openings must be made large enough so that they can serve as doors (Pl. 4, *I I*) through which the wood is charged. It is not necessary, however, to make them very large, for I am not advising that the space between the crucibles be increased. They can be heated very satisfactorily by burning only heavy [*sic*]* billets, such as the heaviest sticks in a fagot; heavy billets must be split if small wood is not available; but the openings *L*, *L* must be enlarged—if necessary in such a way that the two combined form only one which extends down to the bottom of the ashpit.

As soon as the furnace no longer has a bellows, it no longer needs tuyères. The bottom of the space between two crucibles will be open. There will be an opening 2 inches wide over its entire length, or it can be made even wider if an iron bar is placed lengthwise in the middle to take the place of a grating or, if you wish, [143] several small bars are put in crosswise, which makes a better grating as seen in *Y*, Plate 5, Figure 5. This iron bar or these bars, or, what amounts to the same thing, the ledge that runs along this long opening, will be located 4 inches lower than the bottom of the crucible, so that the wood is placed a little lower than the iron in the crucibles.

Even if the real fire chamber is being used, it will do no harm if sometimes pieces of thin wood are placed upright, or almost upright, between the plates, and this practice is even advisable until the furnace has become thoroughly hot. As I recommended in discussing charcoal, the use of too much wood at one time should be avoided, however.

The bottom of the furnace—in other words, the bottoms of the crucibles and of everything else—is built of good, fire-resistant brick. It is unnecessary to point out that these bottoms must be flat; but, if it does not seem desirable to support them by iron bars, there is no reason why on the side of the ashpit they should not be raised into a vault.

If the quick conversion of iron into steel is unessential, if it is just as satisfactory to accomplish in one single furnace run and several days what could be accomplished in several [smaller]

* *Grosses;* misprint for *minces* ("thin")?

furnace runs and almost the same number of days, the capacity of the crucibles can be increased as much as desired (Pl. 5, Figs. 4, 5). Instead of arranging the bars of subsequent layers parallel to each other, [144] they will then be arranged in such a way that the bars of one layer cross those of the two layers on both sides of it; that means, if the bars of one of these layers lie lengthwise, those of the following layer lie crosswise.

I have gone into great detail concerning everything connected with the construction of our furnaces. This seemed necessary because of the importance of the subject. I am nevertheless convinced that there are many points which I have omitted, either because they were not available to me when I wrote this memoir or because they did not occur to me. I am no less convinced that more experience will point to additions and useful changes that can be made in the furnaces. What has been reported seems sufficient, however, to be put into practice and to provide an opportunity to do things better than I could teach them. The most important factor about the design is to arrange the crucibles as I have done it, not only in order to use the heat efficiently, but also to be able to see what goes on in each crucible. Moreover, those who find it too much trouble to be as economical of the wood, the charcoal, and the time as I have tried to be could use furnaces of any other shape.

The Fifth Memoir, on the Nature of the Different Kinds of Iron Considered from the Standpoint of Their Natural Tendency To Become Steel

NOT ALL wrought irons are equally qualified to become good steels. Some ought to be employed in preference to others, and there are some that must be rejected outright. In spite of the changes taking place in their texture during the operation, they preserve something of their good and something of their bad characteristics. Some require a duration of heating that would make of others intractable steels. It is similar, as I have pointed out several times, with the strength and the quantity of the compound by which the irons are surrounded—some irons require less compound or a weaker compound than is suitable for others. This is the point where it is important to have rules. I am herewith giving those which I have derived from observations on a large number of different kinds of wrought iron by making as accurate a comparison as I could of the effects produced on each of these irons by the fire and by compounds of different strength. Although the rules [154] I have derived from these comparisons seemed suitable to me to be applied in practice and although, generally speaking, I have found them reliable, I do not claim that there is none among them to which there is no exception. In order to be useful, the rules I intend to give had to be based on properties discernible to the eye. In addition, wrought irons have internal properties that cannot be discovered by mere inspection; but, since the arrangement and the shape of the visible parts are usually the effect of certain natural tendencies and qualities of the invisible parts, the rules based on the shape and arrangement of the visible parts of which the iron is composed are sufficiently safe and indicate sufficiently well what can be expected from a particular iron and in which way it must be treated.

However, the first rule I shall give is absolutely independent of any knowledge of the internal structure of this metal. It applies to all kinds of iron. It is that the use of bars having a large number of laps or cracks, or any other sort of break, must be avoided. As far as possible, one should choose very clean, well-forged bars. It is advisable that those who wish to build plants for the conversion of wrought iron into steel have at their disposal one of those large forges where pig iron is refined and hammered out into bars. They would then be in a better position to select iron that has come from the forge clean. They would put it aside [155] for conversion into steel and would sell the rest as wrought iron. Bars with laps, cracks, or other similar defects often become steel that has to be rejected. The spots where such tears are found seldom weld well; it is a waste to forge them carefully. Even if they seem to have closed when the bars come from the forge, the weakness is discovered in annealing, at which time they seldom fail to split open. The pains taken in forging a tool out of such a bar are found to be wasted.

There are certain wrought irons that are called "red-short" by the smiths. Properly speaking, they are the same grade among irons which I called "intractable" when I discussed their counterparts among steels. They are the ones which are inclined to go to pieces when forged hot, which sometimes break under the hammer or cause considerable waste because of the quantity of small bits that come loose. I have found some like these among irons of quite opposite natures. I have seen nailrods from Berry which were very red-short, and I have more often found the same defect in the square merchant bar* of Nivernais. It is an infallible rule that one must never try to convert such irons into steel. Irons that are among the most easily forgeable are sometimes made hard to forge by this conversion. There is therefore no reason to hope that the conversion will correct this defect in those which already have it; it may even

* *Quarillon;* see the Glossary, p. 362.

increase it. It is easy to ascertain if the kind of iron one wishes
to use has this bad quality, provided it all comes from the same
furnace and from the [156] same ore. As a test it is enough to
forge some bars so hot that they almost melt—to give them
what the artisans call a "welding heat."

It is known that in general there are soft irons and brittle
irons; irons which in the form of bars can be bent cold and bent
again; and others which, on the contrary, break easily. Soft
irons and brittle irons have different structures; but not all soft
irons have the same structure, and brittle irons also have different ones. When I speak of the structure of wrought irons, I
mean the shape, the size, and the arrangement of their molecules; and it is by means of their fracture, of the surface at the
location where they have been broken, that one can judge how
these molecules differ. When different kinds of stone are broken,
the fractures show the difference in the grains of each one.
When different kinds of wood are broken, fibers of different size,
which are sometimes differently arranged, are seen in their fractures. When bars made of different irons are broken, such obvious diversity will be noticed in their fractures that to the
unaided eye the fractures of these bars sometimes seem to differ
more among themselves than they differ from other metals such
as lead, tin, and silver. There is not only as much and more difference in color, but the difference is even greater in the shape
and [157] the arrangement of the parts. By paying only casual
attention to the fractures of these different kinds of iron, it is
seen at once that they can be divided into two groups: into irons
with only grains or platelets and irons with fibers in their fracture. The fracture of irons of the first group resembles either the
fracture of stones or that of bismuth; and the fracture of irons of
the second group resembles that of wood. (The artisans say that
the latter are fibrous.) But this classification is still too general.
The detailed study we intend to make requires finer subdivisions.

There are in these two groups seven classes of irons, which can
be distinguished by characteristics precise enough to be recognized by those who are somewhat accustomed to looking at the
fractures of this metal. I shall try to describe each one of these
characteristics and shall then indicate how successful I have

been with these different irons after they had been converted into steels and how they must be treated.

In the first class I put an iron that is generally considered to be bad (Pl. 6, Fig. 1). Its fracture shows very brilliant white platelets, which appear to be as many little mirrors, but of irregular shape and arrangement; they rather resemble those in the fracture of bismuth. All these platelets are large, but some of them are much larger than the rest. In the fracture of heavy bars, I have on occasion [158] measured some platelets that were more than 2 lines in diameter. There is some space between the platelets, which is occupied by much smaller parts, which seem to be grains.* I shall call the irons of this first class "irons with large or coarse platelets."

The second class consists of irons which, like those of the first class, have brilliant white platelets in their fracture; but these are smaller than those of the irons of the preceding class, much more uniform, and less irregularly arranged. There is no space between the platelets, or very little space, occupied by grains. Besides, there are among these irons some with platelets which are considerably larger than those of the others. A hard iron known at Paris under the name of *rock iron* may be used as an example of the irons of this class (Figs. 3, 4, 5).

The irons of the third class still have brilliant white platelets which are smaller than those of rock iron. However, a more distinguishing characteristic of this kind of iron is that the platelets do not occupy the entire fracture. There are small areas where one sees nothing but fine grains of a grayish color, which rather resemble those of a moderately fine steel which was broken above the location in the bar where in steel that was quenched very hot the brilliant grains disappear (Figs. 6, 7, 8). However, the grains of this kind of iron do not look as rounded

* The term "grain" relates to a regular fracture made up of more or less rounded parts, in contrast to the platelets, which are flat. Both, of course, are a result of microcrystalline grains, but the platelets correspond to brittle transcrystalline fracture along crystallographic planes, while grains are disclosed either by intercrystalline fractures or by complicated fractures that occur after heavy local distortion of ductile crystallites. The fibers become visible partly as a result of elongated slag particles, partly because of actual anisotropy of grain shape, and do not appear in brittle iron.

as those of the steel to which I am referring. The granular [159] areas are located differently in different fractures of these irons, and neither their size nor their shape is always the same. Occasionally, there are some that are 1 line wide by 3 or 4 lines long; ordinarily, however, they occupy only the smaller part of the fracture. The irons sold at Paris under the name of *ordinary, good iron* are frequently irons falling in this class.

There is justification for having a fourth class comprising irons that differ from those of the preceding one in hardly anything but degree. They also have brilliant platelets and areas occupied by very fine gray grains. The difference between them and the others is that the areas occupied by grains surpass or at least equal the areas occupied by platelets. In addition, the platelets are neither as white nor as sparkling as those of the irons of the third class (Fig. 9). I have always encountered this characteristic in the *irons* sent to us *from Sweden*. But it is not restricted to them.

An even more marked characteristic distinguishes the irons of the fifth class from the preceding ones. They have no brilliant platelets; instead, their fracture appears entirely granular. There also is a difference between their type of grain and that of the irons of the third and fourth classes; their grains are coarser. The irons from the Champagne, Nivernais, etc., that are forged into square bars and are called "square merchant bar" all have [160] this structure. I have sometimes encountered it in very soft iron from Berry, such as that illustrated in Figure 10. However, there are cases where the grains of the merchant bar from the Champagne and Nivernais are not as rounded as in Figure 10, where they are smaller, flatter, and mixed with some platelets, as shown in Figure 12 and still better in Figures 11 [or, rather, 13] and 14, which show the two different kinds of grain development observed in this iron as they appear under the magnifying glass.

There are irons which have some of the characteristics of the five preceding classes without resembling any one of them and which seem to deserve a place in a separate class; they therefore comprise class six. Strictly speaking, these irons have neither brilliant platelets nor grains; at least, the platelets are seldom flat enough to be called "platelets" and seldom convex enough to be properly called "grains." Nevertheless, they seem to have platelets rather than grains, but these never have the whiteness or the brilliance of the platelets of the irons of the first classes. Finally, bundles of fine fibers are more often observed in the fracture of these irons than in the fractures of the others. The iron from Berry that is sold in the form of wide, thick bars usually has this characteristic. It would not have been too easy to illustrate; but Figure 11, which however is nothing but the kind of grain shown in Figure 10 enlarged under the microscope, may be helpful in getting the right idea. These grains appear at least as coarse [161] to the unaided eye as the others appear under the microscope, but they are flatter.

Finally, the irons of the seventh class show almost only fibers in their fracture, which always resembles that of a piece of broken wood. These are the irons commonly called *soft irons* (Fig. 15). Examples are the iron from Berry when it is well forged and drawn out into strip or very thin bars, the irons originating at the forge of Painpont in Brittany, the soft, or mild, irons from Foix, and those of many another forge of the Kingdom.

There are an infinite number of irons that are intermediate between those I have just classified, but it would have been useless to go farther in subdividing them; their characteristics would not be sufficiently recognizable. Moreover, the subsequent discussion of the irons of successive classes will give enough indication of what is to be expected of those irons which fall into a place between two of these classes, depending on whether they are closer to one or the other. Furthermore, in distinguishing seven classes of different irons, I do not mean to imply that the ores or raw irons from which they are made produce essentially these differences; I merely wish to point out that these differences exist. We know that the iron of the sixth class would become the iron of the seventh if it were further drawn out by forging. This does not change the fact that it is a different iron when it has not been forged to this extent. I have shown even further that [162] the iron of the first class could be made to belong to the fourth class if it were worked a great number of additional times, but this could not be done without wasting much iron and without spending much time. In short, it has been my intention to define the differences existing in irons when they are in the state in which they are sold. The more they are worked, the more they are refined; their nature is changed.

What is more, the characteristics described are not invariable in irons obtained from the same ore and refined and forged the same way. Most of them may be found associated in the same bar, so that, when it is broken in one spot, nothing but fibers may be found, but, when broken in another, nothing but platelets or grains. In other bars there may be platelets or fibers mixed in different proportions. I have even seen irons where all these various constituents were simultaneously present in the same fracture.

In spite of this sort of confusion, the application of my observations will not be difficult for those who have to use the iron of particular forges. If the fractures of bars of a particular iron ordinarily contain fibers, this iron will be considered to be fibrous, even though platelets are sometimes encountered. Likewise, irons that ordinarily contain platelets will not be regarded as fibrous irons if some of their fractures have fibers. The rules are based on what occurs most commonly, [163] not on something that occurs always.

Let us now look at the observations that have persuaded me of the necessity for making distinctions among the irons; let us discuss the different classes. The iron of the first class, with large, coarse platelets which are irregularly arranged, an iron which is generally considered bad from the standpoint of the quality of iron, is also very bad for making steel. It is to be rejected outright. Steel made from it cannot be hammered. Even when it is heated very little, it shatters into small pieces as soon as the hammer blows fall; if any part is saved in the end, this will be completely full of seams and cracks. Elsewhere I have said that steels which have been exposed to the fire too long are, generally speaking, hard to forge. Steels produced from this iron fall into the same category, even if they have been given very little fire. Even if a bar is withdrawn from the furnace and forged when it has become only partly steel, everything that has become steel breaks under the hammer or is at least left full of cracks.

The iron of the second class—the kind with smaller, more uniform, and better-arranged platelets, but still with nothing but platelets—this iron, which is much used at Paris under the name of rock iron and is valued by the artisans whose products must be clean and polished, is still a bad iron for making steel. It is just as easy to work it as iron as it is difficult to work it as [164] steel. The steels produced from it are not as completely intractable as those produced from the iron of the first class; but they are sufficiently so that one should not choose it deliberately to make such steels.

Nevertheless, I have sometimes succeeded in making rather good steels from these irons; but, before placing them into the furnace, I had the bars drawn out—that is, I had them forged into new ones which were only half as thick and wide. According to my previous observations, this working could have changed the quality of the iron and made it like those which I have put in other classes—or almost like them.

If, after such preparation, this kind of iron is to be converted into steel, one must above all be careful to pack the bars in one of the weakest compounds. Neither do they require long heating; their conversion into steel is accomplished more easily and more quickly than that of the other irons I shall discuss hereafter but approximately as fast as that of the irons of the first class.

The structure of the irons of the first two classes seems to explain all these facts. They are composed of coarse molecules, which are sometimes badly arranged, and there are always large spaces between them. These already badly cohering parts are spread even farther apart by the sulfurs and salts which are active during the operation.

This [165] reasoning is further substantiated by the observation of which I spoke before that rock iron, the iron of the second class, could be changed into tractable steel when it was forged and drawn out before being placed into the furnace. When it is forged a second time, its parts are brought closer together, and the voids between them are reduced; it is therefore left less spongy, less in condition to soak up the sulfurs and to harbor quite such considerable accumulations of them.

The irons of the third class, which have small platelets but also some areas occupied by grains, ordinarily can be changed into good steels, especially if they are drawn out a second time before they are placed in the furnace; but most of them do not need this extra processing. They should not be packed in extremely strong compound; they require shorter heating than some other kinds of iron; and they become steel which can be given a high degree of hardness and which is much whiter than the kind obtained from the irons that will be discussed in the following. In general, steels have the same color the irons had; steels made from brilliant iron are whiter and those made from dull irons are grayer.

The fourth class of irons comprises the ones characterized by having areas in their fracture occupied by extremely fine grains; and these areas surpass or at least equal those occupied by very small platelets, which are less brilliant than in the [166] irons of the first two classes. These irons belong to the kind that can be used for steelmaking with the greatest confidence. The steels into which they are converted are gray, they forge admirably, and they are suitable for those products which require the cleanest finish. It is not as certain that they are the hardest steels. Those made from irons of the third class and some made of the irons of the classes discussed later have sometimes seemed to me to have the advantage over them in this respect. There is no objection to packing them in strong compounds. Of all the irons, they seem to be the ones that need the shortest heating to become steel, and they are among those that can best stand being heated beyond the point that is actually necessary for them.

The reasons for this are also found in their structure. Since these irons are composed of very fine molecules, and the voids are therefore increased in number and finely divided, the substances introduced during the operation find an infinite number of passages, permitting them to penetrate to the center of the bar; but they do not encounter tiny empty spaces where they could accumulate in excessive quantities, with the result that they would later press too strongly against the parts of iron and prevent them from cohering satisfactorily. This is, no doubt, the reason why this steel has good resistance to the blows of the hammer even if it has been acted upon by the fire and the ingredients of the compound more than was necessary.

There is still another reason why this iron is turned into steel faster than some [167] others. All the granular part of its structure may be considered as a kind of natural steel, still imperfect to be sure, but being nearer than iron to becoming entirely steel. In order to confirm this conjecture, I heated some of these irons and quenched them very hot. I then tested them with the file. There were spots, those which had consisted of grains before the quench, that could not be cut by the file, or could hardly be cut. Like steel after being quenched hot, they had coarse, white, and brilliant grains; the areas surrounding these had a fine, grayish grain and had no resistance at all to the file.

The irons of the fifth class, whose structure consists of coarse grains (such as the merchant bar from the Champagne and Nivernais), take much longer to be changed into steels than the irons of the fourth and even of the third class. Their molecules are coarser than those of the fourth class and apparently locked more tightly together, more difficult to penetrate than those of the third class. Some of these irons become gray steels which are easily worked. I have nowhere found any which give better service as cold chisels for cutting iron. They must, however, not be overexposed to the fire lest they become cracked. It also would be best to use a less strong compound on them than on those of the fourth class. Among these irons, especially among the merchant bar from the Champagne and Nivernais, there are some that as irons are naturally very difficult to forge. I have made [168] it a general rule to exclude all irons of this nature. I have found irons from Berry falling into this [i.e., the fifth] class, which could be converted into steels which were very hard, very fine, and very easy to work.

I have tested the irons known at Foix as hard irons, which are rather coarse natural steels or, if you wish, irons that are related to the fourth and fifth classes. It was impossible to make fine steels out of them, because those I had were naturally difficult to forge.

The irons of the sixth class, which, properly speaking, have neither grains nor platelets, are not always very reliable irons; it happens rather frequently that they become steels which are a little difficult to work. But if this happens only because they are in the form of wide, thick bars, a form in which we often receive the iron from Berry, they must be considered as iron insufficiently worked; they must be reduced to narrower and thinner bars by forging. There is an additional incentive for this, because, as I have said elsewhere, the use of thin bars is preferable in making steel. In addition to the fact that bars of this excessive thickness are suitable for few steel products, this further working makes of them irons of the seventh class or something closely related to them.

If the irons of the seventh class—the irons with an entirely fibrous fracture or one that is mostly fibrous—if these irons, I say, are not red-short, they become excellent steels [169] which above all have much body. These are the irons that have seemed to me to require longer heating than any of the others to be completely converted into steels, which indicates that the fire has more work to do. Before it can arrange the platelets, it has to break up the fibers and reassemble the pieces. These irons can stand rather strong compounds.

The fibrous irons alone present enough combinations to make up a number of other classes of iron, for the fibers occupy sometimes a larger and sometimes a smaller part of the fracture, and the remainder of the fracture is occupied sometimes by big platelets, sometimes by small ones, and sometimes by grains. But it is easy to judge the nature of these irons from what I have said in the foregoing, for the fibers are never what spoils them. If the iron of the fourth class combines areas occupied by fibers with its small platelets and its fine grains, this does not detract from its value. If the fibers are found in combination with platelets as large as those of the iron of the first class, this iron, which with nothing but platelets would be bad, may be tolerable. Sometimes, however, the fibers are found together with platelets of a medium size in certain irons which become rather hard-to-work steels.

The different shapes or arrangements of their parts cause variations in the color of the irons; but, in addition, there are some which in spite of having almost the same fracture otherwise [170] still differ in color—that means they are more or less white, more or less brilliant. Excessive brilliance is not always a good sign; but, if the color is too dull, too blackish, it too is often a bad indication. I have experimented with the iron from a forge in Normandy, from around Caen; the fracture showed a uniform grain mixed with a great deal of fibers. This iron, which thus seemed promising, became a bad steel; but the color of this iron was almost black.

A general rule, and one that may be considered to be the result of the observations I have just discussed, is that the smaller and the more uniformly arranged the perceptible parts are of which an iron is composed, the more suitable will be the iron for conversion into steel. Irons composed of small platelets are good, and the better the smaller the platelets. Irons with a granular structure are the better the finer the grains. Fibrous iron, when its fibers are very fine, is the one that deserves to be preferred in this group.

In conclusion—as the consumption of iron, used as iron, is incomparably much greater than the consumption of steel, it is unnecessary for all the forges of a state to produce iron that can be made into steel; more than enough of the latter kind can be found in most of the provinces of the Kingdom. I have said before that, if it should be necessary to resort to the irons of Sweden, the inconvenience [171] would not be great, as it can be had in our ports at approximately the same price as our own. But we are far from this necessity. I have tried the irons of several forges in Berry and have been very successful with them. I am experimenting with good iron from Nivernais. Some of it has come to me from around Maubeuge, which I was able to convert into good steel. There is no better steel than the kind I have made from the irons sent me from Vienne in Dauphiné, which came from the raw iron of Bourgogne. The Allevard irons, also from Dauphiné, were a complete success. There is a forge at Painpont in Brittany whose iron, which was sent to me, has made good steel. Of the irons of Angoumois, I have tried only that from the forge of Rancogne, four leagues from Angoulême, an iron which can safely be converted into steel if it is usually of the quality I received from there. I have experimented with iron from the Roc forge in Périgord, which has proved to be good. I know of no iron more suitable for being made into steel than that produced from the ore of Biriatou, from around Labour, near Bayonne. This ore has been neglected for a long time. By order of His Royal Highness it was assayed in 1716, and a specimen of the iron resulting from this assay was sent to me. I have tested it as steel, which is of the best kind imaginable.

I could continue much longer with this enumeration; but it is enough to convey the idea that in most of the provinces of the Kingdom good steels [172] can be made. I could also cite irons from most of these provinces that should always be left irons even though, as irons, they are very good; the rules I have given in the foregoing will help in recognizing these kinds of iron. But I repeat once more: it would be wrong to rely sufficiently on the knowledge acquired by these rules to undertake at once the conversion of a large quantity of iron before having made trials on a small scale as described in the third memoir.

The Sixth Memoir, Dealing with Observations of the Perceptible Changes Taking Place in Iron While It Is Being Converted into Steel, with the Precautions Necessary in Forging the New Steel, and the Total Cost of the Conversion of Iron into Steel

IT IS INTERESTING, if nothing else, to follow the iron while it is being converted into steel to see with which changes in its texture it acquires new properties and, one might say, alters its nature. These are observations, it would seem, that would help us to obtain a better understanding of the nature of iron and steel and of how they differ from each other. But, in addition to the interest these observations may hold for a physical scientist, they supply certain rules which will be useful in the operation of a shop in which iron is converted into steel.

However, before we consider the different states through which the iron passes in order to become steel, let us consider the state of a bar on which the process of conversion has just been completed. Let us take this bar as it is when it has been withdrawn from the furnace, [174] and let us also assume that it has been allowed to cool in the furnace. Whether the iron of this bar previously contained platelets, grains, or fibers—in a word, whether it was soft iron or short iron—it has become as brittle as if it were quenched steel, so that, even if it were a wide, thick bar, a few hammer blows would suffice to break it in two. What is strange about this observation is that steel itself is never brittle unless it has been quenched or, what amounts to the same, unless it has been cooled rapidly. We know that if a bar of steel is allowed to cool in the forge, no matter what degree of heat it has been given, it will be found to have a plasticity approaching that of iron. Our bar, which has cooled in the furnace, is, however, definitely brittle.* At present, I shall be content with reporting this fact, which I shall explain later, and which will help to explain others. But we shall derive a rule from it by which we can recognize whether bars have been completely changed into steel. When they have been withdrawn from the furnace, an artisan should grasp each bar in succession by one end, and, as he holds each one, he should deliver with it a heavy blow against the edge of an anvil. When the bar breaks in two, it is steel; but, when it withstands the blow, it must be put back in the furnace. In this way they should all be tried, and this check will not take long. If he prefers, the workman may alternatively place his bar on a somewhat concave anvil or, what amounts to the same thing, [175] he may place a piece of iron under one side of the bar, between the bar and the anvil, so that the bar is out of balance. He then strikes the bar one or two hammer blows. The bar that withstands them without breaking is not steel to the center. It is unnecessary to point out that, the thicker the bars, the heavier must be the blows.

Upon examination, the fracture of one of the bars that did not withstand the blow will be found to be very different from the way it would have looked if the bar had been fractured while it was iron. Instead of the fibers and grains it might then have had, it now has platelets, which cause this fracture to look more like that of ordinary iron—that is, iron of the first class—than of any other kind of iron. Eyes little accustomed to seeing steel in this condition would believe it to be the fracture of bad iron rather than steel. This fracture has nevertheless two points in which it differs discernibly from that of bad irons. In the first place, its platelets, although not uniform in size and shape, are

---

* This brittleness of the furnace-cooled bars is a result of the separation of the proeutectoid carbide to grain boundaries and into plates along crystallographic planes. More rapid cooling causes a more dispersed, less brittle, structure until cooling becomes so rapid as to prevent carbide precipitation altogether and to form hard and brittle martensite at low temperatures. The fracture of furnace-cooled steel of less than eutectoid composition will become more and more dull and of finer texture as the carbon content is increased.

[123]

arranged rather regularly. Their plane surfaces are almost always parallel to the ends of the bar, and they will not be found to be inclined at every possible angle as the platelets of bad irons; neither are there between them the same large empty spaces.

The second difference, which is much more marked than the first one, is that the color of the fracture [176] is more dull and gray than the color of the fracture of ordinary iron. These platelets, which might perhaps seem sparkling to a person who has never paid attention to those of ordinary iron or who no longer remembers what they are like, will seem lifeless when they are compared with the platelets of this iron. They no longer are as white as the platelets of iron; they are grayish and dull compared with the others. They seem to have less polish; and, indeed, they must have less, their surfaces must somehow be rougher, since they reflect the light more weakly toward the same spot. It would be natural to attribute this effect to the substances that have penetrated the iron during the conversion into steel. It seems that they pierce the platelets of which I am speaking everywhere and that they somehow roughen them.

These platelets that appear in the fracture are not always of the same size and color, nor are they dull to the same extent. But, to follow the different states through which they pass, we only have to follow the progress of the conversion from iron into steel. Let us first deal only with a bar of fibrous iron, which is the farthest removed—or seems to be the farthest removed— from steel. The first discernible change taking place in this iron—for I shall speak only of the discernible ones—is that the fibers are broken up; those nearest the surface come first, since they are reached first by the action of the substances surrounding the metal; but all the fibers are progressively broken up and successively destroyed; [177] the ones in the center of the bar come last. If this iron is fractured before the compound has had time to have a strong effect, the fracture therefore consists clearly of two different textures. The center and its environs are fibrous, and the area surrounding them shows only platelets. In the beginning these platelets form only something like a narrow border; but this border becomes wider and turns into a band which, becoming continuously wider, finally reaches the center.

However, the platelets formed in the first breaking-up of the fibers are white and brilliant—like those, in short, of the irons of the first and second classes, but they are arranged with greater regularity. The areas occupied by these platelets are therefore not steel, but they are in a condition close to becoming steel.

When the action of the fire and the compound is continued, the platelets very gradually lose some of their whiteness and brilliance. In the end, after they have become dull and grayish to an extent which I have no proper words to define and which is not exactly the same in all irons, they have become steel. While the platelets nearest to the surface become duller and duller and grayer and grayer, the fibers farther inside are broken up and changed into brilliant platelets, and so one finds in the same bar dull platelets, brilliant platelets, and fibers (Pl. 7, Fig. 4). Subsequently even the center of the bar loses its fibers and [178] becomes occupied by sparkling white platelets, which in their turn become steel only after they have acquired the shade of the others. While these are becoming duller, the other platelets, which during the whole time are exposed to the action of the substances surrounding the bar, do not remain unchanged; they very gradually decrease in size, they become smaller and smaller (Fig. 5), and, when they have been exposed to the fire for a certain time, they disappear. They no longer appear as platelets to our eyes, which see only very slender grains, a little flattened and a little more grayish than the platelets were before and also more grayish than the platelets at the center of the bar have become.

In the conversion of the irons of the third and fourth classes everything happens in almost the same way. They have no fibers; they have only fine grains and small platelets. The first effect of the operation is to reduce the grains to brilliant platelets, which are even larger than they naturally are in these irons. Some of these seem to unite to form new ones, which are arranged more uniformly than those of which they were made, and, finally, these platelets lose their brilliance and their whiteness by degrees. It seems that the fire has less work to do in combining grains or slender platelets together in order to make new platelets than in breaking up fibers and changing them into similar platelets. This helps to explain an [179] observation I mentioned in the previous memoir—namely, that fibrous irons, which are the irons of the seventh class, require longer heating to be converted into steels than those of the fourth class.

One easily recognizes by simple inspection of the fracture of a bar whether it has been completely converted into steel, and this way of judging it is less equivocal than judging it by the ease with which the bar can be fractured, which was discussed above. If there were only very few parts of iron left, they could not have the strength to resist the hammer blow. But these parts of iron, regardless of how few there are, are easily recognized in the fracture by the unaided eye. Everything that is fibrous is iron without any doubt, and the same is true of everything that has excessively white or excessively brilliant platelets. If there are such platelets, they usually are found toward the center of the bar. However, if it has happened by accident that at one side of the bar there was not enough compound, either because none had been placed there or because the fire had found a way into the crucible and had consumed it, this location in the bar which was lacking in that which it required to become steel contains only brilliant platelets, while the rest has only dull ones (Fig. 6).

The information obtainable from fractures goes still further— they also indicate with sufficient reliability whether a steel is of good quality and whether the wrought iron from which it was [180] made is suitable for the conversion into steel, whether this steel is certain not to crack. I have said before that this bad quality [of cracking] can be the result of overexposing the iron to the fire. The fracture indicates whether the firing has lasted too long. If all the platelets have disappeared, if only dull grains are to be seen (Fig. 8), the steel is intractable. On the other hand, if the grains form only a narrow border around the fracture, this is a sign that the steel has been treated long enough to make it hard, although it is still easy to forge. But if this border has become wide enough to form a band, wider than the area where the platelets are left, it would be rare if the steel did not crack. If it does not crack then, the iron is indeed of excellent quality. In general, the space occupied by platelets should be larger than that occupied by grains.

One might say that whatever is granular in the fracture has become too steely. However, certain parts must have passed the condition that is just right for them, so that others can be where they have almost reached the condition which they must attain. From surface to center the bar is therefore graduated into steel of different qualities. The degree of steeliness of the center is rather different from that of the surface. Fortunately, "almost" is good enough in practicing the arts, for it follows from this observation that the quality of the steel in a tool is never uniform.

Let us once more follow the entire sequence of changes [181] taking place in wrought iron while it becomes steel, or all the stages through which its molecules, or at least those visible in the fracture, seem to pass. First, we see white platelets, which are more uniform and better arranged than those of the same color which are observed in bad irons. These platelets become duller and duller and at the same time smaller and smaller; finally, they become so small that they appear to our eyes only as grains. When they are white, they are still pure iron. After having become a little dull, they consist of steel, but this steel is still soft and resembles the kind I discussed in the second memoir, which acquired a beautiful grain in quenching but made bad cold chisels for cutting iron. After having become duller, they are good steel; and, when they have become still smaller and duller, they are a harder and finer steel which, however, is more difficult to work. Finally, when the platelets have become almost as fine as the grains, this is a rather general sign of an intractable steel.

All these different stages of color and grain development may simultaneously be present in a piece of steel, and this is almost necessarily so when the piece is very thick. When the character of the center of the piece changes, a long time has passed since the edges changed. It follows that, the thinner the iron selected, the easier it will be to convert it into a uniform steel.

Excessively long heating has the same effect on [182] wrought irons capable of becoming good steels as the inherently unfavorable disposition of their parts has on those wrought irons which are not suited for conversion into steel. I mean that there are irons in which the platelets nearest to the surface disappear and change into grains before the platelets farther inside have lost their brilliance and acquired the dull color they should have (Fig. 9). These are the irons of the first and second classes. Their molecules soak up the sulfurs and the salts too avidly; they are too easily penetrated by them. Those which enter the bar settle so easily in the parts they first encounter that the newly arriving sulfurs and salts must wait until these parts are saturated before they can advance any farther. The iron a little farther away from the surface of the bar does not start to become steel until after the iron nearer to the surface is already too steely, so that there are some of these bars, especially those obtained from irons of the first class, which are impossible to forge, although only a very small part of their cross-section has been converted into steel.

When coarse-grained wrought irons are converted into steel, as, for instance, the merchant bars from the Champagne and Nivernais, which fall into the fourth class, the resulting platelets are much smaller than those of the other irons, especially those containing a mixture of fine grains and platelets. I believe that in the coarse-grained irons each single grain changes into a platelet, while in the others [183] several fine grains combine to form this platelet.

There are steels which are difficult to forge, although many platelets are still present. But with a little practice in inspecting fractures one could foresee such a case, for the platelets are noticeably duller and grayer than those of the other fractures, and it is the same with the grayish, dull color as with the decrease in the size of the platelets—both must be present only to a degree.

From all I have said it nevertheless follows that irons of different kinds, when changed into steel, will have platelets of different sizes and also of different nuances of color. The different natural disposition of the irons must necessarily introduce variations in all of this. These go so far that a bar of one kind of iron will have become steel after it has acquired platelets which still have a certain sparkle, a certain degree of brilliance, while a bar of another kind of iron will always remain iron at those locations where its platelets are as brilliant as those of the first one.

The thing to be noted in the study of wrought irons is that the most tractable, the most forgeable, steels are obtained from those irons which are converted into steel with the least necessity for the platelets to lose their brilliance and to become of a gray, dull color. The fracture of steel [184] made from Swedish iron—that is, from iron of the fourth class—which has been given the right treatment is much more sparkling than that of the irons of the first, second, and fifth classes.

Generally speaking, the most reliable iron is that which for the same intensity of treatment retains the largest platelets; Swedish iron also has this favorable property. It is peculiar that large platelets should be one of the most distinct characteristics of bad iron and, conversely, a characteristic of good steel. But, as I have said often enough before, the platelets in good steel are very differently arranged from the ones in bad iron, and they have no large empty spaces between them; they are more closely pressed together.

To observe the phenomena of which I have just spoken requires great finesse, but those of which I shall speak in the following can be observed without actually looking for them. The surfaces of bars withdrawn from the furnace often show irregularities, a sort of rash (Figs. 4, 6, 7, *G G g g*), which I believe ought to be called "blisters" or "bubbles," for they are produced by some kind of ebulition which takes place in the iron. These blisters or bubbles are portions of hollow spheres or elliptical spheroids; they are very irregularly distributed on the bars and are of very different sizes. Some of them are less than half a line or a quarter of a line, others are several lines, in diameter. A bar may have three or four large blisters and [185] a multitude of small ones; another may have no large blisters, only small ones; and there are bars with none of these, but that is a rare case.

These blisters prove that the iron has been exposed to a great degree of heat in order to be converted into steel; that inside the bar considerable rarefaction must have taken place, since rather thick layers of iron have been lifted. This formation of bubbles has taken place not only near the surface but even right at the center of the bar where one sometimes finds holes, several lines long, which keep the parts of the iron separated from each other by as much as half a line or even a line or two (Fig. 7, *O*).

I suspected that these blisters were found at locations on the surface of the bars where more saline matter had accidentally collected; but this conjecture could not be verified by experiments. I purposely placed particles of salt on certain marked spots, expecting that I could raise blisters there. What happened was precisely that none appeared on these spots. They probably form at those locations where the iron is more open and has admitted more sulfurous matters which lift up the iron when they rarefy.

Generally, these blisters indicate that the steel has been heated long enough. If it has been overly long exposed to the fire, or if the compound [186] has been too active, they become very numerous. However, they are just as much an indication of the intensity of the fire as of its duration. I have seen bars completely covered with blisters before they had been half-converted into steel; these bars had been given a very lively fire at the start. Thus it seems that the blisters form only when the bar has become quite soft, and for this reason there must be more of them as the bars have been more strongly acted upon by the fire. It follows further that one can convert iron into steel without raising blisters if one gives it a very moderate fire and exposes it to the fire for a longer time.

In addition to this visible rarefaction taking place at certain locations in the bar, there occurs an invisible one throughout the bar; the proof for this is that the bar increases in volume. The amount by which it increases in width and height is not great enough to be measured; but the increase in length is measurable. I have taken the exact length of a bar of iron before I placed it in the furnace; after it had been converted into steel and had cooled, I measured it again and found an increase of more than $1\frac{1}{2}$ lines on a bar 15 inches long.

Not only the volume of the bar increases while it is being converted into steel; its weight increases at the same time. This observation may provide an insight into the causes for this conversion. I weighed a piece of Nivernais iron with all the precision possible before [187] I put it in the furnace. It weighed 3 pounds minus approximately $1\frac{1}{2}$ grains. After it had been converted into steel, I weighed it with the same weights and on the same scales, and it then weighed 3 pounds and 128 grains. As I did not weigh it until four or five days had passed since it had been withdrawn from the furnace, I took great pains to dry it well in order to make it at least as dry and as clean as it had been when it was first weighed. Even if it should seem advisable to deduct about 22 grains in order to be on the safe side, the increase in weight would still be 108 grains, which means 36 grains, or 1/16 ounce, per pound. The weight of the iron therefore increased at least by 1/256 of the original during the operation, and there is no doubt about this increase. When I repeated the experiment on Swedish iron, I found almost the same increase of volume as well as of weight.

I have said before that the bars after having been converted into steel are brittle, even if they have been allowed to cool in the furnace; but I must add that, although they have this characteristic of quenched steel, they do not have the one by which it is usually accompanied—that is, hardness. These bars are a little harder under the file than ordinary iron but much less so than quenched steel. However, when they are heated and then quenched, they acquire all the hardness steel can have.

If [188] the bars are quenched in cold water immediately after they have been withdrawn from the furnace and while they are still quite red, they become still more brittle; they lose their platelets and acquire a type of grain which varies with the degree of heat the bars had when they were quenched but is always less uniform and less beautiful than the grain they can have later, after they have been forged.

When the iron has been in the furnace for approximately the length of time which is considered necessary, some bars should be withdrawn and tested by breaking them either after they have been allowed to cool slowly or after they have been quenched. If desired, they may be forged on one end; this end will be heated, and they will then be quenched and broken. When these tests, performed on bars that have been withdrawn from our furnace at different elevations, indicate that the conversion into steel has progressed to the desired point, no further wood or charcoal is added. If no second furnace run is planned, everything is allowed to cool before the steel is taken out, for it will benefit from the heat given off by the furnace. In this case nothing is withdrawn until the compound seems to be completely extinct. But if the steel has been fired long enough and it is advisable to conserve the heat of the furnace, the furnace is emptied out at once, provided it is constructed in such a way that it can be emptied through the sides. As the bars are withdrawn, the smoldering compound [189] between them is also taken out. It is deposited in a large crucible or some other vessel, where it is smothered as quickly as possible. If it were left exposed to the air, it would soon be reduced to ashes and would no longer be suitable for re-use; but, if one is careful to smother it promptly, it will later be in condition to serve again.

Finally, in order to have the bars which were taken from the furnace and were found to be steel in the state of ordinary [marketable] steel, it remains to forge them. It is necessary to bring their parts closer together again after they have been overly separated from each other during the operation. Before forging them, they are heated as iron and steel are almost always heated before they are worked under the hammer. However, when this steel is not made from an iron of excellent quality and when it has been fired too much, one must be careful not to overheat it, for it would ill withstand the blows. Many small pieces would detach themselves, and it would remain full of cracks; the drastic separation of parts already badly held together is too much. The more fire acts upon any body whatsoever and the more heat it conveys upon it, the more it separates its parts. It is always safest to heat the bars weakly the first time, not to let them get more than red which just begins to pale; they must not be heated so drastically as to become white—that is, to a welding heat.

I have seen steels, made from certain kinds of iron, which could safely be given a welding heat [190] right from the start; but it is safer not to try it.

Furthermore, in order to have these bars heat more uniformly and more exactly to the desired degree, I should like to see them placed in reverberatory furnaces—similar to those in which the bars are heated that are to be passed between the rolls of rolling mills and the cutters of slitting mills—and have them heated in wood fire like those bars. I mean that I should prefer this method of heating to heating them in the forge with charcoal, but this is not one of the absolutely necessary precautions.

When steel is made from good iron and has been carefully made, there is hardly more waste in forging it than in forging common iron. With steel made from Swedish iron I have found a decrease in weight of only one-twelfth when bars 2 inches wide by 4 lines thick were forged into square billets.

I may have advised in the second memoir and also in this one to favor the use of thin bars, but it is necessary to maintain certain proportions of thickness to width. If the bars are too thin in relation to their width, it will not be easy to change their shape under the hammer, it will be difficult to forge them on their sides; and if they are forged and one wishes to reduce these thin bars to [191] approximately square sections, something like corrugations will form on the face of the bar (Fig. 10); even if one later forces these corrugations to disappear, the steel will have a defect which I would not have suspected but which I have discovered by experience. When tools made from this steel are quenched, they are likely to split open. In forging the edge, the fibers of the steel have been separated from each other more than they have been brought together in forging the face, and some remain that cohere badly. Consequently, when in discussing furnaces I said that bars 3 lines thick and 20 lines wide became steel within a certain time, I did not mean to indicate that a ratio of 3 to 20 was the one to be chosen; a ratio of 3 to 10 is better.

By the way, the forge hammers called tilt hammers are the best for forging these bars; they do more work than hand-operated hammers and unite the parts of the steel more firmly.

Finally, after the bars have been forged and given the desired shape, it is customary to quench them. This quenching is not useful for future applications, for every time steel is heated the effect of quenching is voided; and, in order to make tools out of steel, it must be heated. However, those who buy it are a little better able to judge its quality when it is quenched than when it is not. The process of quenching does not belong to those that must be taken into account [192] as making the steel dearer, for all it amounts to is to heat it to approximately cherry-redness and, when it has reached this color, to plunge it in cold water. This is enough to make it hard. When it is broken after it has been quenched, its fracture consists of fine grains; but whether they are more or less fine depends on the quality of the steel and on the degree of heat at which it has been quenched. The time has not yet come, however, to examine the different effects of quenching.

Let us examine at present approximately how much the conversion of iron into steel will cost, so that those who feel like undertaking such an enterprise may know roughly what they can expect. Let us first make our calculations for Paris, which of all localities is the least favorable for such enterprises, and let us make them for a furnace in which only 600 pounds of iron can be converted at one time, which again is not a favorable condition. When this furnace has once been heated, six barrows of charcoal will be enough to convert the iron into steel, provided the plates [separating the crucibles] are thin and the fire is well managed. At Paris, at present, a barrow of charcoal costs 4 *livres* 10 *sols*,* which adds up to 27 *livres* for the six barrows. This is the heavy expense. Soot, ashes, and powdered charcoal are such cheap materials that the quantities needed will probably cost less than 2 *livres*. One will use 12–13 pounds of sea salt, which at Paris may [193] cost about 6 *livres*. A workman will be occupied with the furnace for two days and one night, which is reckoned as three days. Let us add two more days for the time necessary to load the furnace, to lute it, and to pulverize and sift the ingredients of the compound. Let us assume that the workman is paid 20 *sols* for each working day on which he is occupied with something that does not require skilled labor. The sum of these costs amounts to 40 *livres*, so that 100 pounds of iron converted into steel will cost about 6 *livres* 13 *sols* 4 *deniers*. If at present, in Paris, the charcoal were worth only 55 *sols* the barrow, as it was two years ago, 35 *sols* would have to be deducted from the costs

* See Appendix A, p. 369, for a note on currency.

for each 100 pounds, which then would amount to only 4 *livres* 18 *sols* 4 *deniers*. Outside of Paris, where the expense for transportation of the charcoal would be saved, the total cost would not exceed this even at present. In those parts of the country where forge shops are available, the costs would be less than 4 *livres*. And if one were willing not to force those who would build these useful enterprises to employ gabelled salt—in other words, if it could be given to them approximately at cost instead of the 20 *sols* that must be spent on salt for each 100 pounds of iron, the necessary salt would not even cost 5 *sols*. However, even if the salt is bought at the bonded warehouses, it is not necessary to charge oneself with all one uses; if the old compound is employed, it serves more than once; and, if one has this compound leached, more than half the salt used will be recovered. If it were feared that it might be [194] mixed with too much sal alkali, one would only have to use leached ashes in those compounds in which this salt would be employed. If then we deduct 10 *sols* for salt for each 100 pounds, the cost of 100 pounds of steel would now be only 3 *livres* 10 *sols*.

In these computations we have considered neither the cost of building the furnace nor the cost of the plates. The cost of the furnace, distributed over several furnace charges, will amount to very little. If the plates are made of good clay, they should not increase the expenses by as much as 30 *sols* per furnace run, and the same plates will then serve more than once. If they are made of cast iron, they will be still cheaper because of their very long life—although they cost more when they are first bought.

If, instead of charcoal, the furnace I have described is heated by wood fire, the operation will take longer; but the wood consumed will not cost as much as the charcoal would. A load of wood,* which is carefully used, keeps up the fire in this furnace for three or four days. It is true that it will cost more in working days for the man occupied in tending it; but this increase is somewhat less than the saving.

If the maker sold the steel as it comes out of the furnace, it would therefore cost him less than 1 *sol* per pound more than the

---

* *Voie de bois*, now about 2 cubic meters (about 2.6 cubic yards), which is a little more than ½ cord.

[195] iron from which it was made. It would be in the interest of the artisans who use steel in their work to buy it in this state. Nowadays they buy somewhat gropingly; the more or less beautiful grain visible in the fracture of the billets sold to them is a very equivocal indication [of quality], as I shall explain hereafter. They admit that they cannot judge the quality of a steel until they have used it; but, if they bought the steels as they come from the furnace, they would be sure not to be deceived. The fractures of these steels have characteristics by which, as I have explained, we can recognize what can be expected of a steel. By means of these fractures the artisans would soon be able to judge the different qualities of steels at a glance. But there is no hope that for the time being they will buy steel as it comes from the furnace; it will be necessary to have it forged into bars or billets. Moreover, these bars or billets will have to be given shapes similar to those of the steels that come from foreign countries; a different shape would put a stop to the sale. In the beginning it will be difficult to sell the steel at all if it becomes known that it is a product of the Kingdom. The prejudice the artisans of Paris have against this article is quite understandable. They know that many vain attempts have been made to convert our irons into steel, and, what is worse, they have been cheated several times in buying these steels. To make them feel [196] safe, we must promise them to take back any steel they have bought that seems bad to them and to replace it by other steel pound for pound, and the promise must be kept. The state of prejudice at which they have arrived demonstrates that it is important not to leave the experimenting with materials related to the public welfare to just any kind of person; that such enterprises ought to be permitted only to those whose qualifications are recognized and who have the means necessary for success or to whom we are willing to furnish them. Failures in such undertakings become considerable obstacles to those who in the future would be capable of making a success of similar ones.

After our bars have been withdrawn from the furnace, we therefore shall at present be forced to forge them, and this working cannot help but increase the cost. I do not mean that it is

expensive in itself; but with every iron that is forged there is always some waste. This may be as much as one-twelfth, so that
our 600 pounds of forged steel would be reduced to 550 pounds.
These 550 pounds must absorb the costs that were distributed
over 600 pounds and also the cost of the wasted iron. The first of
these items to be added is not very great, but the second is. The
costs of the conversion into steel are augmented for each 100
pounds of steel by the price of approximately 9 pounds of iron,
for the 50 pounds of wasted iron must be distributed over our
550 pounds [197] of steel. At the usual rate, the kind of iron employed for conversion into steel would cost less than 3 *sols* per
pound at the forges, where it actually does not cost more than
that at present. The price of each 100 pounds of steel will therefore be increased by 27 or 30 *sols*. If through this item and others,
of which I have not yet spoken, the increase would rise to 50
sols, the processing of a pound of steel would cost only 18
deniers.

There are many indirect expenses which I have not entered in
my accounts, such as the rent of the workshops where the work
is done or the wages of the clerks hired for the distribution of
the steel. Charged to the steel, these expenses will be the lower
the greater the enterprises are. But there is such a difference between the price of iron and that of the fine steels sold in the
Kingdom that it is easy to see without further computations
that the new steel can be offered very cheaply, and yet everybody would be satisfied. While iron is worth 6 *blancs*, or 3 *sols*,
the pound, fine steels are sold at 18–20 *sols*, and our artisans find
many rejections among these expensive steels. If at 10 *sols* the
pound they could buy steels which are just as fine but not intermixed with bad ones, they would gladly pay the difference [be-
tween iron and steel]. And if the steel were sold at 10 *sols*, the
profit made by the owners of the works would surpass by far the
profit made in the ordinary kind of business.

If certain [198] precautions are neglected—and sometimes in
spite of precautions—accidents may happen to some furnace
runs. One may find steels which have not been converted far
enough, which are not steel throughout, steels in which some
iron remains. As I have said before, the remedy would consist in

putting them back in the furnace; but it would be still better if other factories were near in which tools are made for which this kind of steel could be conveniently used. These steels are quite suitable for making files, sickles, swords, and several other tools which are even better when their center consists of iron than when they are purely steel.

Regarding steels that are defective in the opposite direction, those that have been overexposed and have become too steely, I shall later discuss a means of bringing them back to the state where they should be.

The Seventh Memoir, Where, by Reviewing the Processes by Which Wrought Iron Is Changed into Steel, the Nature of Steel and the Essential Difference between Steel and Iron Are Defined

I DO NOT believe that up to now a clear idea has been presented of what really characterizes steel and how it is fundamentally different from iron. According to the language commonly used by authors dealing with metallic materials, steel is purer iron, more perfect iron, or more highly refined iron. Rohault,* for instance (with a hundred others), uses the last definition, which is not only inexact but actually wrong if the fineness or the purity of iron is defined in the same way as that of all other metals. The finest metal is the one containing the least amount of foreign matters. To refine gold means to free it from the silver or copper with which it is mixed; to refine silver is again to take away the copper or other foreign matters that seem to be one with it. According to this common concept and according to what was demonstrated in the memoirs explaining [204] the manner in which iron is converted into steel, it is obvious that steel should not be called a more highly refined iron, because there is no evidence that any earthy or metallic substance, or any substance of any other nature, is taken away from the iron that is converted into steel. Something is added to it rather than taken away; and that which is added is not iron.

* Jacques Rohault, *Traité de physique* (Paris, 1671), Part III, chap. vi. Though Rohault was wrong on this point, his ideas on the structure of matter were nevertheless important. There is little doubt that Réaumur's concept of the "parts" composing steel and their rearrangement and diffusion under the influence of heat were directly derived from Rohault. Rohault himself was following Descartes (see Introduction, pp. xxv–xxvii).

To call steel a more perfect iron is an even more misleading way of expressing oneself. A metal per se becomes more perfect only when it is made to contain a greater amount of its own substance. In this sense, being more perfect and being more highly refined are the same thing. Even if the degree of perfection of a metal is determined as a function of its uses by us, if the state in which it is more useful to us is called the more perfect state, we still will not find that steel outranks iron. Soft iron is as necessary to us for certain applications as steel is for others. If nothing but steel were ever produced from the ores, there would be a need for finding the secret of converting steel into iron as there has been for seeking the secret of converting iron into steel. Just as we need steel for knives, scissors, razors, and axes—that is, for all cutting tools—we need iron for carriage axles, tires on wheels, crowbars, structures, gun barrels—in short, for all those articles that must resist breakage. Furthermore, with certain products in mind, we might consider brittle iron [205] more perfect than soft iron—that is, for all those products for which toughness is of little importance but which must take a high polish.

There are two possibilities of defining steel better—either by its characteristic properties or by the nature of the process by which it is made. We shall first distinguish it from iron by its observable properties, by those that are brought out in the most common experiments. We then shall see what constitutes its internal nature, from what it derives the properties that are peculiar to it. Such information must naturally be obtained from consideration of the processes that change iron into steel.

What distinguishes steel most obviously from iron is that after having been heated to a certain degree and then being quenched in water or some other cold liquid—or, generally speaking, after having been cooled rapidly—steel acquires considerable hardness and also becomes brittle; and that, if it is broken at a location where it has been quenched, the surfaces of the fractures seem to be occupied by an infinite number of grains which to the unaided eye seem to approach a round shape. All this does not happen to iron that is heated and quenched under the same conditions as the steel.

If steel is allowed to cool in the same furnace in which it has been brought to red heat—that is, if it is not quenched—it can no longer be distinguished from iron by the afore-mentioned criteria. It is almost as tractable as soft iron, [206] its resistance to the file is hardly greater; however, it still resists it a little more than iron, and this is the reason why artisans who make certain products out of steel which could be made out of iron—as, for instance, door knockers—sell them more dearly than the difference in the price of the materials would justify; for the work takes a little longer. The steel is then scarcely more brittle than iron. Its fracture no longer contains grains like those it would have had if it had been quenched, but it still differs from the fracture of ordinary irons. Brilliant platelets will never be found, and the fracture will never be full of coarse fibers as that of soft iron; if it contains fibers, they are fine. In general, it will have some resemblance to the fractures of granular irons. If it differs from them, the difference will consist mainly in that its grains are duller.

A less obvious difference than the preceding ones, but one recognized by the artisans who process iron and steel, is that steel heats up more easily; in the same fire the color that denotes a certain degree of heat is acquired faster by steel than by iron of the same thickness.

These differences between iron and steel are easy to notice; but we must look for those that are not found by simple inspection —that is, for the peculiarities of the internal makeup of the steel. There is no surer way of discovering them than to study the changes [207] that have taken place in an iron that has been converted into steel and how the substances employed in the conversion have operated. Let us therefore review the processes I have described by considering some of their aspects.

Iron bars are inclosed in a crucible; there, each bar is surrounded by a compound, which contains many sulfurous or combustible substances together with saline matters. The iron is heated until it is red-hot or white-hot. The fire dilates the iron as it penetrates it; it moves its parts away from each other; but, as the parts* of the fire enter, they also carry sulfurous parts with them into the iron. Fire itself is made up of sulfurous parts; but not all the parts of this nature carried along by the fire are burning to the degree necessary to be consumed. The fire of our common chimneys proves this. The soot which is deposited there was mixed with the flame—it was part of it—but it has nevertheless remained a highly combustible matter.

The sulfurous parts do not enter the iron alone; they are accompanied by saline parts. A degree of heat violent enough to force these salts to sublimate even on the outside of the furnace, as I have reported elsewhere [p. 47], doubtless has enough force to make them penetrate into the iron which they surround. Furthermore, the sulfurous matters are vehicles that are of very great [208] help to the salts; it is known how much they can increase their volatility. In this instance, however, the help is apparently reciprocal; the salts facilitate the introduction of the sulfurs and vice versa; they are known as powerful solvents of iron. Through their agency the burning fluid in which they float finds itself in condition to act more effectively upon the iron, to open up passages in it more easily. We therefore obtain more active compounds by adding salts to substances which already contain them. Salts alone would, however, act feebly unless they were carried or driven by sulfurous parts, or, rather, they would have no effect at all. We saw this in the experiments in which salts were used alone, the experiments described in the first memoir, where a mixing of fats and salts was found absolutely necessary.

It is evident therefore that sulfurs and salts are introduced into iron which is in the process of being converted into steel, that

* Réaumur's concept of "parts" was essentially Cartesian, acquired from Rohault (see Introduction). From the chemical thinking of the day he adopted the idea of "sulfurous" parts, combining in some measure the qualities of both heat and combustibility. Réaumur could rather easily have concluded that only the "sulfurs" were needed, both for heating and for giving the chemical change accompanying cementation, but the "salts" seemed necessary, because he had noticed the accelerating effect of such materials in the carburizing compound and the rather striking property changes which suggest the presence of a harder matter, which he associated with salt and which we today "know" to be an intermetallic compound, cementite.

the conversion of the iron progresses only as the sulfurous and saline parts progress further inward, and that, when the iron has become entirely steel, these parts have penetrated to the center. The longer one continues to heat this steel, the more one conveys upon it the qualities of steel. This necessarily leads to the conclusion—a conclusion which I had drawn in advance or at which I had at least hinted in some of the previous memoirs—that steel [209] as it is withdrawn from the furnace is an iron into which more sulfurs and salts have been introduced than ordinary iron contains. (It will hardly be imagined that there is continuous circulation, that as many sulfurous and saline parts as enter it continuously issue from the iron that is being treated.) If this concept, which is not supported by any proof, should seem doubtful, the doubts will be dispelled by recalling one of the observations of the previous memoir—that iron which is converted into steel increases in weight. This increase, though inconsiderable, cannot be attributed to anything but the introduction of new substances, which can only be portions of those with which the iron was surrounded.

Freshly made steel, steel which has just been withdrawn from the furnace and has not been hammered since it became steel, thus differs from iron because it is penetrated by more sulfurous and saline parts. In order to put this steel in the condition in which it can be shaped into the articles of commerce, all that remains to be done is to heat and forge it. Its parts, which during the conversion had become too far separated from each other, are brought closer together again by the hammer, and this changes the steel in such a way that when it is subsequently broken—either after slow cooling or after quenching—its fracture is different from the fracture of the same steel before it was forged.

The only question one might still have concerning the nature of steel would thus be whether steel which has just [210] been forged still differs from iron by the amount of sulfurous and saline matters by which it is penetrated as it differed from it when it was taken out of the furnace; whether in heating it directly on the charcoal the matters that had entered it have not been driven out; and, finally, whether the hammer blows do not result in squeezing these matters out when they compress the parts of our metal. It would seem at least probable that, the longer steel is heated on charcoal, the more often it is heated, and the more violently it is heated, the more it would be deprived of its sulfurs and its salts and the more it would also be robbed of its steel quality and be brought back to the state of being iron. These effects are not only probable; they have been proved by experiments, and they are themselves proof that steel differs from iron only because it is charged with matters which fire can take away from it. The best steels become weaker when they are put back in the fire several times. Finally, there is no steel which is not ruined, which is not converted back into iron, when it is exposed to an excessively violent degree of heat or a heating that is not so violent but lasts too long. Every artisan knows it; they call a steel overheated when, after having been overexposed to the forge fire, it has almost lost the properties of steel or these properties have become much less pronounced. They call a steel "burnt" when, because it [211] has been heated still more drastically, it is no longer in a condition to be hardened by quenching. Strictly speaking, this steel has again become iron. It happens comparatively often to careless or preoccupied artisans that they inadvertently reduce steel to one or the other of these conditions. It has happened to me more than once that by talking with them I made them forget the moment when they should have removed from the fire a steel that was to be fashioned into a certain tool. Such steel upon which the fire had acted too much became useless for the intended application.

It would be wrong, however, if we believed that by heating steel once or twice we could deprive it of the additional sulfurs and salts by which it differs from iron. If these sulfurs have thoroughly penetrated the steel, they can withstand prolonged action by the fire without being consumed, for such is the nature of the substances that have been employed. When the bars are removed from the crucibles in which they were inclosed in order to be converted into steel, after having been fired for two, three, and sometimes more than eight to ten days, the substances between the iron bars are found to be still burning lively, still capable of blazing up, although they have burned so long. It is true that they have been inside crucibles which were so carefully closed that few parts were able to escape. But, if the same inflammable matter has penetrated to the center of the small parts of iron, is it not there as tightly shut in as in the crucibles? Would it be easier for it to evaporate? Would not iron, which absorbs sulfurs greedily, hold on to them [212] much more stoutly than charcoal or soot?

It now seems well established that there are more sulfurs in steel than in iron. In order to deprive steel of its sulfurs, one more step is needed than in depriving iron of its sulfurs. I mean that, if iron is overheated, it is burned; it is reduced to scale or cinders; but, if steel is overheated, it is reduced back to being iron, and this iron which was steel, like iron that never has been anything but iron, must then be overheated or burned in order to be reduced to scale or cinders.

Everything I just said of sulfurs is also true of salts. Immediately after the conversion, steel is more penetrated by them than iron, and it remains penetrated by these same salts as long as it stays steel. This is why the most stable salts are needed to change iron into the harder and more durable steels. I reported in the first memoir that, when I used certain salts, iron was changed into a steel which, after having been forged a single time, possessed hardness and a very beautiful grain, but which, after having been heated and forged a second time, was unrecognizable and, after a third heating, was no longer steel or practically no longer steel. This defect did not depend on the sulfurous substances employed; they were the same and were used in the same amounts as in other experiments in which the iron was converted into steel of the most durable quality. [213] It therefore had to be the salts that caused the difference. These steels of low fixity (for one is justified in calling them that) were the product of excessively volatile salts or salts that had become so under the circumstances.

There are steels which, while they are forged and heated, give off an odor of sulfur resembling that of common sulfur. In these steels the vitriolic acids and the fatty part of the iron combine in the proportions necessary to form this sulfur. I have made such steels by packing the iron in a mixture of much vitriol and powdered charcoal; they are difficult to work and also of low durability. In one of the experiments described in the first memoir [p. 37], the compound was soaked in aqua fortis; it changed the iron into a steel that could not stand being heated twice.

Thus, sea salt, which is one of the most stable salts, the one that most readily combines with iron and holds on to it most tenaciously, is of all the salts the one which, according to our experiments, is most apt to contribute to the conversion of iron into excellent steel. But if I were asked if the salt with which the iron becomes impregnated preserves the nature of sea salt, or if before penetrating into the iron it changes its nature, if the acid of sea salt* detached by the violence of the fire, combined with the fatty parts provided by the substances by which it is surrounded, might not form a sal ammoniac [214] which goes into the iron, or if the sea salt enters it as it is—this is something that cannot be decided with such confidence. Our observations do not go that far. However, they have shown that the heat of our furnaces is sufficient to deposit sublimated sea salt even on the outside of these furnaces; perhaps it is no more difficult for this heat to force the salt to penetrate into iron when its parts are farther separated from each other than when it is cold. On the other hand, if one maintained that the salts penetrating the iron are only some kind of sal ammoniac, one certainly would propose something quite probable, for our iron is surrounded by substances from which this kind of salt is made. But perhaps it is still more probable that, together with these sal ammoniacs, not only the acid of sea salt but sea salt itself as the substance in which we see it sublimated is introduced into the iron and that the steel becomes more durable as more of this kind of salt enters into it.

On the other hand, if one maintained that the salts which enter into the iron during the conversion are sal alkalies, which then absorb the acids of our metal, this proposition could also be defended, although it seems to agree less well with most of the facts I have described. In order to confine ourselves to the

* The idea that salts resulted from the association of an acid and a base had been formulated by Tachenius in 1671, but it was well established first by Rouelle in 1745.

incontestable, let us be content with [215] having recognized that steel differs from iron because it is impregnated with more sulfurs and salts and that, of the different steels, the most durable ones are those which are the product of the most stable salts.

We have seen that the shape and the arrangement of the parts of iron are changed in proportion as our sulfurous and saline substances penetrate it. Regardless of whether the iron had fibers or grains, everything is rearranged, so that the fracture will have platelets which are duller than those in the fracture of bad irons and arranged more uniformly. The weight of the iron increases, and its volume increases at the same time. It follows that its parts have moved farther away from each other; the substances that have entered into it have separated them, have subdivided them. The longer the process is continued, the longer the iron is kept surrounded by substances able to convert it into steel, the more are the parts of the metal subdivided. Proof of this is found in one of the observations of the preceding memoir—that iron which has been converted into steel, and which then has platelets of a certain size in its fracture, will have smaller platelets in its fracture if one continues firing it for a longer time. The platelets will finally become so small, they will be divided into so many parts, that they seem to be only grains. The platelets near the surface are always smaller than those toward the center, for the former have been attacked longer and by a larger quantity [216] of sulfurous and saline parts, so that they have become more thoroughly subdivided. We may conclude, therefore, that steel is less "matted" than iron; one might say it has been better "carded." It preserves this kind of arrangement of its parts as long as it remains steel. Even if we hammer it, the metallic parts will always remain separated by foreign substances, just as, even if we compress thoroughly carded wool, it will not mat as it would before it was carded.

Even steel that has again become iron because it was overheated preserves vestiges of this previous arrangement of its parts. When its nature was such that it has become a fibrous iron, the fibers found in it are incomparably much finer than those of ordinary iron of similar quality, for, when parts have once been finely subdivided, they reunite to form thinner fibers.

The reason why steel acquires a greater degree of heat than iron does when both are heated equally long by the same fire is self-evident, one might say. A metal which offers a greater number of passages to the substance of the fire than another metal, and which within the same time interval is charged with more combustible matter, must become heated sooner throughout.

When we examined the different kinds of iron in connection with their tendency to become steels, we found that some could never be changed into anything but bad steels, [217] that others could make excellent ones, and that there are some which can be converted in less time than others. At that time I hinted at the reasons for these different effects of the compounds on different irons, but now we can draw a much clearer picture of the causes for these differences. The result of the memoir to which I am referring was that, regardless of whether the irons belonged to the category with platelets, or of fibrous irons, or of granular irons, the irons of each of these groups were more apt to become excellent steels as the molecules of which they were composed were smaller. Irons having the smallest platelets are to be preferred to all other irons with platelets. Their molecules, which are already greatly subdivided, can be divided to the point which is required by steel without the introduction of a very large quantity of foreign matter; and it is the same with the irons of every other category.

Irons with a non-uniform structure must yield non-uniform steels, steels that are difficult to work. The sulfurous and saline substances will have penetrated the small molecules more than enough when the big ones at the same distance from the surface will not yet have been sufficiently penetrated. When the molecules are extremely big, as those of irons with large platelets, and when these molecules are separated by large voids, as they always are, they will no longer sufficiently cohere when the piece of metal as a whole has [218] reached the degree of rarefaction it must reach in order to become steel. It is likewise easy to see why certain irons are changed into steel in less time than others. What we have learned about the nature of steel in general can easily be applied to any particular case.

Let us remember, then, that steel, far from being a more

highly refined iron or a purer iron as has been claimed heretofore, actually is iron that is penetrated to a higher degree by sulfurous and saline parts, an iron with smaller molecules which are better "carded" than those of ordinary iron. All this has been established from observation of the processes operative in the making of steel, of what happens in the iron during its conversion. Something we might call the [re]conversion of steel served as additional proof when I called attention to the fact that the great violence of the fire converts the steel back again into iron. The next memoir contains as much evidence to support this proof as any proof in physics can ever have. There, the way in which steel is converted back into iron will be demonstrated at least as clearly as the way of making it has been explained.

The Eighth Memoir, in Which, by Means of Converting Steel Back into Iron, It Is Successfully Proved That the Essential Difference between Steel and Iron Consists in the Greater Penetration of Saline and Sulfurous Parts into Steel; and in Which a Method Is Described by Which Most Defective Steels Can Be Reclaimed

THE OBJECT of the preceding memoirs has been to show how iron is changed into steel and to demonstrate what happens in the iron when this conversion takes place. In this one, I shall aim at reconverting our product—at turning the steel back into iron. If we felt that we did not yet sufficiently understand the nature of steel, that its nature seemed not yet sufficiently explained by the way it is made, its reconversion into iron will, I believe, provide as much evidence as we can reasonably ask for. One is fortunate in physical experiments when these two opposite ways of approach both lead to a manifestation of the principles of a body; but a circumstance which is no less fortunate in this instance is that the process of reconverting steel into iron, with which I shall deal, also constitutes the subject matter of one of the most useful branches of our [220] art. We shall first consider this process from the standpoint of its usefulness in practice.

I have so often spoken of steels that are difficult to work, steels that stay full of cracks after having been forged, that it should be very evident that this defect is the one most dreaded and the one most likely to be encountered. There are irons which, regardless of what we do, never yield anything but bad steels, and I have therefore excluded them. But we have seen that even steels made from the best irons will have this bad quality if the substances that have acted upon such irons were not used in the right amounts and proportions and that too prolonged firing can produce the same bad effect. It is true that I have tried to give rules. But how can we be sure that the artisans will always be careful enough to follow them? If they fail to do so, however, losses must be faced which can ruin an establishment that might otherwise have worked profitably. In undertaking something new, one has to be afraid of everything, which is especially true of us who were given no patience to surmount difficulties.

Generally speaking, steel is almost always less easy to work than iron. Hence, since steel differs from iron because it is penetrated by more sulfurous and saline parts, it is natural to assume that steel becomes more difficult to process as it contains more of these parts. Such difficult-to-work [221] steel, as I have said so many times, is steel that has been exposed to the action of excessively large quantities of sulfurous and saline substances or to an excessively long action of these substances, which means that it is steel into which these substances have been introduced in excessively large quantities. One might say it has become too steely; it no longer contains enough molecules of metallic substance, of ferrous substance, in proportion to the molecules of foreign matters. The metallic parts are too far apart from each other. When such steel is heated, which must always be done when it is to be shaped into a tool, the fire further removes from each other these parts that are already too far separated. They are no longer sufficiently tied up with each other to resist the hammer and to hold together. The steel bursts and splits under the hammer blows, or at least stays full of tears and cracks at the locations where its parts were the least cohesive.

Knowledge of the reason for an evil is at least a start on the way to search for the right remedy. It was only natural to try to find one that would prevent steel which had become useless merely through lack of foresight or care on the part of the artisan from remaining useless. According to the reasoning in the foregoing, all that had to be done to make these steels more tractable, or less fractious, was to rid them of the excess sulfurs and salts they had absorbed.

The expedient which occurred to me first, and which it seems ought to have presented itself first, was to place these difficult-to-work steels in the midst of [222] lively burning charcoal and to keep them exposed to this fire as long as indicated by experience; for I believed that in this way the excess sulfurs could be burned out and the excess salts forced to evaporate. It means a lot if reasoning shows one a good way; but one must not expect, in matters concerning physics, that reasoning will make one foresee everything. It was useless that I exposed my steels to prolonged firing, regardless of whether the fire was gentle or violent. They became partly burned; there was considerable loss through scale that detached itself; and their defectiveness was not corrected, or only a little. I had no doubt at all that, if these steels stayed intractable after having undergone this firing, the only possible reason was that the oil and the acids of the charcoal had provided their internal parts with the same amount of these substances as the heat had taken away from them. It was this reflection which almost led me to the correct solution, which is as simple as one could possibly hope for. It requires no processing apparatus, no complication of operations; there is nothing about it that could give it the air of a miracle—all of which makes it the more useful in practice. It was necessary to rid the steel of its excess sulfurs and salts, and fire was the only possible agent to be employed. However, it was necessary to prevent the burning substances from providing the steel with as much of the sulfurs and salts as the fire would take away. The only way to achieve this was by heating the steel very strongly without exposing it to the direct action [223] of the flame. In accord with this way of reasoning, I inclosed some of the most intractable steels in crucibles or earthenware boxes and luted the crucibles and the boxes everywhere so that the flame had no possible way of entering them. When these steels had thus been exposed to a fire of a certain duration, which I shall later on define more exactly, they could be worked as easily as one could hope for; after they had been forged, no more tears or cracks were seen on their surfaces.

I repeated this experiment several times, with the same result. Under certain circumstances it happened, however, that the steels scaled. This was the case when the flame succeeded in penetrating inside the crucible or when the fire was too violent. I therefore thought that I should try to make the process not only more reliable but also faster. Experiments that are unsuccessful with regard to that which one is trying to do often have other uses if one takes the trouble to remember their results. When I tried out the different substances I was considering for the conversion of iron into steel, I tested some which I recognized as being completely incapable of contributing anything in this respect; but I observed, and I was careful to record in the first memoir, that some of these same substances were able to soften the iron and that later a use would be found for them. I shall now tell how they can be advantageously employed. After having observed that several [224] earthy and very alkaline matters increased the toughness of iron, it was natural to believe that they would render steel more tractable. The reasoning recorded in the foregoing helped to strengthen this idea. Materials which avidly soak up sulfurs and salts ought to be able to rid steel of an excess of them.

I therefore tried what effect different kinds of earthy matters would produce on steel. I put in square crucibles layers of bars of intractable steel and separated them from each other by layers of these materials. Some crucibles contained powdered marl, others clay, others the kind of chalk which is generally called Spanish white, others contained quicklime, others slaked lime, others plaster of Paris, others ground glass, and others bone ash (that is, bones that had been burned until they could be reduced to a powder). After having luted these crucibles thoroughly, I exposed them to a heat which I considered suitable. Most of these substances helped to speed up the process and also softened the steels perfectly; but bone ash and chalk undoubtedly deserved preferred rating.

Earthy matters that contain comparatively much salt, such as marl and clay, acted more slowly than the others and also caused the steel to scale in some instances. The effect of plaster of Paris was even worse; it caused the steel to melt when I gave it a somewhat lively heat, and [225] at a moderate heat it caused considerable scaling. Ground glass, it seemed to me, did not effect any softening of the steel.

Whether bone ash is chosen, or chalk, or any other earthy matter, these are not substances which make the process much more expensive. Chalk costs little. Later in this book I shall describe a simple method of preparing bone ash and tell where one can obtain plenty of everything that is needed to make it and how it should be reduced to a powder. It will then become evident that there is no reason to be afraid of a great consumption. This subject will be discussed where it is still more important. Here I shall merely add that this powder should be mixed with about one-third of its weight of powdered charcoal.* The reason for adding charcoal will also be explained at the place to which I am referring.

I have said before that these powders are put in the crucibles layer by layer with the bars of steel. For work on a large scale, however, they will be placed in the same furnaces in which iron bars are inclosed that are to be converted into steel—and in exactly the same manner as described elsewhere in connection with the making of steel; and the crucibles of these furnaces will be luted with the same care.

No general rules can be given concerning the strength and the duration of the fire to which the bars of steel must be exposed in order to correct their defectiveness; [226] this will vary with the shape and the size of the furnaces used and with the quantity and thickness of the bars. In place of more definite rules, it is enough to know that for softening steel, for making it tractable, one needs at the most only one-fourth of the duration of the fire that was needed for making steel out of the iron, provided the same furnace is used. I shall give another, more reliable and more convenient, rule, but only after having made certain observations concerning the results of this operation.

The same steel which could not be hammered when it was put in the crucibles can be forged almost like iron when it is taken out. I have explained more than often enough that what makes

* It is hard to see what purpose the charcoal can serve, since this treatment is intended to decarburize.

it so tractable is that the fire to which it was exposed has rid it of its excess sulfurs and salts without supplying it with new ones. It remains to find out why the result is obtained much faster when alkaline matters such as chalk and bone ash surround our steel than when the steel is alone in the crucible. When it is alone, when it is surrounded by nothing but air, the fire rids the steel just as easily of its sulfurs and salts, but it does not do it in as short a time. As these substances leave the steel, they cannot all at once escape from the well-luted crucibles in which this metal is inclosed. [227] Some of them apparently circulate in these crucibles; the steel reabsorbs them and is charged with them anew. (In a way this is as if one tried to let a wet cloth dry in a very tightly closed vessel. The sun could make the water in this cloth rise up as vapors, but part of the same vapors would soon fall down on it again.) When alkaline matters are present, however, they take hold of the sulfurs and salts which the fire drives out of the steel; and, as they themselves do not contain any, they retain them.

Direct contact between steel and these same substances is useful for still another reason. As soon as the sulfurs and the salts have been conducted to the outer surface of the iron, they are soaked up by our earthy matters. (Anybody who has tried to remove a spot of grease or fat from a garment by means of Briançon chalk, or by any other unctuous earth, has apparently seen something similar to the effect of our chalk or [bone] ash on the surface of the steel.) The outer surface of the steel, its outside layer, is thus quickly relieved of the sulfurs and salts which the fire has carried there, because our alkaline matters soak them up. This outside layer of steel in turn soaks up the sulfurs and salts of the second layer, until even at the center the parts of steel are all relieved of something which they contribute to the evaporation that takes place on the outer surface.

If proof is required that this is what happens, proof which would demonstrate what [228] I have wished to establish so far—that steel is nothing but iron penetrated by more sulfurous and saline matters—a single observation will furnish this proof and will show that our whole operation does nothing but convert the steel back into iron. When a piece of steel in one of our crucibles has been exposed to the fire for some time, and is subsequently heated, quenched, and then broken, it is seen that the whole outside layer is pure iron. It is a bar of steel surrounded by a sheath of iron as thin as a sheet of paper. If the operation is continued longer with another piece of steel—that is, if steel is exposed to the fire for a longer time—a thicker layer of iron is found. A still more prolonged firing leaves steel only toward the center. Finally, if the process is completed, the steel disappears altogether, and the bar returns to its original state of being iron. What is remarkable in this connection is that all this happens without a violent fire, at a degree of heat to which the steel could be exposed on [open] charcoal for the same length of time without changing its nature.

After having demonstrated by a great many experiments how iron is converted into steel, the experiments of this memoir show the manner in which steel is changed back into iron. We thus know how steel is made and how it is reconverted. In order to turn iron into steel, we surround it with substances that can supply it with sulfurs and salts; in order to turn steel back into iron, we surround it with substances that are able to absorb these same sulfurs and salts.

The hypotheses [229] of Natural Philosophy are less often useless to practice than is commonly assumed. We shall later be shown important applications of the present ones. For now, we shall derive from them the most useful rule for determining the duration of the fire to which steels must be exposed when their defectiveness is to be corrected. I assume that in order to soften steel, to make it tractable, it is inclosed in the same furnace that I described for making this steel or that some other furnace is used from which a bar can be removed, if desired, without disturbing the others. In order to be sure of what is happening, a bar of steel will be withdrawn from the furnace after several hours of firing; it will be quenched and then broken. If a ring of iron is observed all round the fracture, it will be time to withdraw everything from the furnace. If such ring has not yet appeared, the fire must be continued and the test repeated on a fresh bar.

All the softened steels, made tractable by our treatment, are then enveloped by something like a sheath of very thin iron. Some people might consider this result as something very undesirable; perhaps they think that this secret process which corrects defectiveness only to cause new defects should not be valued so highly. But, instead of scorning our treatment because of this thin layer of iron with which it surrounds the steel, one should prize this layer as one of its best effects and one [230] that more than compensates for the small expense the treatment involves.

It is true that bars or billets of steel which contain some residual iron are considered defective by the artisans; and they are right. But then the iron is not located as it is in bars that have been subjected to our softening operation. In ordinary steels the iron occurs as irregular veins which often occupy the center or are close to it. There it can only be harmful. When one starts to hammer out the section in order to make a cutting tool out of it, it will happen that some of the iron finds itself in the cutting edge itself, which spoils it. But the thin and uniform sheath of iron that simply envelopes our softened steels can never do any harm. It is never found in the finished tool. It is so thin that there is hardly enough of it to form the scale which detaches itself from the steel while it is being forged into a tool. If there were more than that, the remainder, being on the surface, would be removed by the file.

Instead of considering this layer of iron as harmful, I would advise to make it thicker than the softening of the steel requires. There even are instances when it will be of advantage to have it very thick. If, as a rule, the artisan were guided by reason, he would prefer steels with a surface layer of iron to all others from the moment he tried them out. But it takes more than a day before he becomes accustomed to approving of something [231] that he has not been in the habit of using. It is even difficult to persuade him to try it; but, when he once tries them, he will find that softened steels have many advantages over the others. The following are some of them:

1. Fine steels require great care in heating; they withstand with difficulty the degree of heat to which they must often be subjected; they burn easily. When they are covered with a layer

of iron, they will burn much less easily. There is many an instance when one must give them this layer.

2. In making any tools, whether they are razors, shears, knives, or penknives, there is much work to be done with the file. The file cuts more easily into iron than into steel. It will be an advantage, therefore, if one has to file iron rather than steel, although a steel tool is being made.

3. One of the most outstanding advantages of our new steels is, however, that they save many operations of doubling by hammer welding and of making composite steel. The cutler uses composite steels almost exclusively for edges that must be very keen, such as those of razors, etc. In order to make the so-called composite steels, he separately forges five thin bars of steel of different qualities, one of very fine steel, two of mediocre steel, and two of very coarse steel. He places the piece of fine steel between the two pieces of mediocre steel and these between the two pieces of coarse steel. He welds them together, which means that he heats and [232] forges them until they become one. The result is called "composite steel." In the *Art of the Cutler** I shall investigate the reason underlying this process; but at present I only wish to call attention to the fact that it aims at producing a bar of steel with three different degrees of fineness. Composite steel is graduated into three perceptible degrees [of fineness], and the artisans cannot go any further with this graduation. The softening treatment to which we subject our steels to correct their defectiveness makes of them, without any other manipulation, composite steels that are graduated into imperceptible degrees which can be endlessly varied. The surface is iron; the metal near the surface is, without doubt, not as much steel or not such fine steel as that which is a little farther removed from it. The fineness of the steel increases imperceptibly until the center is reached. This is therefore the most perfect of all composite steels.

4. There is an infinite number of tools and instruments, especially among edge tools, which we are forced to make of steels

---

* Réaumur never published this work. *L'Art du coutelier*, which appeared in 1771 and 1772 as one of the *Descriptions des arts et métiers*, was written by the cutler, Jean Jacques Perret.

that are hammer-welded between two pieces of iron. In thus welding the steel, it is made weaker; sometimes it is burned, and often it is welded badly. Let us soften for a longer time, and we shall have steels sheathed in layers of iron which can be made as thick as desired. Without doubt, the steel will be welded more perfectly to this iron than steel placed between two pieces of iron can ever be, and this processing operation is saved.

5. Those who have read the preceding memoirs, and especially the sixth one, will doubtless remember that bars [233] that have once been wrought iron never become steel uniformly throughout their entire section. The metal closest to the center is always less steely than that which is farther away from it. It is, nevertheless, at the center of the bar that we would like to have the finest steel; but we do not dare give the center the ultimate degree of fineness for fear the surface might become too intractable. Thanks to our softening treatment, we no longer have to be afraid of making the steel too fine at the center. The graduation in softened steel is exactly the reverse of the graduation in steel coming from the furnace where it has ceased being iron; and this graduation is the most favorable possible. Toward the edges the steel will by degrees become less fine than it is near the center.

Furthermore, our softening treatments are not limited in their applicability to steels obtained from wrought-iron bars. They have the same effect on steels made directly from pig iron. They can be used to reclaim great numbers of steels which our artisans have been forced to reject. In other words, there are few steels that cannot be softened by this treatment; and there is none which is not entirely converted back into iron, provided the action of the treatment is sustained long enough.

There are steels which are only little improved by softening and which are never made easy to forge by such treatment. They are the ones that have been made from bad kinds of iron, the characteristics of which are described elsewhere. It is the nature of these irons [234] that their parts cohere badly. It is impossible to separate them from each other by introduction of a new substance; for, if they are separated at all, they are separated too much. Hardly have the first layers of some of these irons started to become steel when they can no longer be hammered without cracking all over. I have pointed out that this kind of iron has a looser, more spongy texture than the others. There are some that give this appearance even to the unaided eye; their molecules or platelets are separated by noticeably larger voids.

When I spoke about the first attempts I made to render steels tractable, I said that I was not successful when I exposed them to the direct action of fire. This general statement needs some clarification; for, when the fire which I let act directly upon the steel was long continued without being excessively lively, it did make them easier to work, but there was considerable discard. The outer layers of the bars disappeared in the form of scale. I put some of these steels in one of those furnaces in which ores are assayed for their metal content. In them the fire is not kept up by the movement of bellows. It is so gentle that the bars could be exposed to its action for a full day. When I was finally ready to forge them, they had been diminished by more than one-third; but the layer of iron with which they [235] were still sheathed was hardly thick enough to be noticeable. This suffices to prove that the direct action of fire is entirely to be rejected.

This experiment and all those that went before demonstrate why fine steels are made weaker by being heated several times and why a single heating by a fire urged to an excessive degree makes of them what the artisans call "burnt" steels. Properly speaking, it means that they have been ruined, have been converted back into iron. Violent heat can rapidly produce the same effect that our gentle softening produces only after a long while.

I believed that I ought to try out if, by softening treatments similar to those to which we subject intractable steels, bad irons could be conditioned to become good steels. I therefore had some of these irons so treated, and after the treatment I put them back in the furnace surrounded by substances which converted them into steel. They always became bad steels. It is true that softening takes away part of the salts or sulfurs of which they have too much, but it does not cure them of the tendency to absorb too much of them. When they are surrounded by substances that can provide them therewith, which we do when we put the conversion into steel into operation, they take up more than they should.

Finally, it would be rather useless to go into [236] details concerning the expenses involved in softening steel to correct its defectiveness. It is easy to see from what it costs to convert iron into steel that they cannot be higher. As a matter of fact, softening should cost less than one-fourth of what the conversion has cost, and it will make good steels out of something that would otherwise have been a complete loss.

The Ninth Memoir, about the Analogy between the Processes Used To Produce Steels Directly from Pig Iron and Those by Which Wrought Iron Is Changed into Steel; about a Method of Making Steel from Wrought Iron Which Has Not Yet Been Discussed; and Why It Is Much Easier To Produce Perfect Steels from Wrought Iron than from Pig Iron

IRON THAT takes up a certain quantity of sulfurous and saline matters becomes steel, and steel that is deprived of these same matters becomes iron. Although these statements can at present be considered to express principles, it is still advisable to examine how well they agree with the different practices employed in making steel. I said in the first memoir that steel is produced directly from pig irons if desired and that, in fact, this is the method commonly used. It is possible, without any kind of addition, to produce either soft iron or steel from the same pig irons by employing different processes, which, however, [238] might not seem to be sufficiently different to make us expect such important differences as those found between iron and steel if we were less familiar than we are now with the principle underlying these differences.

Cast iron, the material produced from the ore by the first smelting operation, is often harder than the most perfectly quenched steel. It cannot be hammered either hot or cold. It is not my intention to explain in detail in these memoirs all the operations that turn it into tractable, soft iron, nor those that turn it into steel. All this is reserved for a more extensive work than this. However, in order to give a clearer and more complete concept of the nature of iron and steel, I can hardly afford not to point out here what analogy exists between steels produced directly from cast iron and those made from wrought iron. The important point is to realize that regardless of the method by which they are produced steels are always penetrated by a larger quantity of sulfurs and salts than iron is. It is true that I just said that steels are sometimes made from cast iron without the addition of more of these substances than when iron is made. But this is not surprising as soon as we realize that cast iron contains more than enough of them. Steel can be converted back into iron; and something similar is done when cast iron is converted into soft iron or steel. [239] The change in the cast iron is, however, more drastic, more is taken away from it, when soft iron is made.

In order to develop this concept better, and in order to prove it at the same time, let us start once more with the ore, and let me repeat once more that every iron ore is a mixture of earthy parts, ferruginous parts, and sulfurous and saline parts. In all metallic ores, sulfurs and salts are present in ample amounts, and it is often necessary to remove a considerable portion of the sulfurs in the ores before the metallic constituents can be separately obtained. In fact, there are iron ores—and ores of other metals— which could not be smelted without excessive losses unless they were first roasted—that means unless some of their sulfurs were burned by a gentle fire. There are among these ores some that, while being roasted, give off an odor exactly like that given off by common sulfur when it burns. Regardless of whether iron ores have been roasted or not, they always contain considerable quantities of sulfurs when they are being charged into the furnace. There, liquefaction takes place; the principal result is that the metallic constituents are brought to a state in which they can separate from the earthy parts. The latter, being lighter, rise to the top after having been reduced to a sort of glass. This glass is continually tapped to remove it from above the metallic bath. [240] However, during this first smelting, the metallic parts release no sulfurous and saline matters or at least release not anything like enough. The fire cannot remove any of these matters from the iron as long as it is liquid; at best, it can act only upon the upper surface of the bath. The molten metal is made to run out of the furnace and is allowed to freeze. It is an iron still mixed with some earthy matter, for the separation of all the matters of this sort has not been wholly accomplished; but it is, above all, an iron full of sulfurs and salts. What has to be done in order to refine this iron, in order to convert it to the state in which it can be hammered hot and cold, is to rid it of part of the remaining earthy matter, to burn out the excess sulfurs and remove the excess salts. Thereafter, the metallic constituents will cohere better, because there is less to separate them from each other. However, larger or smaller quantities of sulfurs will be burned, larger or smaller quantities of salts will be removed, depending on whether wrought iron or steel is to be made.

If the iron is thoroughly purged of its earthy part (I shall explain shortly that this is accomplished by remelting), this iron, which is cleansed of earthy constituents but full of sulfurs and salts, may be considered to be steel—a steel, however, that is too much steel in some ways and is therefore intractable. Once tractable irons which, after they have become steel, are then penetrated [241] by large amounts of new sulfurous and saline matters can no longer be hammered. They have become too steely; they have reapproached the condition of cast iron. Furthermore, if we want to succeed in melting iron and steel, in making them liquid a second time, they must be combined with new sulfurous matters, and after liquefaction they will have returned to being cast iron which resembles that which they were before. This new cast iron cannot be hammered; we cannot work it either hot or cold until the excess sulfurs have been removed. Ordinary cast iron, natural cast iron, is in the same condition as this artificial cast iron. Because it contains too much of sulfurs and salts, its parts hold so badly together that it is very brittle, although very hard. Steel is much easier to soften by fire than wrought iron; and cast iron is much easier to soften than ordinary steel.

If cast iron could be hardened by quenching, it would have all the characteristics of steel. White irons have a degree of hardness that equals and often even surpasses that of quenched steel, so that it is not easy to determine by means of the file if their hardness increases by quenching; but there are gray irons that can be filed. I have heated gray irons of this sort and quenched them red-hot. After quenching, the file no longer cut them or cut only with great difficulty at the same spots that were easily worked with the file before the irons had been [242] quenched. Hence, cast irons, and especially cast irons well cleansed of all earthy matters—that is, those that are the whitest—may be considered to be true steels, but the most intractable steels. The fact that gray irons do not acquire as much hardness by quenching as excellent steels cannot be ascribed to a lack of the sulfurs and salts that characterize steel. It is the fault of the earthy constituents, of which they contain too much. These constituents are not steel, and, although they are vitrified, they yield to the file, as glass itself yields to it. It is important, therefore, that this kind of iron increases perceptibly in hardness when it is quenched; it proves that its metallic grains are, in truth, steel.

Consequently, if we consider a series of terms descriptive of the different states of iron and steel—I mean terms descriptive of masses of ferrous materials whose parts hold increasingly firmly together to give them greater resistance to the hammer when they are forged, materials which at the same time contain increasingly smaller quantities of sulfurous and saline parts than those preceding them—thoroughly purified, very white cast iron will be the first member—it is the highest degree of steel. When the sulfurs of this iron are burned, but only to a certain extent, we come to the second member of the series, which will be an intractable steel, one that will stay [243] full of cracks. Nevertheless, it can be hammered hot to some small extent, whereas cast iron cannot stand any hammering at all; as quenched, it will be extremely hard. When this intractable steel is overheated, when some of its saline and combustible matters are taken away from it, it will be changed into the third member of the series, into steel that is easily worked and can be hardened by quenching. When this easily worked steel is then heated too violently but only up to a certain degree, it becomes the fourth member of the series, an overheated steel, which means a steel that is easy to work but incapable of sufficient hardening by quenching. Finally, we obtain the fifth member of the series, that which the artisans call "burned steel" (or iron), when steel that has already been overheated is once more heated too strongly.

Although cast iron cannot be changed into wrought iron or steel without having to pass through the intermediate states of our sequence, we do not see it appear in these different forms in the forges in which it is processed. It is at once brought to the state of being steel; and, likewise, it is reduced to the state of being soft iron without leaving the finery. But the steps I have indicated are no less real because they are not observed and it is not within our power to observe them. In order to prove this, let us review broadly the differences that distinguish the processes used in changing this cast iron into wrought iron from those used in changing it into steel.

When iron is [244] to be made, and particularly very soft iron, white irons are preferred. These irons are cast in the form of pigs. One end of the pig is placed over the refining hearth, which resembles a large, square crucible made of sheet iron. It is only 7–8 inches deep. The hearth is filled with charcoal, and there is enough of it to cover the end of the pig. Two large bellows maintain a violent fire, which softens the end of the pig and causes it to melt. The pig drips, as the end of a stick of Spanish wax would drip if it were held over a candle. A workman holds a large poker in this refining hearth, with which he collects the matter that drips down; he kneads it, he turns it, and he shapes it into a mass weighing 80–90 pounds. In the forge shops this is called a "bloom." This material, either before having assumed the shape of a bloom or afterward, is surrounded by burning charcoal. The blast of the bellows causes the flame to circulate around the bloom on all sides. There really is no part of the mass against which the flame is not hurled violently. However, the detail that here particularly deserves our attention, a detail which is not included in the process by which steel is made from the same pig iron, is the method of kneading the iron and the bloom with a poker. Thanks to this operation, all the parts of the iron are successively exposed [245] to the direct action of the flame. Experience has shown that the better the bloom was kneaded, the better and the longer it was heated, the softer will be the iron produced and the smaller the amount obtained. More sulfurs are burned and more salts are removed, but at the same time more iron is also burned. Furthermore, the softer the iron, especially when it is obtained from mediocre pig irons, the greater the waste. It is easy to understand that, while the bloom was held in the refining hearth, a large part of the earthy matter and of the vitrified matter, which it still contained, was removed from it. These substances become soft more easily than iron. Some are still squeezed out when the bloom is placed under the big hammer, which weighs 1,000 and sometimes even up to 1,500 pounds. There the bloom is repeatedly forged after having been reheated each time, as is done with all iron bars that must be forged.

If steel is to be made, it may be made from white irons, but medium-gray ones are preferred—that is, irons not of the purest grade. The reason is not that we intend to leave more earthy and vitrified matter in steel than in wrought iron but that it is impossible to employ as violent a fire in separating this matter from the iron destined to become steel as in separating it from iron destined to become wrought iron; and, when pig iron contains a little more of this matter, it is easier to purify it by a gentle fire. [246] The processes used in refining iron that is to be made into steel are more varied than those used in making wrought iron. In general, they agree among each other in that the end of the pig, or the mass of cast iron, is placed over a much deeper refining hearth. There are countries where this crucible, this hearth, is more than 2 feet or even $2\frac{1}{2}$ feet deep. The molten metal which falls into this large crucible is left undisturbed; it is simply covered with burning charcoal. The bellows hurl the flame only against the material that is to be melted. When the hearth contains the desired quantity of molten material—which usually means when it is full of it—the bellows are stopped. In some countries the lower part of the crucible or the refining hearth is opened to let the molten matter flow out and to mold it roughly into thin disks. In other countries it is allowed to freeze in the hearth itself; and whenever a layer, about an inch thick, has frozen, it is lifted off. But, before these layers of iron are taken off, other layers of vitrified matter, which float on top of the iron and have cooled on it, are removed. (When the molten iron is tapped, a layer of a similar matter is found on its surface.) This operation, regardless of how it is varied, thus tends to purify the iron of its earthy matter without, however, removing much of its sulfurous and saline parts. Moreover, in the countries where the best steel is made from pig iron, a practice is [247] employed which seems to aim only at restoring to the iron anything it might lose of this kind of matter during the liquefaction. I mean that the walls of the refining hearth, which are sometimes made of sheet iron and sometimes of brick, are lined with a layer of crushed charcoal, so that the iron melts in something like a crucible of powdered charcoal. The experiments described in the first memoir have shown that such a crucible alone could provide the iron with that which changes it into steel.

There also are artisans who throw into their refining hearths horn, soot, and other similar substances; but it is not even necessary to describe the effect they produce. It is sufficiently obvious what they can impart to the molten metal.

Enough, however, of these more highly developed practices, which contribute nothing to the main subject under discussion. The iron that has been refined by remelting is subsequently transferred to a refinery, to a chafery, where it must be heated to the degree necessary to cause enough of the saline and sulfurous parts to evaporate, so that the metallic parts will no longer be too far separated from each other to be able to hold together. As this is the only work that remains to be done, since in this practice it is unnecessary to convert the vitrified matter to a state in which it separates out—as when wrought iron is produced—it is not necessary to use such violent fire. [248] This material is allowed to heat until it is thought that the fire has conditioned it to withstand the hammer. But while it is heating it is not kneaded, as the bloom was kneaded of which wrought iron was intended to be made.

The important point is to withdraw the mass of material from the fire at the right time. If it has been heated too much, it will be iron; and, regardless of what precaution may be taken, it almost always happens that some portion of this mass, be it one-fourth or one-third, yields only iron. It is impossible for the whole mass to heat uniformly, and everything that has been heated too much will be iron. One end of the bar which will be forged from this material will be iron and the other end will be steel. If the iron and the steel could always be located so far apart from each other, it would not do much harm. But the real trouble, the great disadvantage of this method of making steel, is that one can never be sure that a bar is not interspersed with veins of iron. Their location, which is sometimes closer to the center and sometimes closer to the surface, depends on the original location of the ferrous parts which were overheated and also on where the hammer blows have placed these.

Thus it can be concluded that it is much more difficult to produce from pig iron steels without any remaining veins of iron than to produce steel without this defect by converting bars of wrought iron. It is always [249] possible to convert iron bars through to the center.

In most steel forges, when the refined cast iron—that is, the iron that has been melted a second time—is put back in the fire, the artisans throw on it sand or some vitrified substance that has been reduced to a powder. The slag obtained in remelting provides such material. The sand, or this powder, melts; it coats the metallic mass and prevents the fire from heating it too much or reducing it too much to the state of being iron.

Steels made from wrought iron as well as the steels produced from pig iron, which we have just discussed, are products of the art; they may be called "artificial steels." But it seems that the term "natural steels" can be applied to those which are produced from the irons that are never tapped from the furnace, as, for instance, the steels of Foix, those from around Foderberg in Germany, and others. I have told at the beginning of the first memoir that these irons are allowed to freeze in the same furnace in which the ore is smelted from which they are produced, that these masses of iron there assume a round shape which resembles a flattened ball or cake, and that this is cut into several pieces along lines parallel to one of its diameters. These different pieces are immediately transferred to the chafery, from which they are subsequently removed to be forged into bars. The bars forged from pieces that come from the middle of the cake are almost pure iron, but those forged [250] from pieces that come from the edges are steel, although both have been heated and forged in exactly the same way. The interesting fact is that the material from near the circumference of the mass yields steel, whereas the remainder yields iron. The reason is very naturally found in the circumstance that the molten metal that is suitable to produce steel is more fluid. Its sulfurs make it so; the more fluid metal, which is more suitable to produce steel, has to flow farther and consequently finds itself near the outside. According to the artisans, the parts that come loose from the mass, which flow still farther, make better steels than the rest.

There is one method of converting iron into steel of which I have not yet spoken. It is mentioned by Vanoccio* in his *Pirotechnia*, Book I, chapter vii, and well deserves that something be said about it; but it might have been difficult to explain without the ideas I have developed concerning the nature of wrought iron, steel, and cast iron. A certain quantity of cast iron is kept molten, and into this bath of molten iron a piece of wrought iron is plunged. It is left there to soak for some time, and, when it is withdrawn, it is found to be steel. I had performed this experiment before I read about it in Vanoccio, and it was almost unavoidable that I should have done so, since I had many opportunities to keep iron molten. While this iron was a bath or liquid, a thousand circumstances [251] required that iron rods or coarse iron wires were plunged into it to stir it, and I discovered that iron which was plunged into the bath several times became either entirely or partly steel. I then purposely repeated the same experiment by holding pieces of wrought iron for longer or shorter periods in the middle of the bath of molten iron. I do not intend at present to go into all the details concerning this method of converting iron into steel, a method still practiced in some countries. I have not even performed all the experiments with this method which I consider necessary. I

* Vannoccio Biringuccio, *De la pirotechnia* (Venice, 1540). Réaumur is probably quoting the French translation of 1627 wherein the author's first name is spelled "Vanoccio."

have tried it out on some kinds of iron, but I have not tried it on enough of them. I have not even held the irons in baths of the different kinds of cast iron that I think ought to be tested. Neither have I added to these baths the different substances that could be used as additions. In short, I believe that it still merits a methodical and thorough investigation, which I have not performed. But I am warning those who would like to make these experiments—and who will start, of course, on a small scale, which is always the wisest—that they should not be surprised if they encounter considerable losses. A piece of iron no bigger than a little finger, after having been held in the liquid metal for a quarter of an hour, or perhaps half an hour, will lose a considerable part of its volume and will, itself, partly melt. However, that which is left without having melted will be entirely steel if it has remained submerged in the bath for a sufficiently long [252] time. When the same experiment is made on a larger scale, when the iron that is held in the bath is $1\frac{1}{2}$ inches square or more, it will be converted into steel only after a proportionately much longer time; but this will not be accompanied by a proportional reduction in size. Very thick iron will not melt like very thin iron; the thicker it is, the less it melts.

I shall add, however, that I have the impression that there is a choice to be made here among the irons, as in our other method of converting wrought iron into steel; I found that some of the irons which were converted in the bath stayed full of cracks like those that were converted in our compounds and that, on the contrary, other irons became steels which were very easy to forge.

Let us go back to the cause underlying this conversion. It derives so naturally from the facts we have established that it could even serve to prove them, if new proof were needed. The wrought iron, thirsty for sulfurs, drinks up part of those of the molten iron, which has more of them. After having soaked them up, after having absorbed them, it is in this intermediate state which we call "steel." It contains more sulfurs and salts than it did when it was wrought iron, and it contains less of them than cast iron. One may encounter wrought irons into which the sulfurous parts enter less easily, and cast irons that retain them better. Either one of these conditions, or both together, may [253] give rise to many variations in the degree of success of the experiments.

Be that as it may, this latter method of making steel would greatly deserve that one tried to perfect it. But that would not shorten the task of making a greater success of the steels produced from cast iron. Perhaps we should succeed if we took the pains to perform the experiments which this subject deserves. I had the intention to try it, but I was forced to abandon the project. I could not see my way clear to making trials on a large scale, and, regardless of what I did, I was unable to surmount the difficulties encountered in my work on a small scale. I used an ordinary forge with one double bellows. There, I had 3–4 pounds of cast iron simultaneously melted and refined. With such a small volume, the losses were very considerable. Sometimes I was unable to recover even one-fourth of the weight used, either as wrought iron or as forged steel. In general, I obtained only half of the original weight and in rare cases three-quarters. In work on a small scale there is proportionately more surface exposed to burning than in work on a large scale. A proportionately larger quantity of iron combines with the parts of the charcoal that are vitrified, and, consequently, more of it is reduced to scale.

The inconvenience of waste still would not have stopped me. I would have been satisfied had I succeeded in making better steels. If they had then been made on a large scale, by the same method, the losses would not [254] have been the same; but, in working such a small mass, it is very difficult to prevent some part from heating too much. According to my previous observations, such overheated locations [see p. 168] become iron; and often even the entire mass becomes overheated. Hence it has happened to me many times that, after a certain quantity of cast iron had been refined and divided into two equal parts, which were never put back in the forge simultaneously but always one after the other—it has frequently happened to me, I said, that one of these parts was entirely steel and the other entirely iron. Regardless of how I tried to place them similarly and to give them an almost equal fire, I was far from being successful. More generally, however, it happened to me that the small bars or billets which I produced from these cast irons were partly steel and partly wrought iron.

However, I ordinarily found less iron and more steel when I was careful to have the mass of refined iron well covered by vitrified matter, by molten sand.

There are two main points that have to be watched in order to make good steels from cast iron. The first is to refine the irons well, to cleanse them thoroughly of their purely earthy constituents. The steels will be less hard as more of these earthy constituents are retained in them, for they are less hard than steel and cannot be hardened by quenching. We have previously had reason to suspect that the substance of steels made from cast iron is not as well purified of earthy or vitrified matters [255] as the substance of wrought-iron bars. This suspicion will perhaps be strengthened if we consider that the average steel made from cast iron is not as hard as the steels produced from wrought iron. It seems probable that there is more earthy matter left in the former than in the latter, because the iron from which the wrought iron was made was better refined than that from which the steel was made. All this seems to concur in proving that, contrary to the previously held opinion, steel is less pure than iron, since the average steels not only contain more sulfurs and salts than iron does but perhaps also contain more earthy matter.

If we refined cast iron two times instead of being content with refining it only once or—when the iron used is of the kind that cannot be remelted, when we cannot make it liquid enough—if we mixed it with an equal part or more of still unrefined iron, we certainly would succeed in refining it better. Such practices, however, cause losses, cost charcoal, and it is impossible to make the artisans understand that these expenses will be paid back with interest if they help in yielding a better product. There are a hundred other, similar steps one could take to purify cast iron better.

In some parts of Germany the masses of refined and forged iron are put back in the refining hearth, into a bath of less pure iron. Mixtures of different unrefined irons could [256] well be used.

At Rives, for instance, it would be easy to mix the irons of Dauphiné with those of Franche-Comté.

After the irons have been thoroughly refined, it is most important to prevent their being burned. Sand and the different sandlike powders with which they are sprinkled are helpful in this connection. Powdered scoria, the slag obtained in remelting cast iron, also helps and can even be employed with profit. I have observed elsewhere that I found it to contain much iron. Perhaps, in melting, it transfers part of the iron it contains to the mass of molten iron, or at least it does not absorb as much of the iron of this mass as simple sand does.

Finally, we can try to liquefy in the molten-iron bath old scrap iron, nailheads, etc. Iron thus added will cause the bath to solidify much faster; it will shorten the time during which one must keep it molten. Fewer sulfurs will escape from the parts that are nearest the surface; the iron will take up those which the fire would have caused to evaporate, and they will make steel of it too. I have made steels by this method in an ordinary forge shop, and they have been very successful. Sometimes I have mixed one-fourth and sometimes one-third of scrap iron with the iron bath.

But what should be tried first of all is to mix with the molten iron substances like those used in converting wrought iron into steel—[257] that is, soot, salts, and powdered charcoal. After mixing and combining them differently, I have at times used materials of this sort to line the walls of the vessel that was to hold the molten iron. On a small scale the result was not favorable; but I do not consider it less advisable on this account to try it out on a large scale. It was necessary, in such cases, to keep my irons molten at least three or four times as long as usual before their parts could be brought close enough together, before they could be given enough body to be forgeable. We need not be afraid of this effect in working with a large mass. On a small scale, it was necessary to use too much of these substances, or else it was insufficient; for they would have burned too fast if there had been only small quantities. It nevertheless seems, at least from these experiments, that such compounds increase the fluidity of the molten iron; that they are able to condition it so that it becomes more thoroughly refined; that they can prevent the surface from getting burned and hold it at the point where it must be in order to remain steel; that they will prevent this surface from becoming iron during the time we must heat it so that the center portions can assume the proper body.

It is true that we can restrict ourselves to steels made from wrought iron. It will be easy to make enough of them to satisfy the needs of the whole world, and they will probably always be the best. The others may be somewhat less [258] expensive, and that would give them an advantage if we could make them as good as some other countries produce them. In addition, there are parts of the country whose wrought irons are not suitable for conversion into steel, and there we could make it from pig iron.

The Tenth Memoir, on Methods of Recognizing
Defects and Good Quality in Steel and
on Several Ways of Comparing
Different Grades of Steel

TEEL CAN be so bad that it is recognized as such at the moment of inspection; it can have defects which are obvious enough for that. I have repeated more than often enough that, when there are many cracks (Pl. 8, Fig. 1) or when the corners of billets appear jagged here and there (Fig. 2), one can count on it that it will be very difficult to process the steel. In our country such defects can be considered to be a bad sign even if they are extremely fine. But is it entirely the fault of the steel when it is found to be so bad, or is it perhaps a little the fault of our artisans? This question should at least be asked, and the answer will perhaps not be favorable to our artisans, if one expects from them as much skill in treating steel as the artisans of the Levant possess. His Royal Highness the Duke d'Orléans, himself, gave orders that some of the steels of which the famous Damascus swords are made be sent to me from Cairo. M. le Maire, who was consul at Cairo at the time, responded to this request to the best of his ability. [260] Among the steels which I received from him, and which he assured me were the best, there is a cake which is supposed to be steel from India and the kind to be rated most highly in Egypt. I could find no artisan in Paris who succeeded in forging a tool out of it. It withstood the fire hardly better than cast iron. Other steels from the Levant are ordinarily difficult to forge but less so than this one.

If the surface of a billet is full of laps (Fig. 8, M), one should not expect to be able to forge it into sound products. When the steel is sold, it has been quenched and broken; if veins of iron or spots with non-uniform grain—that is, numerous brilliant platelets mixed with gray or dull grains—are noticed in the fracture, the steel contains much iron and consequently is no good.

But the defects of steel are not always so easily recognized. A bar or billet may appear very sound and nevertheless belong to the kind that is hard to work. The test that will really show if steel is without this defect [of being non-workable] is to forge it after it has been given a welding heat. This means that it must be given the heat necessary to force the two ends of a bar, after one has been doubled over the other one, to be united by hammer blows perfectly enough to give the impression that both of them are one and the same body. This is what the smith calls "welding." A bad grade of steel can still look very sound if it has been forged at red heat; but it will be full of cracks if it has been heated [261] until it was whitish-red or if it was brought almost to welding heat. It would be impossible to weld it without giving it almost this latter degree of heat. With a bad steel, the two ends that are to be welded together will not weld perfectly; but, when good steel is broken at the location where it has been welded, it will be difficult to recognize where the two parts once were separate.

Even at the time of heating steel to the degree necessary for welding, it is possible to predict whether it will be able to stand as much heat as it must be given. One only has to listen. A noise is heard which can be distinguished without much practice from the noise made by the flame or from that of the blast of the bellows. It is the result of something like boiling which takes place in the steel. Steel that boils this way will not forge well. Another bad sign concerning the quality of steel is observable while steel is in the forge; this is when its surface continues to look dry, when something like a gloss does not appear on it after it has been heated thoroughly and has even been sprinkled with some sand.

When well-heated steel is put on the anvil and breaks under the hammer, or if it splits or breaks at least partly in the bend when one end is bent over in order to weld it on to the rest, such steel will not be easily workable (Fig. 3, *D*).

The smith should beware, however, not to blame the steel for defects which may be caused by his own negligence [262] or ignorance. Good steel can be made bad by excessive heating, by causing it to melt or almost to melt.

One indication of a good steel, which the merchants of Paris mention most boastfully and to which much importance is attributed by artisans of mediocre skill, is the rose.* What they call the "rose" is a certain spot found in the fracture of some bars of steel. This spot can be compared with a rose only when it is round, but it is often oval and frequently has other, very irregular outlines (Figs. 4–7). The center of the fracture often is

---

* See also p. 251.

The rose seems to be a transverse fissure which has become somewhat oxidized to show temper colors. Its appearance must depend on many factors, and it is indeed astonishing that it should ever have become a mark of anything but inferior quality.

A century earlier Jousse (*La fidelle ouverture de l'art de serrurier* [La Flèche, 1627]) had remarked that the best steels that were used in France were those imported from Germany and Hungary under the name of "*aciers de Carmes ou à la rose.*" They were recognized, he said, by the fact that "the bars could be bent by hand, were without laminations or burned spots, and showed in the middle of the fracture a nearly black stain, tending toward violet, having a very fine grain, flawless and with no patches of iron. If this stain covers practically the whole of the bar reaching all sides, it is a sure sign that the steel is good. On the contrary, if the bars are laminated, overheated, and with some veins [of iron] intermixed in the fracture it is not good."

A good description and essentially accurate explanation of the rose was given in 1771 by Jean Jacques Perret. This was in his *L'Art du coutelier* published under the auspices of the Académie des Sciences as one of the *Descriptions des arts et métiers*. We translate in full the section relating to the rose: "In the old days a German steel which is called *Carme* steel was very good; but it has now deteriorated, at least as steel for razors, although it is still very good for making knives. It often displays the rose. This is mistakenly considered to be a mark of quality. If the middle of the fracture of a bar of Carme steel is blue, black, or violet (which is what is meant when we say *it displays the rose*), it is an infallible sign that the texture of the steel is internally broken. Experience has proved that this rose is not found throughout the whole length of the bar and that a light hammer blow will cause the bar to break at the spot where it displays the rose, whereas a much heavier blow is required to break it at some place where the rose does not occur. I believe that this rose has its origin partly in the quench and partly in the process of making the steel, in which connection it should be stated that this is a *natural* steel, which means that a cement is not used in making it, but only 'boiling.' Furthermore, I will say, to explain the formation of the rose, that certain bars are quenched much hotter than the strongest cherry-red and are plunged suddenly into very cold water. The outside thus cools suddenly, while the inside of the bar is still hot. Even if the inside takes much longer to cool than the outside, and the contrac-

the center of such a spot. There are some that occupy the greater part of the fracture and others that occupy only a rather small part. Their color is as variable as their shape. Some are a rather light blue and others are dark blue, almost black; there are yellow ones of different shades of yellow; some are just a little duller than the rest of the fracture. Finally, there are some where these different colors form concentric bands. In short, the color of the roses of steel may be like any of the colors that can be given to the surface of steel or clean iron heated gently over charcoal to be either colored or tempered. I shall discuss these colors elsewhere, and, when I explain what causes them [see p. 250], I shall also give the reason why the spots called "roses" [263] are produced inside of some steels. They vary as much within the same bar as among different bars. A bar broken at one location will have a rose of different color, different size, and different shape from a rose found when the bar is broken at some other location. The bar may even be broken where there is no trace of a rose.

There really is no more unreliable sign of good quality of steel than this rose. It is true that it is found in some steels that come from Germany and are very good; but it is also found in mediocre steels. Some of the steels from the Champagne and Limousin

---

tion of the parts has to be proportionate to the cooling, both inside and outside must eventually shrink to the same extent. But, as the outside has suddenly felt the full effect, it has been left in the condition which it must reach; then, when the inside finds itself compelled to contract slowly, the grains are forced to break or spread apart in order to yield to the force of contraction. During this operation internal cracks are formed, or, at least, the parts are not brought close together at certain spots, because the outside, which has also shrunk, has operated first. This is, I think, how the rose is formed, and the best proof I can give is that, if the end of a piece of steel displaying the rose is inspected under a light [*sic; lampe* misprint for *loupe*, 'lens'?], it will be noticed that all around the rim, to a depth of 1 or 2 lines, this steel is white and has a very dense texture, while the rest is blue or violet or black and of a much looser texture. I believe, therefore, that the occurrence of the rose is not as important as certain people would like us to believe. Good cutlers ought not to be guided by such an unreliable sign in choosing the material on which their reputation depends. They should not let themselves be seduced by the talk of merchants who practically always ignore that which constitutes a good steel and who, desiring to make a sale, attempt to make the bad qualities of their merchandise pass as perfections."

sometimes have it, and the greater part of the good steels from Germany do not have it. I have encountered it in steels from Foix (Fig. 4), which are so coarse that not even the people who produce them consider it right to call them "steels"; they call them "hard irons." What the rose indicates most reliably is that the steel in which it is found is steel produced from pig iron. I have never seen it, at least not well marked, in steels produced from wrought iron.

Furthermore, this spot is not permanent. It depends on the degree of heat the steel is given before it is quenched. When a bar with a rose is heated very hot, the rose will disappear in the first heating or will at least become fainter. It will not be found in the finished product.

In some of the provinces of our country where steel [264] is made from pig iron, it is forged into small billets, one end of which is hammered out into a point (Fig. 8). This pointed end (*F*) is quenched and is used in a test, of sorts, of the quality of the steel of the bar. To make this test, the bar is held in one hand, approximately at the middle, and a rather light blow is given the thick end (*L*). When the steel is good or at least reasonably so, the end of the bar opposite the one that has received the blow—the pointed end—will break. This test proves that there was no sizable vein of iron at the place that broke; but this is really all it proves. However, it means something if no vein of iron is found in the steels of this category.

If we except the afore-mentioned rough tests of which I have just spoken, the average artisan has almost nothing to guide him concerning the quality of the steels he wants to process. He does not know if his steels are suitable for the tools for which he selects them until the tools are finished, and in other cases only when those for whom they were made have employed them. Some honest cutlers, who belong to the more skilful in their profession, have repeatedly confessed to me that they did not know if a new steel which they had used for razors was suitable until the barber had given them a good report on the razors they had sold him.

The most valuable information concerning the steels with which they work is to know from which country [265] they come. The cutlers of Paris recognize as good only those from Germany. If they are offered steels from England or Italy, just because they are from England or Italy they will not buy them, even though they may be better than those from Germany. They work only according to routine. They are accustomed to certain shapes of steel. If the same steel is given a different shape, they will reject it, because they have no means at all by which to judge its qualities.

It would be especially important to have means by which to judge the merits of different steels and to decide for what purpose one kind is more suitable than another. I shall suggest some possibilities that have occurred to me; but I hardly expect that the common artisan will bother with them. However, they may at least be useful to those who try to distinguish themselves in their profession. Specialists, and scientists who wish to have certain products made that require carefully selected steels, can have the selection made according to these rules. They will be especially useful in steelworks; they will provide the makers with a means to be sure of the properties of the steel produced.

Thus, the difficulty here does not consist in detecting the defects that are more or less common in average steels. Steels in general have certain qualities which make them suitable for products that cannot be made of wrought iron. The difficult part is to determine the degree of perfection reached [266] by each of these qualities in every steel. The three principal ones are (1) that of acquiring a certain type of grain after having been quenched at a certain degree of heat, (2) that of being more or less hardened according to the degree of heat at which a steel has been quenched, and (3) the tendency to preserve more or less body after the quench.

The word "body" is ordinarily used to describe the ability of a quenched steel to resist the force that wants to break it. Of two steels of equal hardness which have the same resistance to the file, the one that is easier to break is the one that has less body. Of two flat bars of equal thickness which have been quenched in the same way, the one that is less rigid, that can be bent more, has more body. Of two chisels used to cut iron cold which have been quenched in the same way and which are equally hard and have edges of the same shape and size, the one with more body is the chisel that chips and breaks less easily while being hammered to cut the iron or some other material. It is in this sense that I am using the word "body" and shall use it in the future. It will always be descriptive of some kind of toughness which the steel keeps in spite of the hardness it acquires when it is quenched. The artisan who is little accustomed to connect clear concepts and well-defined meanings with his terms sometimes uses the word "body" to mean hardness. When the edge of a chisel folds back when it is used to cut iron cold, the artisans say that "it [267] has no body"; but I shall avoid using the word in this sense, which is improper. I shall say instead that such a steel "lacks hardness." A lack of hardness is the reason why its grains can be compressed and brought close together. We also hear it said that a steel lacks body when it does not readily withstand violent heating, when it becomes too weak therefrom. Of these meanings and still others which are sometimes given the expression "body of steel," we shall reject all but the first one.

If we assume that a steel has no laps, no cracks, no overheated areas, no veins or platelets of iron, and that it is easy to work, we must, then, examine three things in order to decide about its worth and about the applications for which it is best suited. These are its grain, its hardness, and its body. We must look for methods of determining if one steel is better than another in any one of these properties. For example, of two steels, the one that can be made to develop the finer grain will also be called the "finer steel." We still have to determine how these three properties are combined in the same steel, for we must realize that a steel loses body and fineness of grain as it gains hardness. The further problem is, therefore, to decide in which steels these combinations are the most favorable. However, before we go on to the combinations, let us review each of these principal qualities separately.

The fineness of steel or, differently expressed, [268] the fineness of grain that can be attained in a steel seems to be the most easily recognized of these three properties; it also can be most easily compared. Our eyes will make the decision. A good artisan admits, nevertheless, that by looking at the fracture of a quenched steel he does not know if it is finer than another. His reasons are very plausible. Heat a piece of very fine steel almost to white heat, quench it in this condition, and break it. Its fracture will show nothing but a coarse grain. Heat a mediocre steel, or even an agricultural steel, only to cherry-red and quench it. When it is broken after the quench, it will have a fine grain. The fineness of the grain thus seems to depend on the degree of heat a steel had when it was quenched. It actually does depend on it; but the important thing to know is whether, of two steels which have been quenched at the same degree of heat, one may not have a finer grain than the other. This is how excellent steels should be—and actually can be—distinguished from mediocre ones. However, it is not easy to decide by ordinary methods which of the two steels is the better one, because it is difficult (1) to heat two pieces of steel equally hot and (2) to break these two pieces in exactly the spot where they were equally hot when they were quenched.

In order to recognize better of what these difficulties and the inadequacy of the ordinary test consist, it should be [269] noted that a piece of steel that is being heated does not acquire the same degree of heat over its entire length; that, if it is heated at one end, this end may even start to melt (Fig. 8, *F*), while the other end (*L*) is still cold or at least black. When this steel is quenched and broken* near the end that was heated until it was

---

* This test was still in use two hundred years later. To quote from Harry Brearley, *The Heat Treatment of Tool Steel* (London, 1916), p. 90: "The following means of determining in an ordinary smith's hearth the degree of redness, at which the finest-looking fracture is induced in steel by quenching, is generally attributed to Metcalf. A bar of the steel being used of about one-half inch diameter is notched for a length of three or four inches, each eight or ten millimeters from one end. The notched portion is then heated in the smith's fire until the extreme end is white hot, and in such a manner that the heat tapers gradually backwards. After quenching, the bar is dried and broken at each successive notch. The first piece or two will break off very easily—if they do not break in quenching—and exhibit a coarse, staring white fracture. Subsequent pieces will break off less readily, and become gradually finer in fracture until a smooth amorphous appearance of well-hardened steel with a faint bluish-grey tinge is reached. After that the fracture gets coarser down to the unhardened part."

almost melting (*G*), the grain will be coarse (Fig. 9, *f g*). When it is broken at a location a little farther away, the grain will be found to be less coarse (Fig. 9, *g h*); when it is broken still farther away, it may be found to have a fine grain (Fig. 9, *h i*); and when it is broken a fourth time, at a location still farther removed from the hot end, the fracture will have a much finer grain (*i k*). If another piece of steel which is to be compared with the first one is treated in the same manner, we may perhaps be able to decide which one of the fractures of these two steels represents the most beautiful grain; but we will be unable to decide which of the two steels really has the more beautiful grain. There is reason to wonder if the steel that appears to be inferior might not have outranked the other if it had been broken farther away from the end or if it had been broken at the middle of one of the pieces that were obtained by two successive fracturings. This doubt is especially justified, because the finest grain sometimes occupies only a very short length of the entire piece of steel.

When one end of a piece of steel is heated until it almost melts while its other end stays black, we can be sure that this steel has undergone all the different degrees of heating possible; for from the melting-hot end, which is the upper [270] limit of heat to which steel is susceptible, to the other end, the degrees of heat diminish very gradually, and the heat at the end that remained black may be considered to be zero, because it was unable to produce any effect. It follows that, when this steel is subsequently quenched, it undoubtedly is given all the different grain sizes it can have, as the degrees of fineness vary with the degrees of heat. In order to obtain a complete range of grain sizes, in order to observe all the degrees of fineness, and in order to make a comparison between two steels, it would therefore be necessary to break the steel lengthwise. This is impossible if the steel is left in its ordinary condition. Hammer blows break it transversely and at the location where it has been quenched most drastically, which is the location where it is the weakest.

To increase the accuracy of the comparison I have in mind, we have to concentrate, therefore, on eliminating the difficulties that prevent us from breaking a piece of steel lengthwise through the quenched part. There are several methods by which this can be done, all so simple that to find them only requires to decide to look for them. I shall suggest two from which to choose. The first is as follows: Of the steel which I wish to test, a flat bar is forged (Fig. 10). Its thickness and width can be chosen at will. A length of 2 inches is enough, but if it is 5 or 6 inches long, it will be even more convenient. Then I have this steel bar welded to an iron bar (Fig. 11) of at least the same [271] length and width but of greater thickness, if desired. When these two bars are thoroughly welded together, I take a cold chisel and cut through the iron bar down to the steel over its entire length. In the steel I cut a groove, something like a channel or furrow, which is then still widened a little by a file (Fig. 13, *g h h i i k*). That is all the preparation needed, the result of which is probably already anticipated. When one end of this bar, which is part steel and part iron, has been heated almost melting-hot and the bar has been quenched, it can be broken in two lengthwise; there is no reason to fear that it might break transversely. At the location where it has been quenched the hottest, and where the steel is most brittle, this steel cannot break transversely, because it is joined to the iron; it forms one body with it. The iron, which is not at all brittle, supports the steel. This is not the case at that part of the bar where the groove has been cut. All along this groove the steel is no longer supported by the iron, and the steel can therefore be broken longitudinally but no longer transversely. However, if the steel bar is several lines thick, and if such a long one has been chosen that a large part of it has not been heated and therefore is not in a quenched condition, the steel itself will be difficult to fracture in this [unaffected] area, as unquenched steel is hard to break. It can be done, nevertheless, by putting in the groove, at the locations that resist the most, a big, [272] somewhat blunt, chisel, something like a wedge (Fig. 14, *n*), which is hammered to force the steel to open up. Each of the pieces which has thus been separated from the other will show the whole range of different grain sizes (Fig. 15, *o, 1, 2, 3, 4, r*). Getting ready for the preceding experiment is in itself a test of the steel, as it shows whether the steel can be easily welded to iron.

There is still another method, which is easier than the previous one. One side of the piece of steel that is to be tested is left its original thickness; the thicker this side is, the better. The opposite side is hammered out over its entire length. To give a picture of the shape I wish the piece of steel to have, let me say it shall be forged out to resemble a blank for a razor (Pl. 9, Fig. 1) with the exception that longitudinally its width shall be the same all over. The experiment will be the more successful, the thinner the hammered-out side is made or the thicker the opposite side has remained. The steel is heated melting-hot at one end and is subsequently quenched. Nothing remains but to break it, which is done by gentle blows upon the thin rim, from which different fragments are thus successively broken loose until the piece has been fractured over its entire length. It will make the fracturing easier if, before the steel is quenched, a groove is cut along the line where it is to be broken (Fig. 1, *B C*)—or at least all along that part which will not become hot enough to be brittle after quenching.

In the fractures [273] obtained by one of the methods just described, one glance reveals the whole range of different grain sizes a steel can be given by all the different degrees to which it can be heated. We are now able to compare the finest grain of one steel with the finest grain of another. Artisans who wish to know what they are doing should have a stock of such fractures of every grade of steel known in the Kingdom. These would serve them as standards to measure the degree of fineness of the steels which are offered them for sale. These bars would be for them what the touch needles (made of gold and silver mixed in different proportions) are for goldsmiths who must decide quickly about the fineness of gold that is offered them. Once made, these fractures will serve an artisan all his life, provided he is careful enough to put the bars in a dry place and to keep them in a box. I have had some for several years, the fractures of which are almost as white and brilliant as they were the moment they were obtained. I have taken the precaution, however, to put them in a box which, itself, is kept in another, much larger one, which is filled with bran.

Without a certain sensitivity of vision and, moreover, without some experience in inspecting steel, it would be hard to decide which of two steels of not too drastically different qualities has [274] the finer grain. But our fractures enable unschooled eyes to make a decision and provide a method of measuring the fineness of this metal by dividers. To explain this method, and to show upon what it is based, I shall demonstrate that the different grain sizes observed in the fractures (obtained by one of the methods just explained) can be divided into four types which are very easy to recognize. The first division contains only white, brilliant, coarse grains (Pl. 8, Fig. 15, *o, 1;* Pl. 9, *L, 1*); no other kind is seen, and we therefore refer to this type as white, brilliant [or coarse] grain. In the second division the white, brilliant grains are mixed with dull ones (Pl. 8, Fig. 15, *1, 2;* Pl. 9, Figs. 2–6); but here the brilliant grains are less coarse than the first grains of the first division. We call this type the mixed grain. The third division has only one kind of grains, which are all fine, dull, and often gray (Pl. 8, Fig. 15, 2, 3; Pl. 9, Figs. 2–5). This is the fine grain. The fourth division begins where the preceding grain ends. Here we again find much coarser grains which, though dull, are less dull than those of the preceding division (Pl. 8, Fig. 15, 3, *4*). These grains are ill defined; they do not seem to be quite detached from one another; they are, one might say, not lined up. This is the location where the steel has not been hot enough to respond to quenching. We therefore are interested only in the first three divisions. The grains in each of them are not of the same [275] size over the entire extent of the division; they become smaller as they approach the next order. Near the location where the mixed [or, rather, the coarse] grain ends, where the second division just begins, the white, brilliant grains are less coarse and also less brilliant than the first grains of the first division. Similarly, among the mixed grain, there are more white grains and fewer gray ones toward the location where this order starts and, conversely, more gray grains than white ones where it ends. Thus I might have divided this order into two different ones if I had not been afraid to increase the number of divisions needlessly. The third division consists of much more uniform grains.

It follows from the foregoing that the dividing lines between the types are not very sharply defined—that they have to be approximated. Astronomers have to do the same when they must define the dividing lines between the umbra and penumbra of an eclipse and between the penumbra and full light. However, the dividing lines we have to deal with can always be defined accurately enough for our purpose. Furthermore, they can be defined with some precision when the eye is aided by a strong lens. The first grains of the fourth division are sometimes so fine that they would seem to belong to those of the third division (Pl. 8, Fig. 15, *3, 4*)—that means to those produced by quenching. But when they are viewed through a lens, when they are enlarged, one recognizes [276] the difference between them and the preceding group without the possibility of any doubt.

From these remarks, which I might have omitted if they were related only to the physical science of steels, and from my observations concerning the length of the divisions occupied by different types of grain in different steels, I am able to derive the promised rule for assistance in judging the fineness of every steel. I have observed that, as steels become finer, the extent of the third division becomes greater—it becomes longer compared with the second division. This difference is sufficiently considerable in steels of very different grades, so that we have no reason to fear that we might make a mistake in measuring them; we do not have to worry that we might misplace the border lines between the groups. I have seen bad steels from Nivernais in which the space occupied by the fine grain was not half as long as the mixed-grain division. On the other hand, I have seen fine steels in which the fine grain occupied more than twice as much space as the mixed grain (Pl. 9, Figs. 6, 7). Consequently, these fine steels had at least four to five times as much fine grain as the coarse steels.*

If the fine grain of both grades of steel has the same degree of fineness and the same hardness, the one with the larger area of

---

* The control of grain size is an important aspect of modern steel production, and steelmaking practice is adjusted specifically to increase the range of temperature over which proper grain size can be maintained. Réaumur's test would also show the effect of varying carbon content, for part at least of his second type of fracture would be due to ferrite plus austenite structures in hypoeutectoid steels at the time of quenching.

fine grain should be preferred for making tools which require this type of grain. It will be easier to obtain this grain in the cutting edge of tools made from such [277] steels. For, if of two steels one shows in its fracture a larger area of the same type of grain which the other one has, it follows from the manner by which we heated these steels that this grain can be produced in the first by a greater number of degrees of heat than in the second. Thus, when we heat a steel (after it has been forged into a tool) in order to quench it so that after quenching it will have a certain definite type of grain, we can be much surer of succeeding in obtaining this grain if the steel can acquire it at different degrees of heat than when it acquires it at only one degree of heat. This degree of heat is difficult to attain exactly, and more so than one would think. Furthermore, we can rarely be certain that we have obtained it in all parts of the cutting edge. The parts which have become hotter will not have the grain size we wished to produce.

Finally, in the fractures of two steels, of which one is finer than the other but which have been heated equally over an equal length, the range of the quenched structure is greater in the finer steel. All this logically follows from our observations concerning the nature of steel. The finer ones, which acquire more [quenched] grain and finer grain, are composed of more detached parts which are richer in sulfurs and consequently of parts that are more easily set in motion because of these two factors. [278] There would be nothing better than this method of measuring the fineness of steels by dividers (one might call it) if doing it were as simple as one would like it to be. However, it requires great care on the part of the person who wishes to employ it in practice. It is necessary that the steels which are to be compared be heated to the same degree over the same length, and it is very difficult to accomplish this with ordinary wood or charcoal fire. Later in this memoir I shall give the means for overcoming this difficulty, which will once more become a problem in determining the body of steel.

If the steel that has been fractured is thick and was heated more on one side than on the other, the grain size at a particular location on the fracture may not be the same on both sides; but we can still observe the same sequence of divisions on each side; the relative position of each division will still be the same.

The coarse grain, the first division in the series, enables us to judge the fineness of steel at least as well as the fine grain does. Steels which have a finer grain than others in the third division often have a much coarser grain in the first. Something that is less subject to variation is that the coarse grains of this first division are whiter, more sparkling, and more brilliant in fine steels than in coarse steels; [279] they are also more uniform. The coarse grains of coarse steels seem to be mixed with dull grains. The first grains in the coarse division of a fine steel may at times also be dull if the end of the steel has been almost melting-hot; but the subsequent grains will have the most sparkling luster. The entire coarse-grain division of coarse steels resembles the beginning of this division in fine steels that have been heated until they were melting-hot; and sometimes the grains are even duller. Furthermore, in coarse steels the grains of the group under discussion sometimes seem to be arranged in layers. A similar arrangement is never found in the same type of grain in fine steels.

Let us now consider the methods by which the degrees of perfection of the second property of steel, its hardness, can be recognized and compared. All the difficulties encountered in judging the degrees of fineness are again encountered in judging the degrees of hardness. The same steel is more or less hard, depending on whether it was more or less hot when it was quenched. In general, the hardness decreases as the grain becomes finer. The location where the grain is the coarsest, the location where the steel was quenched the hottest, is ordinarily the hardest. Nevertheless, there are occasional exceptions to this rule, and these exceptions are enough to make trouble for those who must decide where a certain grade of steel becomes hardest on quenching. However, something which nobody has attempted to [280] determine, but which is nevertheless important, is which one of two steels that were quenched at the same degree of heat is harder. We have absolutely no rule on that. Again, our fractures furnish the means for formulating rules concerning this problem. These rules are as accurate as one could wish them to be and, what is more, independent of the difficulty of heating the steels uniformly before they are compared. If we wish to know at which degree of heat a steel must be quenched to acquire the greatest hardness, all we need know is with which order, or type, of grain it is the hardest; for the different types of grain are proportional to the different degrees of quenching. In order to compare the hardness of two different steels, all that is necessary, therefore, is to compare the hardness produced in each at its different divisions of grain size, and this comparison is easily made on our fractures.

The artisans know only two degrees of hardness—that at which the file takes hold and that at which it does not cut. These two expressions do not even come close to informing us of the degrees of hardness different steels can have. There is practically no steel—or, actually, there is no steel—which, after having been quenched at a certain heat, does not resist the file. We therefore must have files with a larger number of different degrees of hardness than ordinary files possess. Several kinds of stones or other hard materials serve me [281] as such files.* I use seven different kinds. The first is glass, which is less hard than ordinary files are. The second is the softest rock crystal. Pieces of hard transparent crystal, such as the crystal of Médoc, serve as the third kind; pieces of agate or a certain kind of faceted stone found near Perpignan as the fourth; oriental jasper as the fifth; oriental topaz or another of the transparent oriental stones, such as the sapphire, as the sixth. The diamond is the seventh and final one. I give these stones only as an example; everyone can choose others according to his liking and can increase or decrease their number depending on whether he intends to go more or less far with his tests. As long as the stones differ from each other in hardness, it does not matter. Glass may be followed by the ordinary file, and emery may also be given a place among the testing stones.

By means of these different files, by means of our different

* The mineralogist will recognize here the anticipation by nearly a century of Friedrich Mohs's scale of hardness, which consisted of ten minerals, the hardest being (in decreasing order) diamond, corundum, topaz, quartz, and orthoclase.

stones and our fractures which show all the different types of grain, we are able to determine and to compare the hardness of steels with accuracy. All that is necessary is to find out for each grain size with which stones one can make an impression, with which stones it can be scratched. The test is not made on the fracture itself but on one of the flat surfaces of the bar very close to the edge of the fracture. A few examples will make it [282] clear how this method works. If I successfully try to scratch with glass, or the file, the third type of grain, the finest grain of a steel, I conclude from this fact that this steel is not hard enough at the location where it has the fine grain—that no hard tool could be made of it with the degree of quenching that produced this grain, especially as I have seen that in other steels the same type of grain cannot be scratched even by emery. If I must make tools of very great hardness, to which the fineness of the grain is of less importance, and if I have found that the mixed grain of a particular steel cannot be scratched by agate or jasper, whereas the corresponding grain of various other steels can be scratched by rock crystal or the crystal of Médoc, I shall select the steel that resists agate. Finally, if I need extraordinarily hard tools, and I have found by my tests a steel (a kind which does exist) whose coarse grain resists oriental topaz, although other steels can be scratched by jasper or even crystal where they have the same type of grain, I shall choose the steel which can resist topaz. This is enough to show how the different degrees of hardness of different steels can be compared and what advantages can be derived from this comparison.

The same method also provides the means for [283] discovering how the two essential properties which are under investigation are combined in one steel. For instance, my tests may tell me that the fine grain has as much hardness, or almost as much hardness, as the mixed grain—the second type of grain. Since fine grain is in itself an advantage and since, in addition, it is combined with the advantage of body, tools made of this steel will never be given anything but the quench that results in fine grain. On the other hand, if the steel that is to be employed has a much greater hardness in its mixed grain than in its fine grain, and unless its mixed grain is extremely coarse, a tool made from this steel will be given the quench that results in mixed grain. If I recognize that the white [or coarse] grain of a steel is not much harder than the mixed grain, I shall always quench the steel at the degree of heat that will result in mixed grain, even if I need a very hard tool.

Of the three essential properties of steel, body is the one whose determination, in order to make it subject to rules, requires most in the way of preparations. I have succeeded in determining the degree of toughness, or the degree of least rigidity, left to a quenched steel. In order to decide which of two steels has more body, all that is really necessary is to be able to judge which one of two steels of the same dimensions in every direction, after both have been quenched at the same degree of heat—which one, I said—can be bent [284] more. But this also involves two difficulties. The first is to give two pieces of steel exactly the same dimensions, and the second is to heat both to the same degree. After these two difficulties have been overcome, all that remains is to have a reproducible method of bending them, one that permits to determine different degrees of bending, which is not difficult.

In order to make two pieces of steel quite alike in all dimensions, I know only one sure way, which is to have them drawn into wire. We can be satisfactorily certain of their gauge after they have been passed through the same holes several times. One could forge them in dies or else work them with the file and measure their thickness; but all this would not approach the precision of the wire-drawing die and would take much longer.

Suppose, then, that we have made wires of equal diameter of the steels which are to be compared for body. We are still faced with the great difficulty that the entire length of both must be heated to the same degree before they are quenched. This would, indeed, be an insurmountable difficulty if it were necessary to lay them directly on the charcoal as is ordinarily done. The heat of a fire never acts uniformly upon two pieces of steel, nor even upon the entire length of one, for the pieces of charcoal are unequally distributed, and the wind of the bellows blows unequally upon the charcoal. In order [285] to heat them with perfect uniformity, both must therefore be surrounded over their entire length by an equal quantity of equally hot matter. This gave me the idea to let them get hot by immersing them in molten lead. First, I took a round (Pl. 9, Fig. 12), exactly cylindrical crucible, similar to those I discussed for the trials on a small scale but of much smaller diameter, in order not to be forced to melt a larger quantity of lead than required by the experiment. The crucible was 8–9 inches long—that is, a few inches longer than the steel wire the body of which I wished to determine. In the beginning one cannot think of everything. The trouble is that, when lead is kept molten for a long time, part of this metal is lost if the crucible is made of a porous clay. The lead penetrates the walls of the crucible; it imbues them and then drips out. For ironworkers it would be easier to use the barrel of a pistol or a piece of a musket barrel (Pl. 9) as a crucible, provided the barrel is well welded throughout; it must have no channels. Even if there is only the tiniest crack to permit the opening of a passage, the lead will find it, and you will see it come out in drops which may be more or less big depending on the size of the exits it has made for itself. However, no great sums of money are involved. We have time to make very many experiments of the kind I am suggesting before a [286] quarter of a pound of lead has run out of our little iron crucible.

If one wishes to use earthenware crucibles, tin may be melted in them instead of lead; it does not pass through the walls with anything like the same ease.

Regardless of whether lead is molten or tin, regardless of whether an earthenware crucible is chosen or a piece of musket barrel, we shall not be content with making the metal liquid but give it the highest degree of heat the forge is able to produce. The prepared steel wires will then be plunged into this lead bath and will be held in it. Being completely surrounded by the same, uniformly hot matter, the equal wires will take on an equal degree of heat. If they are left there for any desired time, provided they are withdrawn together and are quenched simultaneously in cold water, they will both have been quenched at the same degree.

After these wires or any other pieces of steel have been held in the molten lead or tin for a certain time, we have reason to believe that the steel has been given all the heat to which it can be brought in this metallic liquid and that this degree of heat will be a constant degree, a determinate degree of heat; that under certain circumstances, of which I shall speak later, it can be considered to be a fixed degree of heat. One of the most interesting [287] experiments of the new physical science is that performed by M. Amontons,* who observed that water which was brought to the boiling point had acquired the highest degree of heat to which it could be brought. It is useless to urge the fire; it cannot give it anything additional. Lead and tin which just start to melt may be compared with ice which just starts to thaw. The heat to which these metallic liquids can be brought is considerably greater than that of boiling water, but it probably is a determinate degree of heat, which has its limits as the degree of heat of boiling water has its limits. One produces this degree of heat in lead or tin when the fire has been driven as violently as possible and perhaps much earlier. What I just said of lead and tin probably is also true of all metallic liquids. Apparently there is a limit beyond which, when it has once been reached, ordinary fire adds nothing more to their heat, and this limit is most likely different for different metals. It would be interesting to know this limit and to know what relationship exists among the highest degrees of heat of which the metals, all the liquids, and other substances are susceptible and what relationship exists between these highest degrees of heat and the specific weights of these substances and also between them and the difficulty we experience in melting them. There was a time

* G. Amontons (1663–1705), French physicist who made important observations on thermometry, though in the particular observation referred to he was foreshadowed by Newton and Huygens. It is interesting to see this early evidence of Réaumur's interest in heat measurement, which culminated in his thermometer and temperature scale (*Mém. Acad. Sci.*, 1730, p. 452). He was wrong, of course, in supposing that in the forge fire tin or lead would reach a constant temperature through boiling but quite right in believing in the existence of such a point. Lead boils at 1,740° C., tin at 2,270° C., while the forge fire would not exceed about 1,450° C. A lead bath is nevertheless a very useful means of quickly and uniformly heating parts to be quenched and prevents scaling or decarburization. For further observations on heat see p. 234.

when I made a great many experiments in this field, but I [288] have made not nearly enough to have come to any conclusion.

One thing seems very certain—that other metals are susceptible of a higher degree of heat [than lead and tin] and that each has a different *maximum* heat. To prove this, melt lead in a crucible; melt the same amount of pig iron in another similar crucible, increase the degree of heat of these two metallic liquids as far as it is possible, and plunge into both an equal piece of iron. The end of the piece that was plunged into the iron bath will take on the whitest color that fire can produce in iron; and, if nothing heavier than an iron wire was used, the iron wire will melt in the bath. But the iron wire that was immersed in the lead (or tin) will be far from having melted.

As we use lead in order to heat equally hot any steels which we wish to test for body, so shall we use molten iron to heat equally hot any steels whose range of different grain sizes we wish to observe accurately. The iron can be put in ordinary crucibles; it is not necessary to use an iron crucible, as for lead. This, then, constitutes the reliable method I promised for heating equally any steels whose different types of grain are to be compared.

Let us come back once more to the testing of the body of steel. [289] When wires of the same thickness and length are plunged into molten lead or tin or even in an iron bath, if desired, and are simultaneously withdrawn and then quenched, they have been quenched as identically as possible. If one of the two is more flexible than the other, it has more body. There are many possible methods of measuring their flexibility. The one I have most frequently used requires the construction of a small machine* (Pl. 10). It consists of a copper or iron plate (Fig. 1, *BB*) placed horizontally and held by screws on a piece of iron that is

---

* This is the first materials-testing machine on record, although Leonardo da Vinci, Galileo, and Hooke had all performed simple experiments to determine the breaking strengths of wires by hanging weights on them until fracture resulted. Shortly after the publication of Réaumur's work, Musschenbroek in Holland published an excellent study of the mechanical properties of materials of all kinds (*Introductio ad cohaerentium corporum firmorum* [Leyden, 1729]). His machine was a greatly improved version of one used by Desaguliers (*Phil. Trans. Royal Soc.*, XXXIII [1724], 345–47).

bent twice into a right-angled brace. I shall not give the dimensions of the different pieces of this machine, for they are rather arbitrary, and with the scale given [at the bottom] on Plate 10 the dimensions of the machine that I had made can be found. At one side of the plate there is a little vise (Fig. 1, *C*) which is attached to the same piece that supports this plate. The purpose of this vise is to hold one end of the steel wire the body of which is to be determined. The two arms of the rectangular brace which supports the plate extend beyond the plate. Either by bending them at right angles near their ends or by adding another small piece, each of these ends is made to be higher than the rest and is provided with a square opening (Fig. 1, *DD*); it has something like a lunette guide, similar to that of some lathes. The two guides, or openings, receive a piece of iron forged into a billet (Fig. 1, *E*) which is longer than the plate. It can be moved to and fro [290] in the guides. This piece is thicker in the middle, where it is traversed by a threaded hole into which a long, coarse screw (*F G*) is fitted. One of the arms which grasp the piece holding the coarse screw is also pierced from above by a screw hole into which a small screw (*I*) fits, which, when tightened, holds this piece firmly in place. As this piece can be moved in the guides whenever desired, it is obvious that the coarse screw can be held at different distances from the vise.

Using this machine is simple. One end of the quenched iron wire (*N O*) is clamped in the vise. In doing so, one is careful to place the wire horizontally and so that it has the same elevation as the screw. After the screw has been turned until it touches the wire, it will push the wire forward when turned further. It will force the wire to bend, and, finally, after the screw has advanced to a certain point, the flexibility of the wire will have been strained to the limit, and the wire will break.

The location on the plate up to which the screw has advanced when the wire breaks will be noted down. In order to make this easier, the plate can be divided into as many parts as desired by drawing lines perpendicularly to the direction of the screw. Then take the broken steel wire from the vise, put another one in its place, let the screw gradually force it to bend more and more, and observe once more where the screw was when the wire broke. The more flexible of these two wires, the one that has [291] more body, is the one that before breaking permitted the screw to advance farther. The difference between the two locations gives a measure of the flexibility, or the body, of the steel.

I should mention that the end of the coarse screw (*G*) must be drilled hollow like that of a key and that there must be a little piece with a round spindle which can be put into this hole (*H*) and turn in it freely. Outside the screw, this spindle must end in a small fork in which the iron wire is placed. Otherwise it would be difficult for the screw to push the wire ahead, as the wire would slide over or under it.

Instead of graduating the plate, it would be still easier to have a small graduated rule, which can be moved over the plate. A piece of iron which is bent so that its two parts are parallel to each other can be used as such a rule (Fig. 1, *K L*). The distance between the two parts will be only a little greater than the thickness of the plate. The plate fits easily into the space between these two parts. The lower one will have a screw (Fig. 2, *M*) which, when tightened, will hold the rule in the place selected for it. The upper part, which is the rule proper, will have divisions at intervals of a line or at closer intervals if desired.

This is how the little rule is used: When the iron that is to be tested is in place—that means when its one end has been clamped between the jaws of the vise and the other [292] end has been placed in the small fork of the coarse screw—the rule will be brought over and will be made fast, so that its end is quite close to the end of the lower tine of the little fork. The coarse screw is then turned slowly, and, as we turn it, we observe with which division on the rule the end of the lower branch of the little fork is even. The moment the wire breaks, we stop turning the screw and note down the division of the rule which one end of the fork had reached when the wire broke. For instance, if it had arrived at the eighth line, at the eighth division, and if when some other wire is broken the end of the same tine advances only to the sixth division, we know that the first wire is made of steel with more body.

The wires that are placed in the machine will not always be

as straight as one might wish them to be; they often warp in quenching. The shorter they are, the less they will be inclined to warp, but they will also bend less before breaking. However, it rarely happens that they warp enough to make it impossible to judge the outcome of the experiment.

After two steels have been compared concerning their body, it should not be neglected also to compare their grain; for, if the steel with more body is found at the same time to have a coarser grain, it indicates that it would have much more body if it were quenched less hot in order to give it the type of grain [293] of the other one. One would reason in the opposite way if the steel that broke closer to the end of the rule had the coarser grain; by quenching it less hot, it could be given more body and the type of grain of the first one.

Body, or flexibility, could also be determined by means of weights. It is enough to make this suggestion without supplying sketches or even an explanation of the way in which a cord could be fastened to the steel, and how this cord would then pass over a small pulley and would be loaded at its other end with weights, to which others would be added as long as it is necessary.*

For the makers of springs for watches and clocks it is more important than for any other artisan to obtain steels that have body. They treat their steels by tempering, an operation of which it is not yet time to speak. They must coil their steels; but those steels which have no body cannot be coiled. We could determine the body of steels by a method that derives from the way they are processed—I mean by using small, hollow wheels of different diameters, something like rings (Pl. 9, Figs. 14, 15). The steel that could be wound upon the ring of the smallest diameter would be the steel with the most body; but then it would be necessary to forge the steel into thin strip or to draw it into fine wire, because otherwise it would not have enough

* This second method would, of course, measure the bending strength as well as the maximum strain in bending which Réaumur had earlier defined as body. The term "body" is currently used to imply a vague aggregate quality, a combination of hardenability, toughness, and reliability in service. Réaumur is far ahead of his time in attempting to reduce it to quantitative measure and shows wisdom in matching the type of test to the intended service.

flexibility to withstand the test. One end of the strip or wire would be fastened on the ring by a screw (Fig. 15, *a*), and the artisan would then attempt to fit the rest [294] of the steel on to the circumference of the ring, either by hand or with a small hook (*b d*).

These methods of testing the body of steel really are as precise as one could wish; but they require a little too much in the way of apparatus to be adopted as ordinary practice. I doubt that we shall become as progressive as these methods show we could become. At least, we could hardly expect the ordinary artisan to have recourse to them. Those who use the steel are far from being equipped with the machines needed to draw it into wire, and, although this operation is very simple, they might get into difficulties. They would need a drawplate and something corresponding to the *bench* of the goldsmith. They also could use a small jack similar to the ones described by M. Dalesme in the *Memoirs* of the Academy of 1717.*

Instead of these precise methods, a cruder one could be used which is still good and provides a means to determine the hardness of a steel at the same time as its body is being tested. This is practically the only test known to our artisans, and I shall suggest some improvements which will be useful. In order to try out a steel, a cold chisel is forged from it. Either the chisel is forged entirely of steel or only its end is made of steel, which is sufficient. The chisel will be quenched, and the degree of heat, the color at which it has been quenched, will be noted down. Then one [295] tries out if this chisel can cut iron cold. If the edge folds back, it will be heated and quenched hotter, for the first quench has not given it the necessary hardness. If it spalls after the second quench, it has not been left enough body. One will then aim at quenching it at a degree of heat intermediate between the two previously used. If none can be found at which this steel does not fail because of one of the two extreme possibilities—that is, either by folding back or by spalling—this is a sure indication that this steel cannot combine sufficient body with much hardness. Instead of being quenched at lower degrees

* Dalesme, "Crics nouveaux," *Mém. Acad. Sci.*, 1717, pp. 301-4.

of heat, it is additionally tempered; but this is not yet the time to talk about tempering.

If the chisel successfully cuts iron cold, it can be made to cut it in two different ways, either obliquely or perpendicularly (Pl. 9, Fig. 17). If it is used to cut obliquely (*m*), it is usually made to rest on the long edge of the bar that is to be cut. Chips are taken off as they would be taken off a piece of wood, first thin ones and then thicker ones, which means that the chisel is held sometimes more and sometimes less inclined and that it is more or less strongly hammered, depending on the size of the chip that is to be cut off. The cut in the iron, the spot from which the chip has been taken (*n*), itself gives an indication of the hardness of the steel. The harder a steel is, the cleaner, more sparkling, and brilliant will be the cut. A steel is given a good rating if it lifts [296] large chips without spalling or breaking. But, if the steel spalls, the rating it should be given is not so certain. If the hand holding the chisel wavers when the chisel is struck with the hammer, the edge will break without fail, even if it has sufficient body.

This kind of test provides no means of comparison; it is not able to tell whether one steel outranks another; but it can be made more precise as follows: Out of the worst grade of steel, the one of the least hardness (Pl. 9, Fig. 16), I have a thin bar forged. This is quenched mildly at one end (*f*); I then divide it into several parts, like a rule, and use it as a measure of hardness and body of steel. After a chisel has been forged out of steel, I have it successively quenched and tempered at different degrees of heat, and I also give its cutting edge different degrees of thickness. I then determine after each operation up to which location, up to which division and which part of this division, my chisel can cut the quenched steel without spalling. When I have found the limit beyond which I cannot make it cut into the steel, I note it down. Let us suppose that our chisel could make no impression beyond the third line. I have a similar chisel forged out of another steel and determine which kind of quenching and tempering gives it the greatest hardness and body. If I subsequently succeed in making this second chisel cut up to about the second division, I know that this steel has more body than the other one [297] and probably more hardness.

There are few chisels made of steel which can cut another quenched steel, even where its grain is fine. In order to be able to test all classes of steel, they must be opposed to something less hard. For this purpose, I am using a flat bar of a naturally hard iron, one end of which has been heated and quenched almost melting-hot. Not every steel can cut into this end, not even at some distance from the actual end. Thus I could graduate, and I have graduated, such an iron bar for the purpose of comparing the quality of different steels.

Instead of using a hammer, one could strike the chisel, placed vertically, by means of a weight, which would fall from a certain constant height in a constant direction. This could be done easily by employing a machine similar to the one with which pinmakers form the heads of pins, and to my mind this would be a good method of selecting the steels that are most suitable for very sharp cutting tools. I assume that I have a number of chisels made of different steels that are to be tested; they have all been given the same width and approximately the same angle, and they have been used to cut iron or wood or some other material. It is clear that the best-cutting steel would be the one that, struck less often, would cut a piece of equal or greater thickness. If one chisel cuts only after thirty blows what another cuts [298] after twenty, one has a means of judging the difference in quality between the steels from which these chisels were made. But at the present state of the arts, as long as we do not attempt to encourage high-minded competition among our artisans, as long as we neglect to reward those who distinguish themselves in their profession, we cannot expect that they will devote their time to similar investigations and that they will do anything with precision.

Besides veins of iron which may be found in steel, other irregularities may be encountered in their texture which are not so easily recognized. We have seen that these textures vary from each other in their degrees of fineness and hardness. These differences, which we have considered only in different steels, can be found in the texture of one and the same steel and can make it defective. The best method known to me for recognizing if a steel is of the same quality throughout is to have a piece of it worked on a lathe, to have a cylinder made of it, which may be more or less long, more or less big, as desired.* Watchmakers must often have such cylinders turned, as they use them for the shafts of wheels and gears, etc. They know from experience that there are steels with a non-uniform texture; the graver cuts deeper into spots of less hardness, digs into them more deeply than into the rest. Whereas our other tests are meant for quenched steels, this one is used on unquenched steels.

In general, the [299] quality of unquenched steels can also be judged to some extent by examining their fractures. I should like to see the careful artisan equipped with the fractures of all grades of unquenched steels as well as of quenched steels. The thing that is shown most plainly by the fractures of unquenched steel is whether a steel contains grains or platelets of iron; for, provided they are present, they show up by a brilliance which permits to distinguish them from the other grains. If there is a scattering of them in quenched steel, these platelets of iron are not so easily recognized. It would be impossible to distinguish them among the [coarse] white grains. Among the mixed grains they may be mistaken for part of the mixture. And, if they are present among the fine grains, one may sometimes wonder if they are not still part of the mixed grain.

Another thing I have observed in the fractures of unquenched and very well-annealed steels is that, as the grains of these fractures become finer, they become grayer, and the steels become more difficult to work; those with coarser grains are more easy to use. It is the same with those of a less dull color.

I believed that I could compare the hardness of two different steels after they had been forged in a swage, in which they were given the shape of prisms with the same right-angled triangle as

* One of the mysteries of metallurgical history is why etching was so late in being used to distinguish between metals and to show heterogeneity. Etching was used for decorative purposes on armor and weapons very early, both through a ground with a scratched design and to show the water in Damascus blades. Perret (1771) used nitric acid to distinguish between iron and steel, but it was not until the nineteenth century that etching was used to show structure.

bases. It seemed to me that, if the right angle of [300] the one prism were placed upon the right angle of the other one (Pl. 10, Fig. 3), and the upper one were then struck with a hammer, the harder of the two steels ought to notch the other one. However, I usually found both of them notched. The blow is not as instantaneous as it would seem. The upper prism is propelled forward. If, at first, it has forced the parts of the lower prism to yield, or to break, the sharp edge of the lower angle will have become thicker after it has yielded, or has broken, and is then, in turn, able to force the sharp edge of the upper angle to yield or to break. The same would have happened if the upper angle had yielded first. I am mentioning this experiment only so that those who might have the same idea as I had will be saved the trouble of trying it out.

The comments accompanying the Plates, which were purposely made very detailed, should help to clarify anything that might still be obscure about the means I have suggested for recognizing the different qualities of steel and for comparing those of different steels.

I T HAS BEEN sufficiently demonstrated that the most important characteristic of steel, considered from the standpoint of its usefulness to us, is its property of becoming hardened by being quenched. It is this property by which so many of the arts profit and without which they could not exist. Without the quench, an infinite number of machines and tools would not have the hardness which is absolutely necessary to them. If we consider the simplicity of the operation which gives steel so much hardness, and after having recognized the great usefulness of this effect, we will not hesitate to include quench-hardening among the most wonderful phenomena of nature, as Rohault has done.* I shall add that in the interest of the arts it would be extremely worthwhile to understand its causes and that I believe that such understanding has not been attained so far, in spite of the attempts to explain them, because we have had no sufficiently clear-cut concepts of the nature of steel. Several physicists have tried to explain the reason for this sudden hardening after having developed their own theory of the reason for [311] the hardness of bodies in general. However, even if we assume that the cause of hardness is well known, whatever it may be, the cause for the hardening of steel by quenching involves its own particular difficulties. When steel hardens, it seems to deviate from the general rule. Quenching is nothing more than sudden cooling. If we are mindful of the circumstances which accompany and precede this operation, it would at first seem as if the steel should be softened rather than hardened by the quench.

A piece of steel is heated. When it has become red, it is plunged into cold water. This is the basis of the whole mystery

* Jacques Rohault, *Traité de physique* (Paris, 1671); see note, p. 211.

of the ordinary quench, and it is all that is necessary to give considerable hardness to this steel, which would have remained soft to the file if it had been allowed to cool slowly, surrounded by the same charcoal that brought it to red heat, or even if it had been allowed to cool exposed to the ordinary air. If we had to guess under which of these two circumstances the steel acquired greater hardness, if this were one of those truths about which experience can tell us nothing, reasoning would lead us to think that exactly the opposite of what we observe would happen. We started by giving the steel a great degree of heat, or, what amounts to the same, we introduced into the steel torrents of particles of fire, which separate, remove, detach the parts of the steel from each other. In brief, we increased the volume of the steel. In [312] this state it is plunged into cold water. The water quickly arrests the movement, the action, of the substance of the fire which has penetrated the outer layer [of the steel]. Now this layer is fixed to preserve part of the increase in volume which the fire has caused, for it could not lose what it has gained without reoccupying its old place. However, the inner layers, which have not yet cooled or have not cooled to the same extent, prevent it from doing so. And, after the first layer has once cooled, what force could make it move back again toward the center? The same is true of all the other layers. It seems to follow that one of the effects of quenching is to give steel more volume than it would have if it had been allowed to cool slowly.* However, the general rule† is that bodies of the same nature decrease in hardness as they increase in volume relative to the same mass; decrease in hardness as they become more rarefied, because their parts, being farther removed from each other, hold less well together. According to the general rule, quenched steel should therefore be less hard than steel that has cooled slowly.

As far as we know, only water (as it freezes) increases in vol-

* One cannot but admire Réaumur's correct deduction of the origin of internal microstresses in rapidly cooled bodies, even though they are a relatively minor factor in producing hardness.

† This rule follows, of course, from general experience with materials of the field and kitchen and particularly from the behavior of clays on being fired.

ume while it becomes harder. Strictly speaking, water itself does not increase in volume when it freezes. The amount by which the volume seems to increase is due to dilation of the air it incloses, as shown by the beautiful experiment by the late M. Homberg. After [313] he had removed for a long time, and with great care, the air contained in some water, he found that this water from which most of the air had been pumped decreased in volume upon freezing.

If the foregoing discussion had not sufficiently proved that, by quenching, steel is forced to preserve its increase in volume, this reasoning could be given additional weight by a simple inspection of the fractures of steel in the two different conditions. Quenched steel seems to be more porous than unquenched steel. But I have more; I have an experiment which furnishes absolute proof of the correctness of this reasoning. It consists of measuring the dimensions of steel before it is heated and measuring them again after it has been quenched. M. Perrault* observed before I did that a quenched steel wire could not pass through the same die through which it had passed before it was quenched. I have repeated and varied this experiment in very many ways, and I have always found an increase in volume in the quenched steel. But I wished to know additionally how far this increase went and if it was large enough to be measured. I had an iron gauge made into which a piece of steel, 6 inches long, fitted exactly. These pieces of steel usually were 2 inches wide by 6 lines thick. When I quenched them after they had become whitish-red in the fire, I always found that they were at least a line longer after quenching than they had been before [314] they were heated. There was an increase in all the other dimensions as there was in length, but it was not so easy to measure it. This is no reason not to believe that it was propor-

---

* Claude Perrault and Pierre Perrault, *Essais de physique* (Paris, 1680). The statement referred to is as follows: "Pour être assûré que l'acier s'enfle par la trempe, j'ai fait faire dans une lame de fer un trou rond & parfaitement juste pour recevoir un fil d'acier, qui ayant été coupé en deux, & l'un des morceaux ayant été trempé, n'a pu passer par le trou, dans lequel il entroit avant que d'avoir été trempé; & où l'autre morceau, qui n'étoit point trempé, passoit aussi fort aisément."

For comments on Claude Perrault see Introduction, note, p. xxvi.

tional to the increase in length. Granted this, the diameters of the volumes of steels which were quenched at a certain degree of heat are to the diameters of the volumes of unquenched steels at least as 145 to 144.* It follows that the ratio of the volume of quenched steel to the volume of unquenched steel is greater than 49 to 48; for 145 cubed is 3,048,625; 144 cubed is 2,985,984, and the difference is 62,641, which means that the volume of steel is increased by at least 1/48 by quenching.

Thus, it has been satisfactorily proved that steel hardened by quenching has a more rarefied texture than the softer steel, than the unquenched steel. The causes that may be suspected of being able to increase the hardness of this metal while increasing its volume can be reduced to three. (1) Either the fire or the water may add to the mass a substance which is responsible for the increase in volume and also causes the parts of the steel to cohere more firmly. (2) Or, on the contrary, the fire may remove from the steel a substance which prevented its parts from being as perfectly bonded as possible. (3) Or, finally, changes may take place inside the steel—in the shape or the arrangement of its parts—which [315] cause these same parts to hold more firmly together.

I have made the experiments which seemed best suited to indicate in which of these possible causes we should believe. These experiments have convinced me that the first and the second cause are entirely to be rejected. Reasoning is not favorable to the first one. The only substance that might penetrate into steel at the instant of quenching is water (for the subtile matter can be taken into consideration only for empty space); but it is hard to see how water can find passages by which it can reach the center of a bar of steel. If it found any open passages in the first layers, in cooling these layers it would soon close those it would need to pass on to the center. Furthermore, water introduced into steel would hardly seem very suitable as a hardening agent.

---

* Réaumur either made a computational error or inadvertently recorded the change of length as 1 line instead of $\frac{1}{2}$ line. The latter is more in keeping with modern determinations, which indicate maximum density changes of about 0.8 per cent, corresponding to a length change of 0.27 per cent. This would amount to 0.016 inch in 6 instead of the 1 line (0.083 in.) reported.

In order to harden a body, one must add a substance whose parts are more cohesive. Let us now consider the experiment which could have saved us the foregoing argument and which proves that steel owes its increase in volume neither to water nor to the introduction of any other heavy substance. I weighed a piece of steel in one of the finest balances, reduced it to the exact weight of 1 ounce, and then heated it until it had become more than cherry-red and subsequently plunged it into cold water. After it had been taken out, I wiped and dried it and finally weighed it. I not only found no increase [316] in its weight; I found that it had lost half a grain. Now, if the increase in volume were caused by the introduction of a substance as heavy as the steel, the weight of this piece ought to have increased by about 12 grains —that is, it ought to have added 1/48 of its original weight as it added 1/48 of its original volume. And, if the capacity of new volume had been filled with parts of water, the increase in weight still ought to have been noticeable and in proportion to the ratio of the weight of water to the weight of steel.

It has thus been well established that the increase in volume and hardness observed in steel after quenching is not caused by the introduction of a heavy substance. It seems to me that the observed decrease in weight by half a grain deserves no further attention. I had taken every precaution possible to prevent the fire from burning my steel, from taking anything away from it. If it took half a grain, it really means that it took practically nothing.

Finally, if the introduction of water played a role in the hardening of steel, the steel would harden more when it is quenched in boiling water than when it is quenched in cold water; for boiling water would penetrate it more easily. However, certain experiments, which I shall discuss in my detailed report of investigations concerned with quench-hardening [Mem. 12], will demonstrate that boiling water cannot give a [317] high degree of hardness to steel—that it hardens steel less than cold water.

The arguments I just used against the introduction of water are just as strong when used against the introduction of parts of fire, or parts driven by the fire, which we might imagine to have become imprisoned in the steel when the water, in cooling it, closed the pores of the surface on the outside—of such parts, in brief, as those which remain in the calces of lead, tin, and several other substances after they have sustained prolonged firing. These parts increase the weight of the bodies into which they penetrate. There is, therefore, no introduction of any substance into quenched steel unless it is a substance without weight—that is, subtile matter.

As far as the second explanation is concerned, I mean the one that would make the hardening of steel dependent on a substance which is driven out of the parts of steel by the fire and then finds its return cut off by the water, I shall confess that, at first, I found it rather attractive. It seemed natural to me to suspect air of being inclosed and compressed between the parts of unquenched steel (where isn't there any?) and to believe that this air, having the tendency to distend the parts of the steel, prevented them from holding firmly together; but that the fire, in rarefying steel, in opening its pores, might drive this air out from between the parts of the steel. In air [or, rather, steel]* cooled suddenly, re-entry would be barred to this air, whereas the same air would gradually re-enter a steel which lost its heat by imperceptible degrees. [318] In explaining the phenomena of physical science, we start with hypotheses; it is the experiments which decide whether we guessed right. For fear that somebody else might adopt this idea as I was tempted to do, I am reporting herewith the experiment which disabused me and which, in my mind, should leave no doubt. It occurred to me to let a very hot piece of steel cool in a space that was empty of ordinary air, or almost empty. There, the steel ought to harden as when quenched in cold water if its hardening were caused by the inability of ordinary air to re-enter suddenly cooled steel after it has been driven out of the steel by fire. The space where my steel was cooled furnished no more air of this nature than water could have done. I shall not go into great detail concerning the method I used to make this experiment. I placed a piece of steel, which was more than red at one end, in a long glass tube filled

* *Air* is obviously a misprint for *acier*.

with mercury up to near the red end of the steel. Suffice it to say that I barred all entry to ordinary air by surrounding the empty space which the steel left around the upper opening of the tube with a compound of wax or resin. It is evident that it was easy to have the steel in the tube located in a vacuum by letting the mercury descend (as is done with barometers) and to determine the rarefaction of the air by the height at which the mercury stood. After having repeated this experiment several times, and in some of them having cooled the steel [319] in a space in which very little ordinary air remained, the steel always stayed as soft as if it had been cooled in ordinary air.

Since the hardening of steel is caused neither by the introduction of a new substance nor by the expulsion of air, it remains to look for its cause in the changes produced in its texture. This is also where Messrs. Rohault and Perrault believed it ought to be found. The former claims that its texture is made more uniform by quenching, because the water arrests its parts in a state approaching that of fusion; that its parts are not given enough time to collect in the form of gross component parts* which would leave perceptible spaces between them, into which the points of gravers and the teeth of saws or of files can enter. But, if he had had many opportunities to see steel being quenched and to fracture quenched steel, he undoubtedly would have observed that, the hotter a given steel is quenched, the greater will be the number of component parts, or grains; at the same time, the voids between the component parts, or grains, will be larger, and yet the steel will be harder. Its hardness increases in propor-

---

* Rohault says (English trans. by John Clarke [London, 1723], II, 156–57): "In order to account for this effect (which perhaps is one of the most admirable, and doubtless one of the most useful properties that we know) we must suppose that the heat of the fire which makes the steel almost ready to melt, puts the small particles, which each component part is made up of, into motion, and thereby causes the particles of the two nearest component parts, (whose distance from each other was very small, though far enough) to approach a little nearer one another, so that the metal becomes more uniform than it was before; after this, being cast on a sudden into the cold water, the metallic parts lose the motion they were in, before they have time to gather together into gross component parts [*grumeaux*], with considerable intervals between them: whence it follows, that the points or edges of gravers and the teeth of files can only slip over them without entering into them."

tion to an increase in the size of each of the perceptible spaces
between the grains. If steel is harder after quenching, it does not
mean, therefore, that the spaces where the teeth of files and the
points of gravers can enter are smaller than before quenching; it
really means that each grain is harder, [320] the parts of each
grain hold better together.

M. Perrault recognized before I did that the grains of steel are
harder after quenching, although the gaps that separate them
have grown. He attributes this hardness of the grains to pressure by subtile air, the subtile matter which he assumes to be the
general cause of the hardness of bodies. He claims that sudden
cooling locks this matter in. But this matter, thus imprisoned,
would be free to escape, and surely would escape, when a bar of
steel is broken in two. Consequently, the surface of the fracture
should become soft instantaneously, whereas it keeps all its
hardness. Furthermore, since the way in which subtile matter is
here supposed to act is tied up with the general cause of hardness, those who are not satisfied with the explanation given for
the general cause will not be satisfied with this particular explanation, and it is not easy to satisfy physicists in regard to this
important question.

I believe that the cause for the hardening of steel can be found,
without connecting it with the general cause of hardness,
through our understanding of its nature as acquired in the preceding memoirs. It is necessary to see simultaneously why
quenching hardens steel very much and why it hardens iron very
little. This remains something which cannot be rationally explained by M. Perrault's theory. At present we know that steel
differs from iron only [321] because it is penetrated by more
sulfurs and salts. Now, then, that by which they differ from
each other must be the prime cause of the differences found between them after they have been treated in a similar way. The
ability of steel to harden must, therefore, depend on the sulfurs
and salts, of which steel has more than iron. Let us try to discover how they are able to make steel hard when it is cooled
suddenly and, conversely, to leave it soft to the file when it is
cooled slowly.

We know, and it is important to remember, that iron and steel

soak up the sulfurs; but we also know that violent fire can remove them from the metals. For the present, in order to eliminate as many unnecessary factors as possible, let us look at a
single grain of an unquenched steel, one of those visible to the
unaided eye, and let us then compare it with a grain of quenched
steel of approximately the same size. This grain (Pl. 10, Fig. 5,
G), which is easily seen by the eye, is itself an accumulation of
an infinite number of other grains, which we shall call the
"molecules" of this grain (Fig. 5, *MM*). The microscope brings
these molecules into the field of our vision. But these molecules
are themselves composed of other parts (Fig. 6, *p p*). It is possible, if it seems desirable, to suppose that the latter are the elementary parts, although in reality we may have to continue the
division vastly much farther before we reach them; however, we
can stop here. We thus have to consider [322] a grain, the molecules of which it is composed, and the elementary parts of the
molecules. As the salts and sulfurs intimately penetrate the iron,
we can at least assume that those by which steel outnumbers
iron penetrate the molecules of the grain. If I expose to the fire
a soft steel containing the grain on which we have concentrated
our attention, the fire will melt the sulfurs and the salts of the
molecules of this grain before it melts the molecules themselves.
It will drive part of the sulfurs and salts by which steel outnumbers iron out of the molecules in which they were wedged.
Whereas, before this, they had penetrated these molecules, they
will now, as a first step, go into the gaps between them. This
will be all the effect caused by a moderate fire.* It is not just
because it helps me to arrive at my explanation that I make this
assumption. Reconversion of steel back into iron, accomplished

* Had Réaumur only reversed the effect of fire in this admirable theory, he
would have precisely anticipated the modern theory: Slow cooling permits
the carbon to aggregate in the spaces between the iron grains, while heating
to a temperature for quenching distributes the carbon uniformly in the interstices between the iron atoms. Réaumur's belief that properties of steel depended upon the relation of the main parts of the material and the salts and
sulfurs (which today we know to be just carbon atoms) indicates a physical
intuition of the highest order. It is curious that his approach was not made
use of by his successors—indeed, the physical study of metals as opposed to
the chemical or engineering study of their properties was long delayed.

either by a slow but long-continued fire or by a violent fire, has proved that the fire robs steel of its sulfurs and salts. Those which it has forced to come out of the molecules first occupy the spaces between these molecules. Let us therefore not hesitate to admit that, when our grain has reached a certain degree of heat, the empty spaces between the molecules of which it is composed will be partly filled by a sulfurous matter which was not there previously and of which the molecules have been deprived; that part of this sulfurous matter, which the fire has started on its way out of the iron, has passed from [323] the molecules themselves to the intervals left between them. In this state let us plunge the bar of steel with the grain we are studying into cold water. We shall instantaneously fix the sulfurs and the salts which float around together. We shall deprive them of their fluidity; they will no longer be in condition to re-enter the molecules. However, the small intervals between these molecules of the grain will now be more completely filled, and filled by a substance which we can suppose to be almost as hard as we want it to be. The molecules of the grain will therefore be more firmly bound to each other. For this reason our grain of steel will be more difficult to divide or to break; in other words, our grain of steel has now become harder. The same thing has happened to all the other grains of steel that had acquired the same degree of heat. Consequently, our steel has now been hardened; or, to be more precise and in order to keep in mind what we actually wish to explain, we should say all the grains of our bar of steel have now become hardened.

It is in no way difficult to agree that the sulfurs of the steel can be melted, can be brought to the liquid state, before the parts of the steel are reduced to the same state. I just spoke of what happens during the reconversion of steel back into iron when the sulfurs are removed although the metallic parts stay behind. A much more obvious example demonstrates that one part of the substance of a very solid compound can become liquid while the rest retains all [324] its solidity. I am referring to one of the methods invented to separate silver from copper, one of the most convenient methods for work on a large scale. It consists of having this silver pass into lead, from which it can

be recovered more easily than from copper. In order to have it
pass into the lead, certain quantities of lead and copper which
contain silver are melted together; the two metals are thoroughly combined and are then allowed to cool. After cooling,
they form one single mass. Subsequently this mass is exposed to
a degree of heat that suffices to melt the lead but is too weak to
melt the copper. The lead melts; it runs off after having seized
the silver and leaves the copper behind as a spongy mass.*
Something similar to what happens in the mass of lead and copper also happens in the molecules of our grain of steel. The sulfurs of the molecules melt; they run into the spaces between
these molecules, where they bond these molecules more firmly
together and thus create a harder grain after they have become
fixed by sudden cooling.

The pyrites, a class of sulfurous rock well known to natural-
ists, make me inclined to believe that sulfurs and salts mixed
together can have considerable hardness. It is known that the
pyrites are almost nothing but salts and sulfurs; but they are
nevertheless so hard that they were once used with wheel-lock
harquebuses in the same capacity in which flints are used today
with muskets. Even if these substances [i.e., sulfurs plus salts]
were less hard, as long as they occupy [325] the intervals between the molecules, the molecules will be more thoroughly
bonded together.

By the way, when I speak of the sulfurs of iron and steel, I
rarely mean sulfurs pure and simple. I consider them a kind of
common sulfur, like the substance of our pyrites—that is, sulfurs
mixed with a great amount of salts. And if somebody should
claim that these sulfurs, which we have forced to run between
the molecules of the grains, do not harden the grains—or,
rather, harden the grains principally because of the salts which
they carry along with them—this claim will later be found to
be supported by certain observations. These observations will
prove that salts introduced into iron harden it, even though it

* The best description of this liquation process for the desilverization of
copper that would have been available to Réaumur would be that of Ercker,
published in 1574. For an outline of the process see notes to the English translation of Ercker (Chicago, 1951), pp. 224–26.

loses some of its oily part. But in any case it seems certain that the hardening of quenched steel is caused by solidification of the substance which runs into the interstices of its parts; and this substance is not a simple substance [i.e., not elemental matter]; it undoubtedly is a sulfurous matter charged with a great deal of salts.

The processes of box-hardening are so appropriate to confirm this explanation that expressly planned experiments could not possibly be better. If steel is to be given a greater hardness than ordinary quenching will give it, it is heated, inclosed in certain boxes or crucibles in which it is surrounded by soot, charcoal, and salts—in other words, by substances which can provide it with sulfurs and salts. Here again we have the [326] interstices of the molecules or, if one prefers, the molecules themselves, which take up sulfurs and salts. In this condition the red-hot steel is taken from the boxes and quenched in ordinary water. Quenched at the same degree of heat, it hardens more than it would have hardened if it had not been heated surrounded by sulfurous and saline matters. My explanation gives the reason for this difference, and this difference confirms my explanation at the same time. The grains of steel heated in the box have been penetrated by more sulfurs and salts than the grains of steel heated directly over charcoal; cooling fixes more sulfurs and more salts in the one case than in the other.

Even iron that has been heated in a box containing these substances and is then quenched acquires at its surface a hardness approaching that of steel. While it was heated, the interstices between its parts have been filled with sulfurs and salts, and where that has happened it is in a state resembling that of steel.

However, I do not wish to conceal two rather severe objections [to my theory], nor would I try to make them seem less important. One is common to all the explanations of the effect of quenching which have been given so far. The other is particular to mine. The first of these objections is that quenched steel, hardened steel, apparently ought to be weaker than unquenched steel. I mean that it seems impossible to deny that, if [327] two pieces of steel of the same diameter—two steel wires, for instance—are pulled by both ends, less force ought to be required to break the quenched steel than the unquenched steel. Since the volume of steel is increased by quenching but the substance proper is not, it is clear that the number of points of contact must have become smaller; in other words, that the sum of the surfaces that touch after quenching is smaller than before quenching. Furthermore, the intervals between the grains are perceptibly larger after quenching. If the bond is proportional to the contacts, we thus have a smaller sum of bonds. The steel as a whole is therefore less strong after quenching than before quenching. It seems difficult to admit that quenched steel, which resists the file and pressure incomparably much better than unquenched steel, should be weaker when it is pulled. I must confess that this conclusion at first surprised me. For, although I knew that a quenched steel becomes brittle by quenching, this did not seem to prove in any way that the bond between all its parts taken together should therefore have become less strong. The hammer blow that breaks a piece of thick glass does not break a straw, but this same piece of glass can hold a considerable weight suspended, whereas the straw can hold only a light one.

Conclusions which seem hard to understand [328] sometimes are therefore no less true. I wished to make sure whether this one was true; whether steel hardened by quenching was therefore actually less able to resist the forces of tension. For this purpose I took a very long steel wire which had passed through the drawplate (Fig. 4). I then heated and quenched part of this wire, a length of 2 or 3 inches (Fig. 4, *h*). I used a silk thread to mark the location which seemed to me to have been quenched the hottest. Then I fastened one end of this wire to the ceiling, so that the wire was now in a vertical position. I loaded its lower end with weights, to which I added until the wire broke; or, to make it easier, I broke it by means of a lever after having twisted the lower end of the wire around it. Now, then, when it broke, it always happened in the part where it had been quenched and almost always at the location I had marked as being quenched the hottest, which consequently was the hardest.

I have repeated this experiment so many times, using all the precautions necessary, that there is no doubt left in my mind. The wire had some laps, where it had to be weaker than elsewhere; but I avoided quenching it at these spots. The last few times I performed this experiment I took an additional very important precaution to avoid that the wire became warped in quenching; for, when it is warped, it no longer represents a wire pulled vertically, and it would break in [329] being straightened, as a steel lever would. I started by placing the wire in a vertical position (Fig. 4) in which it was held by a weight, which put enough load on it to stretch it tight. Lighted charcoals were held near this tightened wire by placing them on a little iron plate through which the wire passed. I heated it at the spot which I estimated to be the strongest, until it had become red; then I threw water on it. The weight with which the wire was loaded prevented the quench from causing any warpage; in spite of this precaution, the wire always broke in the quenched part.*

I did not make sufficiently accurate experiments (and it is not easy to make them) to determine by how much the force necessary to break a piece of quenched steel in tension is smaller than that required to break the unquenched steel. But I know that the difference is considerable and much greater than the increase I found in the volume of the steel would make one expect. There were spots in the wire from which I removed laps which occupied more than one-third of the circumference and were as thick as one-quarter or one-third of the diameter. Spots thus weakened but not quenched still were stronger than those which had been quenched.

Thus, while steel gains strength to resist friction and pressure, it [330] loses some of its strength to resist tension; its strength is

---

* In planning this well-conceived experiment, Réaumur anticipated the effect of bending stresses on a brittle material but failed to get the right answer, either because he did not heat his material above the critical point before quenching or because fracture actually occurred at a part outside the hardened area. This experiment has been cited as an early attempt to determine the tensile strength of materials at high temperatures. Though the apparatus clearly could have been used for this purpose, it was not Réaumur's intention. He provided means of heating merely for heat treatment, not as an environment for testing.

being differently distributed. There is some sort of compensation by which it is given back in one direction what it loses in another.

The second objection, which is particular to my explanation, is that the molecules of the grains must be less hard after quenching than they were before the quench. In order better to understand the importance of this objection, let us assume that we are viewing under the microscope the grain of an unquenched steel (Fig. 5) and that the grain has been vastly enlarged. Let all the crosshatched areas (*M M M*) inclosed by lines be the molecules of this grain; their number is vastly larger than it would here appear. Any white spaces (*V V*) are the gaps between these different molecules. The molecules of the grain are in turn composed of other parts, which I have called the "elementary parts" of iron and steel. Let Figure 6 of Plate 10 be one of the molecules of the grain, where lines mark the boundaries between the elementary parts of which it is composed. When the grain of steel is heated, the sulfurs inside the molecules of this grain melt and will then occupy part of the interstices left between the molecules. As soon as quenching fixes them in this position, the grain will be a unit composed of better-joined parts, and the unit will be harder. The difficulty is that at the same time the molecules of the steel will have become less hard. [331] After quenching, the *M*'s of Figure 5 will hold better together than they did before; but the parts of which the *M*'s are composed, the *p*'s of Figure 6, will be less well joined. This is a necessary conclusion. But, if we take it under careful consideration, we shall not hesitate to grant it. What is there to be afraid of? That it must follow that steel, after quenching, has less resistance to the file than before? First, the file does not attack one part of a molecule or even one single molecule of a grain of steel at a time. It simultaneously attacks a multitude of the parts (such as *M M M*) of which this grain is composed; there may be thousands like them in the path of every tooth of the file. The file will therefore encounter more resistance, the steel will be harder to the file, when the grains and the parts which compose the grains hold better together. Second, if the above conclusion proved that the molecules of the grain are composed of elementary parts which are bonded together so firmly that they are still able to resist our tools although their bonds have been weakened, why should we object? Third, and finally, is there any actual proof that the molecules of the grain are less hard, are easier to detach or to break, in quenched steel than in unquenched steel? Would this be proved by the fact that quenched steel takes a better polish than unquenched steel and that the polish it takes [332] is the more beautiful the harder the steel has become by quenching. The fine powders used in polishing then act upon smaller parts; it is smaller parts that yield to them.

Even if we grant that the grains themselves hold less well together in quenched steel than in unquenched steel, quenched steel will resist the file and the chisel better than unquenched steel, provided that the parts composing the grains are more firmly bonded together. Whether the file acts upon steel or upon very soft irons, it does not lift the grains whole. This is proved by the fact that the fractures of iron and steel, even if they are very smooth, are rougher than spots that have been filed. When a piece of sandstone is worked with the file, it does not look smoother afterward, because the file removes the grains themselves. The reason why steel and iron look smoother is, therefore, that their grains are cut. Similarly, the chisel cuts steel only because it divides its grains; it rarely cuts its way precisely between two grains. Thus, if the parts of the grains hold better together, the steel will appear harder to the file and the chisel, which are used as the means to test its hardness.

But I believe, nevertheless, that the grains of quenched steel hold more strongly together than those of unquenched steel. Some of the sulfurs driven from the molecules apparently have moved as far as the intervals between [333] the grains; portions of these intervals have been filled with them. Even if quenched steel is weaker, less able to resist tension, each of its grains can still be more firmly bonded to the others; but the sum of these forces is less in the case of quenched steel. This is explained by the fact that quenched steel really has coarser grains than unquenched steel. Suppose that R and S (Figs. 7, 8) are sections through rows of grains of steel and that these grains are approximately round. We give them this shape, which in reality they have not, to simplify the argument; but it can be applied to any other shape. Thus, let S be two rows of grains of unquenched steel and R two rows of grains of quenched steel and assume that both pairs are of the same length but that in R the grains are not only coarser but also a little farther apart from each other. The increase in volume caused by quenching requires the last assumption. The sum of the points of contact in S, the measure of which is obtained by putting these points end to end, will be greater than the sum of the points of contact in R, greater than the length of these points put end to end. If the force to resist tension is proportional to the quantity of contacts, it will require more force to separate at one time all the grains of SS than to separate at one time all the grains of RR. On the other hand, it will require less force to detach a single [334] grain of S than to detach a single grain of R, as the latter, being coarser, touches its neighbors in more points.* A steel composed of grains such as those in S will, therefore, be more difficult to break in tension. And it will be more difficult to detach grains from a steel composed of grains such as those in R. Unquenched steel belongs to the former and quenched steel to the latter kind; and, further, the coarser the grains of one and the same steel, after it has been quenched, the harder it will be, generally speaking.

There is still another reason for the increase in hardness in proportion to the increase in grain size. This is a natural consequence of the explanation I gave of hardening by quenching. I have stated on very many other occasions that the grain of a steel will be the coarser the higher it has been heated, the hotter it has been quenched. As it is heated higher, more sulfurs and salts are driven out of its elementary parts by the fire, and the intervals between the particles that compose the grain are consequently better filled. However, there are limits to the increases in heat that can be used to increase the hardness of steel. If this heat is such that it drives the sulfurs out of the steel it-

---

* This is not true. If the shape of the grains remains constant, the number of contacts per grain will not vary with size. Réaumur may have been considering the number of contacts of a constant-sized molecule, more of which will be in a large grain.

self, the steel is no longer in condition to be hardened by quenching, or at least to be hardened as considerably. It then has been
reduced, or almost reduced, to the state of being iron.

The reason why the grains of steel are the coarser [335] the
hotter it has been quenched is that more parts of steel have
been joined together, because the heat has softened the steel
further. When the intervals between two grains are filled with
parts of sulfur, these two grains form only a single one, for the
sulfurs which surround these grains unite them.

At last, all the phenomena of quenching are clearly related to
our explanation. It has been shown why quenching hardens
steel; why it hardens it more when the steel has been quenched
hotter, when the grain of the steel has become coarser; why
such steel has less body, which means that it cannot be bent
without breaking—or can be bent only a little. The grains can
no longer yield when they are hard and rigid. They would be
more rigid for the sole reason that they are coarser. Glass, the
most brittle of all our bodies, is tough to an astonishing degree
when it has been drawn into thin threads, as I have demonstrated in the *Memoirs* of the Academy of 1713, page 210.*
Among equal quantities of the same material the one composed
of the smallest parts will be the most flexible. A glass cylinder
will be brittle, but the glass of this cylinder drawn into thread
will give a flexible skein; its flexibility will be the greater the
finer the threads of which it is composed. Unquenched steel corresponds to a skein of finer threads and quenched steel to a skein
of coarser threads.

It remains to [336] be seen why this quenched steel becomes
soft again when it is heated or, what amounts to the same, why
it would have stayed soft if it had been allowed to cool on the

* This memoir ("Expériences et réflexions sur la prodigieuse ductilité de
diverses matières," *Mém. Acad. Sci.*, 1713, pp. 199–220) is an interesting fore-
taste of Réaumur's many scientific interests. He discusses at length the properties of thin fibers of various materials, including spider web and silk from the
insect kingdom that was to be his major preoccupation through life, and he
describes experiments on the extreme ductility of gold and of gold-clad silver
which impressed upon him the extremely small nature of the ultimate parts of
metals. This paper is included in Vol. IV of the English translation of the
Mémoires, published in 1742 by Martin and Chambers.

charcoal. To give a reasonable explanation, it is enough to recall that iron avidly absorbs sulfurs and salts. I shall not try to
explain how this is accomplished; perhaps I could not do it. If,
in physics, we tried to explain everything connected with the
simplest question, we would be forced to give a complete course
in physics with every question. All the truths of physical science form a chain, any link of which can be considered separately. I assume, therefore, that it is well enough established
that iron avidly absorbs sulfurs and that a violent fire is needed
to rid it of those it has seized, those by which it has been penetrated. As the action of the fire becomes weaker, when it is no
longer able to drive more sulfurs out of the molecules of the
steel, some of those which had left return. They insert themselves once more and do so firmly; for, in this case, the action
of the fire decreases continuously. This action, which is too
weak to expel the sulfurs that have re-entered into the elementary parts, has enough force to maintain the fluidity of those
which are still outside. If the heat diminishes very gradually
over a considerable duration of time, more sulfurs can re-enter
the molecules and the elementary parts. Thus, the more slowly
steel has been cooled, the farther it will be removed [337] from
the state it had acquired by quenching. The more suddenly it
has cooled, the greater its hardness; the more slowly it has
cooled, the greater its toughness.

If iron that has just been converted into steel is withdrawn
from the furnace completely red and is then quenched, it hardens
like ordinary [forged] steel. It therefore must be provided with
the sulfurs and salts that are necessary to produce this effect.
If it is allowed to cool slowly, it is still in the state of unquenched steel; it has little hardness. What distinguishes it in
this state is its brittleness, which indicates that its parts have
been considerably removed from each other during the operation. They will continue to be badly joined together until they
have been brought closer together by the hammer—that is, until the steel has been forged. For the same reason, the grain of
steel is not as beautiful when it is quenched before forging as
when it is quenched after forging.

Since iron and steel differ only by degree, it seems that the effects produced on each of them by quenching must also differ only by degree—that it must be possible to give iron some measure of hardness by quenching. And it is. If iron is quenched when it is cherry-red or whitish red, it will not be hardened to the point where it resists the file. But every artisan knows that quenched iron is less soft, less pliant, than unquenched iron. And, whenever very soft iron is required, he is very much on his guard against cooling [338] it suddenly. But if you wish to observe what maximum effect quenching can have on iron, heat it until it almost melts and then plunge it into cold water. I have often found that iron thus quenched from a melting heat had a hardness approaching that of steel—that it resisted the file. Since iron has fewer sulfurs than steel, a more violent heat is required to force enough of them out of its molecules and its elementary parts to fill the interstices left between the molecules which make up the grains. I imagine, therefore, that fire which almost melts iron drives only as many sulfurs from the parts of the iron as it does from those of steel to which it gives a cherry-red color. Everything I have said about the nature of both must give one this idea. In general, steel is easier to heat than iron, and steel cools faster. The same degree of heat increases the volume of steel more considerably than that of iron, which is proved by the following. I heated a piece of steel and a piece of iron, each of them 12 inches long, until they had the same color as far as the eyes could judge. In this condition I measured them both; the length of the steel had increased by 3 lines and that of the iron only by 2. I repeated this experiment several times. Regardless of what color I gave the steel through the fire, when I gave the same color to the iron, the volume of the steel always increased more than that of the iron.*

* The expansions observed by Réaumur—2 and 3 lines, respectively, for 12-inch long pieces of iron and steel at a red heat—correspond to 1.4 and 2.1 per cent, respectively. How close Réaumur must have been to observing the sudden shrinkage on heating iron through the transformation point! Although the expansion of solids by heat had been known for a long time and had been studied by the Florentine Academy, these experiments by Réaumur seem to be the first quantitative measurements published. In 1716–17 Derham had shown that iron rods long enough to swing seconds (39 in.) expanded 0.2 inch on heating to a "flaming heat" and shortened 0.03 inch in a freezing

After having [339] measured the piece of steel and the piece of iron when they were equally hot, I quenched them and measured them again. The steel kept at least one-third and sometimes half of the increase in volume caused by the fire, but I found that the iron returned almost to its original volume; it never kept a measurable increase in volume. The sulfurs are easier to cool, they solidify more easily, than the metallic parts; and steel containing more sulfurs must cool faster. Its parts have less time to return to their original position. Furthermore, as soon as the sulfurs have solidified, the return of the parts which they separate is arrested.

Whenever I have spoken of the cooling produced by quenching, I have indicated that it is very sudden; still, I did not mean to give the impression that it is instantaneous. Iron and steel are not cold the moment after they have been plunged into water; for some time thereafter they hold a considerable degree of heat. If the pieces are thick, it is seen through the water that they stay red for some time. During the quench, part of the sulfurs which the fire had driven between the molecules of the grains re-enter into the molecules. When a steel which has been quenched white-hot has cooled, there are perhaps only as many sulfurs between its molecules as there are between those of steel

---

mixture of salt and snow, but he did not publish these results until 1736 (*Phil. Trans. Roy. Soc.*, XXXIX, 201). Nine years after Réaumur, Musschenbroek, in the notes to his Latin translation of the Florentine Academy's report (*Tentamina experimentorum naturalium captorum in Accademia del Cimento* . . . [Leyden, 1731]), described a "pyrometer" with a dial gauge of adequate sensitivity. Using bars 5.8 inches long, he observed a maximum extension resulting from the heat of five spirit lamps of 230 scale divisions (each 1/12,500 in.) for iron as against 310 for steel. The expansion from freezing to boiling water for iron was 53 divisions, while steel expanded 56 divisions. This corresponds to 7.3 and 7.6×10^{-6} per ° C., respectively, compared with modern values of 11.9 for iron and 11.6 for annealed steel (0.9 per cent carbon). Quenched steel has a higher expansion coefficient, and the fact that most of the early measurements show steel as expanding more than iron is probably due to the use of quenched samples. The measurement of linear expansion was a popular subject for English scientists of the eighteenth century and provided the excuse for some excellent instrument-making. The principal dilatometers are those of Ellicott (a good differential instrument—*Phil. Trans. Roy. Soc.*, XXXIX [1736], 297), Smeaton (*Phil. Trans.*, XLVIII [1754], 598–611), and Ramsden (*Phil. Trans.*, LXXV [1785], 385).

which has the degree of heat accompanying a cherry-red color. When steel quenched [340] cherry-red has cooled, it has perhaps only as many sulfurs between its parts as steel that was heated to a red just beyond black. We must believe, therefore, that iron from whose elementary parts few sulfurs have been driven will reabsorb almost all of them; that its sulfurs do not bar the return of the molecules of iron, so that these will resume almost their original positions. Consequently, the mass of iron will almost regain its original volume.

The foregoing observations explain one of the fundamental rules of quenching, which will be discussed later—namely, that of two steels of different fineness which have been brought to and quenched at the same degree of heat, the finer steel acquires more hardness. It is farther removed from the state of being iron; more sulfurs are fixed between its molecules.

I hope that everything I have said about the general cause of the effect of quenching will also shed light upon the different methods of quench-hardening; that the effects produced by different methods of quenching can be foreseen; and that, in turn, the effects of these different methods of quenching will give additional support to an explanation which to me seems already well proved. I therefore consider a somewhat more detailed discussion of quench-hardening indispensable. This will be the subject of the following memoir.

The Twelfth Memoir, on the Different Ways [341]
in Which Steel Can Be Quenched and Is
Often Tempered after the Quench

INCE QUENCHING steel is nothing more than cooling it rapidly, all the different ways of quenching may be reviewed under two general headings; namely, in relation to the condition of the steel at the time it was cooled and in relation to the media and the condition of the medium that cooled it. The steel could have been more or less hot when it was quenched, and we shall first study it in relation to the degree of heat it had before it was quenched. Subsequently we shall investigate what happens when it is quenched in different media; but we shall then go back to the different effects of quenching considered in relation to the condition of the steel itself. We shall examine the possibility of causing the steel to be in such a state that it can acquire greater hardness even though it is quenched at the same degree of heat into the same medium. This is done by means of pack-hardening.

However, I have no intention of dealing with this subject in its entirety. To do that it would be necessary to review the effects of quenching on [342] different steels; deal with the media in which steel can be cooled in prodigious detail; and determine what degree of quenching is suitable for each tool. (The latter subject alone would lead us far afield; it would be necessary to explain the functions of every tool; and such discussions can be dealt with at the proper length only as part of a description of the arts that produce these tools, which I hope to prepare eventually, one at a time.) At present, I shall be content to give general information, to discuss the fundamentals of quenching. I shall state only the principal rules and give these rules support by a few experiments I have performed, which however could be carried much further.

I shall also come back once more to some of the facts I have already discussed in the preceding memoirs, in order to show consecutively everything that is concerned with quenching. Elsewhere I omitted certain details which then ought to have been omitted, but they should not be left out now. Let us start with ordinary quenching, quenching in ordinary water, the method by which the larger part of the tools we use is hardened—tools like knives, scissors, razors, penknives, cleavers, hatchets, etc.

The degree to which a steel has been heated is recognized by the color of its surface; but, of all the colors it can have, only those which begin to contain some red [343] render it noticeably responsive to quenching. It is necessary that the steel has at least started to become red. The first shade of red is brownish red; as the steel becomes hotter, the red becomes brighter, more vivid, and finally reaches the shade which the artisans call "cherry-red" and which actually resembles ordinary cherry. A greater degree of heat makes this red paler; it becomes mixed with yellow. Finally, when the heat of the steel has risen to the utmost degree, when the steel is almost melting, its color is a yellowish white, which the artisans call "white."

The color which steel is given in the fire thus indicates the degree of heat it has acquired. This color is a guide in quenching the steel; it indicates if the steel has arrived at the degree of heat at which it is to be quenched.

The most general rule concerning quenching is that the grain of a steel becomes coarser and whiter as the steel is quenched hotter and that, conversely, the grain becomes finer and increasingly gray and dull as it is quenched cooler. This was illustrated in the tenth memoir, where the different types of grain are described. The only exception to this rule would be that, if steel has been overheated, if it has become melting-hot, its grain will be neither so white nor so coarse as if it had been heated a little less hot. Excessive heat causes it to lose some of its steel quality.

The second rule is that steel increases in [344] hardness as it is quenched hotter. However, this rule is subject to some exceptions. I have known artisans who were more observant than most of them are in general and who did not agree with this rule. They had noticed that steels are occasionally less hard when they are quenched very hot than when they are quenched a little less hot. They must have had this experience with very fine steels, as I have had it. If such steels are heated almost melting-hot, it sometimes happens that, at the location at which they were white-hot, they have no greater hardness than at the location where they were only cherry-red. The explanation is that excessively violent fire weakens such steels; it even may destroy them entirely, turn them back into iron, make of them what we, following the custom of the artisans, have called "burnt steels" [see p. 144]. Since they have been exposed to a degree of fire which makes something less than steel out of them, it is not astonishing that they are less hard. The rule is nevertheless valid. In general, it is true that, the hotter a steel has been quenched, the harder it will be.

There is, however, a third rule, which will help to clarify the previous one—namely, that among steels of different grades the finest ones become harder at the same degree of heat. Take a steel suitable only for agricultural implements and one suitable for the finest cutting edges, quench both when they are cherry-red, and the latter will be harder than the former. However, you can [345] quench the finer steel at such low degree of heat and the other one at such high degree that the coarse steel will be harder than the fine steel. In the class of fine steels, increasing fineness requires decreasing degrees of heating for quenching.*

This is the place to describe an experiment (which I promised to do elsewhere) that is well suited to confirm this rule and to show the underlying fundamentals. According to my theory of the nature of steel, the finer steels are penetrated by a larger quantity of sulfurs and salts. In order to make (from wrought iron) a steel as fine as it could become, even at the risk of making it too hard to be worked, I repeatedly put several pieces of this steel back into the furnace. Each time I surrounded them

---

* This is a direct consequence of the different carbon content of the various kinds of steel. Modern practice calls for a quenching temperature lineally descending from about 1,670° to 1,410° F. (910° to 765° C.) as carbon content increases from 0.1 to 0.9 per cent.

with the ingredients capable of changing them into steel if they had not already been steel. When they contained as much of the sulfurs as they needed, they absorbed more. The ends of these pieces of steel were then forged very gently and were quenched at a little above cherry-red. What happened to some of them seemed peculiar to me. There were some which went to pieces as soon as they were plunged into the water. Others were withdrawn from the water whole, but, when I started to tap upon the end, even lightly, this end crumbled into grains almost as sandstone would have done. I had a coarse sand of steel; its grains were hard and even very hard, but the aggregate of grains was friable.

A fourth rule, which is a corollary of the third, is [346] that, if hard tools are to be produced from steels which are not fine, they must be quenched very hot at a color exceeding cherry-red, verging on white. However, to quench steels at a melting heat is to be avoided; this can be done only on rare occasions and only with very big pieces which are to be hardened very far inside; this is sometimes done with edge tools. In order to have the effect of quenching penetrate to the center of the piece, one is forced to give the surface too much heat.

Coarse steels resemble iron; their elementary parts are much less charged with sulfurs and salts than those of fine steels. Only considerable heat can melt a sufficient quantity of these substances and cause them to move in between the molecules of the grains and sufficiently fill their interstices. The sulfurs and salts are much faster liquefied in fine steels, which contain much more of them. In extremely fine steels, in those which are too steely, which are surcharged with sulfurs, a very low heat suffices to disengage them from inside the metallic parts, cause them to run into the spaces between them, and even make them collect there in such quantities that the metallic parts are thereby too much separated from each other. When steel in this condition is quenched in cold water, it will crumble in the quenching medium; or, if it stays whole, it will decompose into grains at the slightest touch, as if it were a piece [347] of sandstone. In short, if what we have learned about the cause for the hardening of steel by quenching and about the nature of steel is applied to these phenomena, everything about them becomes clear.

A very important rule, which is not sufficiently observed by very many artisans, is never to heat steel to anything but the exact degree at which it is to be quenched. There are some who think that they are careful enough if they quench their steel at the proper color. They often heat it more than is necessary, and, after having withdrawn it from the fire too hot, they let it cool until it has come back to the desired color. After having cooled down to a certain color, the parts of the steel will not be arranged exactly in the same way as when the fire had simply given them this color. There are parts which are no longer able to return to their first position. In order to be quenched well, steel should therefore be quenched as soon as it has reached the degree of heat at which it is to be quenched.

Thus, an alert artisan must not take his eyes off his tool while he heats it for quenching. In order to quench exactly at the desired degree of heat, it is necessary when dealing with small pieces (which would cool in the air if they were carried only a distance of four or five steps from the forge) to have the water in which they are to be quenched right on the forge itself. Good cutlers do this with penknives.

In order [348] to obtain definite proof to support the statement I made a while ago, I took two pieces of the same steel. I heated one of them exactly to cherry-red and then quenched it. I heated the other piece until it was almost white, far beyond cherry color, withdrew it from the fire, and waited until it had cooled down to that color before I quenched it. After these two pieces of steel had been broken, the fracture of the first one always gave the impression of consisting of finer, more uniform, and better-defined grains than that of the second piece. I have repeated this experiment very many times, always with the same result. In order to make the comparison more dependable, I sometimes used steel wires which came from the same rod and had been drawn through the same hole of the wire-drawing plate.

I have watched quite intelligent artisans who intentionally gave their steel a higher degree of heat than the one at which they intended to quench it; but, instead of letting its heat decrease by holding the steel on the charcoal of the forge or in the air, as one usually does, they placed it on the anvil and forged it by light blows until it had cooled to the proper degree. Their idea was to prepare it to acquire more hardness on quenching by bringing its parts, which the fire had separated, closer together again. This quite plausible argument has seemed to me not to agree with experience. The fractures of steels which had been given this small amount of working before they were quenched seemed to me not to have the same beautiful grain as the fractures of [349] steels quenched at the same degree of heat immediately after they had been withdrawn from the fire. It is possible that the hammer blows which compress the steel force some of the sulfurs to go back into its parts, so that there are fewer sulfurs in the interstices than there would have been otherwise. Furthermore, these blows may cause an arrangement of the parts which is less favorable for hardening than the arrangement caused by fire alone.

From these rules or statements concerning only the condition of the steel at the moment of quenching let us now go on to the different media, and to the condition of the different media, in which steel can be quenched. Let us start with water. In connection with quenching in water the most important item to be watched is how cold the water is. If of two equally hot steels one is quenched into colder water, it will be harder and more brittle than the other one after quenching. It also will have a somewhat coarser grain. Almost every artisan knows that tools quenched in very cold weather are more brittle. The artisans call this being quenched *drier*, and the more skilful ones therefore heat their tools less under such circumstances. There is something like a compensation between quenching a piece less hot in colder water and quenching a piece hotter in water that is not so cold. If one extends the explanation of the reason for hardening by quenching, these two facts can also be explained. The hardening [350] is caused by the salts and the sulfurs that solidify between the molecules of the grains, by the sulfurs whose return [into the molecules] is arrested. There are fewer sulfurs and salts between the grains of a steel that is heated less hot; but colder water solidifies these substances in less time—it ends their fluidity sooner. There will be fewer that can re-enter the parts of the steel when it cools in less time. Steel does not cool instantly. Even under water it stays red; and it will keep the red color longer the hotter it has been quenched.

In order to obtain still more complete proof of this kind of compensation I have just explained—in order to make sure that quenching a steel less hot in colder water is somewhat the same, as far as hardening is concerned, as quenching a steel hotter in water that is less cold or even warm—I heated a steel until it was only cherry-red and plunged it into boiling water. It did not acquire enough hardness to resist the file. It hardened somewhat, but not as much as it would have hardened in cold water. It had not even become brittle; it could be flattened by hammer blows. I then heated the steel to a much higher degree; I let it become very pale red. When it was then quenched into boiling water, it acquired the same hardness it would have had if it had been quenched into cold water after having been heated only cherry-red.

Since [351] quench-hardening steel is nothing more than cooling it, it is clear that any medium that can cool steel, that can arrest the movement of its parts, is capable of hardening it and that different liquids can produce similar effects or come close to producing the same effect as water. Even solid materials that can be made to surround hot steel intimately will quench-harden it. Here are some examples: Under certain circumstances tools with thin tips are quenched in lead. After the tip of the tool has been heated, the tool is pressed against a lump of lead and forced to penetrate into it. The lead melts a little in order to make room, and it will invariably quench the tip to almost the same hardness as water would have done.

If it were as easy as with lead to make a hot tool penetrate into gold, silver, and copper, tools could also be quenched in these metals. Tin comes closer to the softness of lead. I have tried if it would not also quench steel and found that it hardened without fail the part that was pushed into it; but, because it is a little harder to melt than lead, it is necessary to press harder upon the tool or even strike it to make it penetrate far enough.

I have quenched the points of red-hot steel by forcing them

into bismuth, and I have quenched steel by driving it into a regulus of antimony.

As different as these substances are [352] from water, they have not seemed to me to convey upon the steel any quality other than that conveyed by water. I have not found that antimony has a bad effect upon it, although it is very apt to alter iron and steel. The act of quenching is of such short duration, the steel is cooled so rapidly, that the substances that come in contact with it have scarcely time to react with it effectively other than by making it cool more quickly.

A substance which seemed to me to deserve more than any other to be tried as a quenching medium for steel was mercury, and I therefore did not neglect this experiment. When, after the act of quenching, I happened to put my finger into the mercury, it seemed to me that it had been heated much more than water would have if a piece of steel of the same size had been quenched in it.* However, since a given volume of mercury is about thirteen times heavier than an equal volume of water and the mass that must be set in motion is approximately thirteen times as great, it would seem that mercury ought to require a much greater degree of heat than water does to be heated to the same degree. It was not natural to expect the opposite—that mercury would become hotter than water when exposed to the same degree of heat. In order to convince myself of a fact which I had not foreseen, I took two quite similar pots and filled one with water and the other with mercury; then I quenched into both equal pieces of steel wire equally heated. If by chance one of them had become hotter, it was always put in the pot containing water. After the steel had been quenched [353] in both, I put my finger in both liquids; the water had acquired just per-

* This seems to be the first observation of the different effects of the same amount of heat upon the temperature of two different materials. Modern values of specific heats indicate that mercury should increase in temperature 2.2 times as much as an equivalent volume of water. Somewhat later Fahrenheit made quantitative observations of the temperature differences obtained by mixing mercury and water varying in amount and temperatures. It was Black who first formulated the modern concept of specific and latent heats and who first made extensive accurate measurements (see D. McKie and N. H. de V. Heathcote, *The Discovery of Specific and Latent Heats* [London, 1935]).

ceptible warmth—it barely had the degree of heat of lukewarm water—whereas the heat of the mercury was such that I could not keep my finger in it for long—it burned me. I know (and who does not?) that one cannot judge with certainty by the sense of touch how hot or cold a substance is. I wish I had had thermometers handy, of a size and shape suitable to give me greater assurance of this fact or—to speak more plainly—to prove it incontestably to others. For, although I know that mercury which is less cold (or less hot) than water may cause a greater sensation of heat (or of cold) because a greater number of the parts of this liquid are applied at one time to the body which is in contact with it (just as water causes more of a sensation than air)—although, I said, I am aware of this fact, the difference in this case was so considerable that there was no reason to be afraid of an error caused by the senses. If there was any doubt left in my mind, it was removed by something that provided as good proof as thermometers could have done. I am referring to the fact that the pot which contained the mercury had become noticeably hotter to the touch than the other one. Why would a quantity of heat which ought to heat mercury approximately thirteen times less than water actually heat it more and considerably more? One might say that the [354] parts of mercury are more easily set in motion than those of water or that they better conserve the heat they have acquired. These may be good reasons and may play some role in the phenomenon, but I have a better explanation which apparently gives the real reason for the difference. When red-hot steel is quenched in cold water, one hears a certain noise, a kind of hissing known to everybody, which resembles the sound heard when water is thrown upon a firebrand. When steel is plunged into mercury, there is not the least hissing. What one hears when red-hot steel is plunged into water is the result of a boiling that takes place. This boiling is apparently caused by the considerable and sudden rarefaction of the air contained in the water. Whatever its cause, it is enough to know that the water boils around the steel which is quenched in it. These bubbles are spaces which the water does not occupy, and consequently there are from time to time empty spaces around the steel. It is true that they do not last long, but they recur frequently, so that the water must not be considered to be in continuous contact with the steel. It is not continuously in condition to receive all the heat the steel can give it. Part of this heat passes into the substance that forms these bubbles and is lost with them. Mercury, on the other hand, being more difficult to lift and containing less air, is always in intimate contact with the red-hot steel; it absorbs more heat and keeps the heat it has acquired.

Steel [355] quenched in mercury has always seemed to me to have a coarser grain than the same steel quenched in water at the same degree of heat. In order to obtain equally fine grain in steel quenched in mercury, it was necessary to quench it colder than when it was quenched in water. Mercury cools steel more rapidly, although it heats up itself. According to one of our previous observations, steel quenched in mercury, although quenched at the same degree of heat, will therefore be in the same condition as a hotter steel quenched into a colder liquid, because it is cooled more rapidly.

The artisans of many countries loudly boast about their water for quenching purposes. If there are any waters that are better than others, it looks very much as if they are better only because they are colder. If one kind of water could produce a greater effect than another on a steel that is quenched in it, this could be only through the sulfurs and salts which it might contain, and I am not convinced that there is reason to believe that any water contains enough sulfurs and salts to produce a greater effect than some other water. The following experiments will shed some light on this question. What I have said of ordinary water is very probably also true of dew, although it is acclaimed for quenching; and it is the dew of the month of May which is praised most highly.

In order to find out whether a great deal ought to be expected of waters that are naturally charged with certain salts, or whether [356] ordinary water could be made more potent by the addition of salts, I filled several pots with river water. These pots were quite alike; they were all turned on the same mold. I added to the water of each pot a different salt to be dissolved, and I even added more than the water could dissolve. Thus, the water of one pot contained sea salt, another glass salt, a third sal ammoniac, a fourth saltpeter, a fifth alum, and a sixth vitriol. In order to make an accurate comparison between the effects of these waters and of pure water, I also put pure water in a small pot like the ones containing the solutions. After all these preparations had been made, I simultaneously heated two steel wires and plunged one into the pot with ordinary water and the other into one of the pots containing water in which salt had been dissolved. For each new experiment I put fresh unsalted water into the pot for ordinary water. Steel quenched cherry-red into ordinary water or into water containing some salt always hardened to such an extent that it was impossible to judge by the file if it had acquired more hardness in the one medium than in the other. The file could not cut the steel quenched at this degree of heat.

In order to discover, therefore, whether water containing certain salts was able to produce a much greater effect on steel than pure water, I heated the steel in molten lead to different [357] degrees of heat below the color of cherry-red. I simultaneously quenched pieces of steel wire in pure water [and in one of the salt waters]. When the steel was not hot enough to acquire a considerable degree of hardness in ordinary water, to harden enough to resist the file, I found without exception that it had acquired no greater hardness in the water containing salt, which makes me inclined to believe that there is little to be accomplished by dissolving salts in water to increase the effect of quenching.

However, if somebody would like to carry these experiments through to the finish, they could still be performed on steels which are fractured lengthwise, as I have described it in the tenth memoir. This would show whether the salts caused changes in the different types of grain. If the hardness of each type of grain were then tested with stones [p. 191], the results would provide complete information on this subject, which may or may not be of much practical value. I said, however, that I did not intend to deal with quench-hardening in all its details. I only wished to give the most general concepts and some hints for their possible improvement.

[237]

When steel is quenched in cold water when it is extremely hot, hotter than cherry-red, its surface, after the steel has been withdrawn from the water, is white and clean; there is no dross, nothing blackish, on the surface. The steel is then called [358] well *descaled*. If a steel, after having been quenched at a lower degree of heat than another steel, emerges white from the quenching bath, we say that this steel *descales* easily. Steels descale much better in water containing salts than in ordinary water. Steel that does not descale is steel on which dross remains. This dross is composed of earthy substances mixed with fatty ones which derive from the charcoal and the iron itself. The fatty substances hold the earthy ones together and cause them to adhere to the steel. If steel is plunged into water in which salt is dissolved, the salt dissolves these fatty matters. It removes the spots, as the salt of soap removes spots from linen and fabric. This dross, this kind of stain, is not retained on steel or even on iron that is quenched extremely hot. After the heat of iron and the heat of steel have reached a certain point, anything fatty or greasy occurring on their surface is consumed as soon as it forms.

Steel quenched in vinegar descales perfectly. It has also seemed to me that it hardens more than in ordinary water and that it becomes more brittle. Verjuice produces an effect similar to that of vinegar.

Among the secrets mentioned in connection with the hardening of steel one almost always encounters the juice of radishes. I have quenched steel by pushing it into the radishes themselves. I have also squeezed juice out of radishes after grinding them up. [359] Steel quenched in this juice or in the radish itself did not seem to be hardened any more than steel quenched in vinegar. I am not even sure that it was hardened as much.

However, one liquid which has an unmistakable effect is aqua fortis. I have used it to quench steels in different conditions. I have sometimes used it to quench a steel heated to such a low degree that it hardly showed any shade of red even when viewed in the dark. If the steel had then been plunged into cold water, it would have emerged amply soft enough to be filed; but, when it was withdrawn from the aqua fortis, it was thoroughly quenched, and the file could not cut it. Such noticeable difference can be attributed only to the penetrating spirits of the aqua fortis. There is no doubt that they entered into the steel, and it is not astonishing that these active spirits can penetrate into steel, whereas a simple salt dissolved in water cannot accomplish anything. There is a great difference in activity. The steel itself would soon be completely macerated, dissolved, if it were left for a long time in this liquid. If it is left there only a moment, nothing happens but that it acquires great hardness. Even a very fine piece of steel would not be marred by this immersion. The result of this experiment indicates that the effects of the other kinds of spirits on the hardening of steel ought to be investigated.

I have investigated the effect of the spirit of sea salt. It hardened steel quenched at a degree of heat at which ordinary water would not have hardened it at all; but I doubt that it had as much effect as aqua fortis. Neither is this spirit as fast [360] in dissolving iron; it does not possess the same facility with which to penetrate into its parts.

Any substance that cools steel can be used as a quenching medium. Steel can be quenched in fatty or oily substances such as tallow, linseed oil, olive oil, spirits of wine, spirits of turpentine, resins, and others. It is easy to foresee, however, that these readily inflammable substances will soon attain a degree of heat approaching that of the steel which is being quenched without having greatly reduced the heat of the steel. Consequently, they will cool steel neither as much nor as rapidly as other liquids, including common water.

Nevertheless, there are instances which call for a method of quenching which does exactly what is accomplished by these media. Certain tools need be hard only to a certain degree. It is unnecessary that their hardness is such that they resist the file; what they need is body. The maker of mathematical instruments who must quench the ends of compasses heats them with a candle, the flame of which he repeatedly darts against one of the ends by a blowpipe. When this end has become colored, he thrusts it into the tallow of the candle itself, and this produces enough hardness. But the scythe is a much more important example of a case where this mild quenching is necessary. If a scythe were hardened to the same degree as an ax, a razor, or a knife, [361] it would, of course, cut the grass even better. But, with the amount of grass it has to mow down, it is impossible to prevent its cutting edge, however it may be quenched, from becoming dull very many times in a day. If it were hardened to the same degree as the other tools I just mentioned, the scythe-man would then be forced to have it sharpened several times a day. What a waste of time if he had to carry it to an edge-tool-maker every time. One of these artisans would have to be stationed in every field. The most ordinary appliances used by the arts are based on ingenious inventions to which we pay no attention. It was necessary to enable the mower to perform the work of the toolmaker. For that reason the idea was conceived —and nothing could have been better—to quench the scythe in such a way that the steel is left with enough body, with enough toughness, to be flattened by the hammer without breaking. Thanks to this invention, as soon as the edge of the scythe has become too thick and too blunt, the mower can place it upon a small anvil, which he always carries along with him, and can thin and flatten it by light hammer blows. Instead of having it ground on the large grindstone of the toolmaker, he only sharpens the edge with a stone which is hardly larger than the stones used for razors but which has a much coarser grain. It is true that the edge of the scythe is not as keen as those of tools quenched so that they have become more brittle; even the file can cut it. But the size [362] of the aggregate of which it is a part, the length of the handle to which it is fastened, and, finally, the swiftness with which the scythe is moved all work together, so that its edge can cut the grass, although it is not extremely hard.

I have tarried a little over this tool, but I do not intend to go into details concerning the different ways in which different artisans quench it. That belongs under the subject of toolmaking and would mean straying from my set path. A page would hardly be enough to enumerate all the ingredients which some artisans incorporate in the quenching medium used for this purpose. They make it up of most of the minerals and also preparations obtained from minerals, plants of a great number of different species, and especially plants with a strong odor. This is the theriac of toolmakers. I do not know if as much should be left out of the real theriac* as out of this one, but I know that there are artisans who use very many useless substances in quenching their scythes and some others that may be harmful. Fundamentally, the scythe should be quenched in tallow or in something equivalent. I am not even sure that its edge would not be given the necessary degree of hardness and toughness by quenching it in water that boils or has been heated to a certain degree. But, as I said before, this is the concern of a different art.

However, let me include a word about these fatty and oily substances. I have quenched steel in tallow, butter, wax, oil, [363] rosin, spirits of wine, and soap. In all these media steel is hardened less than in cold water. They are in the same category as boiling or hot water. For instance, if steel is quenched cherry-red into spirits of wine, the hardness it acquires is not enough to resist the file; and, when steel is quenched hotter into the same liquid, it emerges so hard that the file can make no impression upon it.

When the quenching medium is aqua vitae, steel will harden if quenched at a degree of heat at which it would not harden if it were quenched in spirits of wine. Aqua vitae hardens it almost as much as ordinary water; and the strongest aqua vitae actually contains a considerable amount of ordinary water, as shown by the interesting memoir of M. Geofroy, Jr., which was published in the *Memoirs* of the Academy of 1718, page 35. He therein describes the most precise methods of assaying aqua vitae and spirits of wine. He finds that good aqua vitae, either pure or commercial, after having been distilled, leaves half of its weight of pure phlegm. The part that has been distilled off

* The theriac was a complicated compound originally intended as an antidote to poisons but widely recommended as a specific against anything. An essential part of its ingredients were vipers, which had to be gathered at the right time and by the right people and compounded with other components with a great deal of essential ceremony. According to Galen, it had more than sixty-one ingredients. (For an interesting description and an illustration of the ceremony see M. T. Gnudi and J. P. Webster, *The Life and Times of Gaspari Tagliacozzi* [New York, 1950], pp. 67–79.)

would give spirits of wine if it were collected in a receiver. If this in turn is subjected to this assay, it yields very much more than half of its weight as phlegm. And the amount it yields is probably not nearly all it contains of phlegm.

We now shall consider how steel can be conditioned to become more responsive to quenching. According to what I [364] have said about the reason for the sudden hardening of steel and also for the change of iron into steel, it seems that the best thing to do would be to fill the interstices between the molecules of steel with more sulfurous and saline parts. In order to accomplish this, what could be better than to heat the steel surrounded by substances that can furnish these parts? This is the purpose of "box-quenching" [or pack-hardening]. I have spoken about this method of hardening on more than one previous occasion. It really is not a special practice of quenching steel, for the actual quenching of the steel is ordinarily done in cold water; but the method stipulates a special way of heating [or soaking] the steel before it is quenched. Instead of letting it become cherry-red by placing it directly on a bed of charcoal, the steel is inclosed in sheet-iron boxes the joints of which are well coated with clay, so that the flame cannot possibly find a way inside these boxes. The steel in the boxes is packed in suitable ingredients. It is then heated for an hour or more, and, the moment it is taken out of the box, it is plunged into water.

The basic materials used in pack-hardening, the principal substances with which one surrounds the pieces that are to be soaked before quenching according to this practice, are soots or charcoal. Ordinary soot is very frequently used. Each artisan has his own method of adding refinements to his way of pack-hardening and, following laudable custom, makes a mystery of them.

Nothing better [365] and more useful has ever been invented in connection with hardening than this practice. We have seen very many times that, as soon as the hardness of steel is increased, the steel becomes more brittle and its grain becomes coarser at the same time, which is a real disadvantage. By means of pack-hardening, steel can be made harder without becoming more brittle and without acquiring a coarser grain. The reason is that steel which is box-quenched or, to be more precise, which is quenched after it has been soaking in a box—the reason is, I said, that this steel acquires the same hardness when it is quenched cherry-red which without the soaking would require quenching at white heat. In this way one obtains hardness while retaining the body of the steel and the fineness of its grain.

But this pack-hardening is practiced not only on steel; it is also used to harden iron and to make it responsive to quenching. It is by means of pack-hardening that iron files are given almost the same hardness as steel files possess and that the locks and several other parts of firearms are hardened.

In order to get a clearer picture of the effects of this method of hardening, let us consider first what is accomplished when iron surrounded by soots and other substances is heated by exposing it to a fire of long duration. It is obvious that this treatment tends to convert the iron into steel. The experiments I have described in the memoirs [366] dealing with this conversion could leave no doubt about it. As a matter of fact, it was this soaking that helped me the most in discovering how this conversion is accomplished. When iron is withdrawn from the box in which it was inclosed, its outside layer has become steel. When it is then quenched in water it is, therefore, not astonishing that this outside layer acquires a hardness which it would not have acquired before. If this piece is broken, one sees all around it a band formed by grains which resemble those of quenched steel. But, if pack-hardening has led us to the art of converting iron into steel, this art in turn enables us to understand why this method of hardening is effective and to perfect it as much as possible.

When steel is soaked before being quenched from the box, the substances surrounding it will make of it, one might say, more of a steel; they will raise it to a higher degree of steel, will make of it a finer steel. It will then harden more when quenched at the same degree of heat, in accord with one of the rules given in this memoir. Steel being heated in the box is surrounded by substances that impregnate its surface with sulfurs and salts. The quantity of sulfurs by which it was naturally penetrated is thus increased; and, consequently, there are more sulfurs between its parts than if the fire had merely caused a portion of those present inside its parts to leave them. When this steel containing more [367] sulfurs and salts is quenched, it will have greater hardness than it would have had otherwise after quenching even though it is quenched at the same degree of heat.

The most remarkable thing in this connection is that, if the soaking that precedes the quench has not been of long duration, the sulfurs and salts will not have penetrated far; only the area near the surface will have been conditioned to harden better; the rest will then have as much body as if it had not been quenched to the same hardness.

Although the soaking of steel before quenching and the soaking practiced in converting iron into steel are fundamentally identical processes, there are, nevertheless, substances that are suitable for use in the one but not in the other. There are some substances that should be avoided in converting iron into steel and some that should be preferred in pack-hardening steel. Understanding these differences will at the same time show a way to obtain better results in hardening. After iron has been converted into steel, this steel must be heated several times; it must resist the hammer without splitting, without cracking, and its parts must be capable of being joined. In making steel, we must therefore be careful not to employ substances that render it too difficult to work; we also must avoid the use of substances which are too volatile, which would disappear in repeated heating, which would let the steel become too weak. It is different [368] with steels that are soaked in pack-hardening. They already are shaped into tools. It is a fact to remember that steel is never pack-hardened unless it has first been given the shape it is meant to keep. After such tools have been soaked, they are quenched, and there is no reason to worry whether they are difficult to hammer-forge; they no longer require forging. If their hardness stems from very volatile substances, it does not matter either; for they need not be put back in the fire.*

* The difference between the two classes of substances lies in the fact that the case-hardening operation then in use involved a partial nitriding from the nitrogenous materials present in the compounds. Steel nitrided throughout would be excessively brittle, but a thin case is not harmful and can be applied much quicker than a true carburized layer of the same hardness.

The substances we seek for use in pack-hardening are those capable of giving tools greater hardness and at the same time penetrating into them very fast. Whereas in converting iron into steel the sulfurous substances must reach the center in order to make perfect steel, in this instance it is desirable that the substances used do not penetrate beyond the surface layers. It is these surface layers that must become hard. In the subsequent layers we require body, a fact which leads to the following rules:

1. Those substances which are best suited to harden steel and penetrate it readily are best suited for pack-hardening.

2. The best pack-hardening practice is one in which the soaking takes the shortest time and requires only a gentle fire. If the degree of heat applied should color the surface only dark red, or blackish, or a little beyond that, the operation would be more perfect on that account; for the inside of the workpiece, which is always less hot, would then still have only the degree [369] of heat corresponding to black; and it follows that the sulfurous and saline substances, which enter only those areas to which they are carried by the fire, then would not be carried much beyond the surface.

3. Now, in order to combine short soaking and a gentle fire, we need materials that are especially capable of penetrating into iron. To make an intelligent appraisal of the efficacy of the substances that can be used in these soaking operations, in trying them out, we therefore must pay attention not only to the degree of hardness which different substances can convey upon iron or steel. (There are a number of substances capable of giving both iron and steel as much hardness as desired by quenching them from the box; and it would not be easy to distinguish among the different degrees of hardness produced by these different materials.) The important point is to find out which substances give iron the greatest hardness in the shortest time and at the lowest degree of heat. I say "iron," because it is much better suited than steel to demonstrate the effect of the soaking operation. As steel is always considerably hardened by quenching, the outcome of the experiment would be more difficult to evaluate.

In those I have performed to gain knowledge of pack-hardening, I therefore chose iron. The substances which, according to these experiments, yield the best results will also be the best for pack-hardening steel. I inclosed in different boxes pieces of iron of the same dimensions and the same quality, [370] surrounded by different substances. I shall describe some of the principal experiments I have performed, for they can serve as a guide to a practice that will, it seems to me, produce the desired results. But, if it should be considered to serve the purpose better, these experiments can be extended, and the subject would then only be more exhaustively studied.

1. I tried chimney soot by itself.

2. I also tried old leather burned to charcoal. Artisans who pride themselves to be expert at pack-hardening prefer it to soot; but it was difficult for me to notice any difference in favor of leather. If it has any advantage, it is so insignificant that it is easy to restore the advantage to soot and to give it an even greater advantage by adding one of the substances of which I shall speak. Furthermore, soot is easier to obtain, which is of some importance if a great quantity of iron is to be hardened.

3. I then tried soot moistened with urine. Most of the artisans who practice pack-hardening on files do not look any further. They prefer very old, very thick urine. The soot is moistened with the urine until it has become a paste, and the pieces of iron are packed in this paste. [In my experiments] the urine accelerated the effect of the soot; the iron was sooner in condition to be quenched.

4. I tried leather charcoal moistened with urine and compared its effect with that [371] of soot also moistened with urine. Again I failed to recognize in this experiment any advantage in favor of leather.

5. I mixed one part of flowers of sulfur with two parts of soot without adding urine. The sulfur seemed to arrest the effect of the soot. The iron did not harden, although soot moistened with urine had hardened it well in the same time.

6. In another experiment I mixed one part of sea salt which had been reduced to a powder with nothing but soot. Soot

moistened with urine did not come close to harden the iron as much in the same time; and it must always be kept in mind that the soaking time is here of principal interest.

7. In continuing to test the effect of salts, I stirred sea salt into soot moistened with urine.

8. Into another batch of soot moistened with urine I put the same amount by weight of powdered sal ammoniac.

9. I mixed glass salt with soot moistened with urine.

10. I mixed potash with soot moistened with urine.

The last four tests were made in the same furnace run; the iron packed in sal ammoniac became the hardest, although its location with regard to the fire was among the less favorable. The mixture to which sea salt had been added caused hardening, but less than the preceding one. The mixtures containing the other two salts [372] accomplished nothing. If the effect of soaking is accelerated by sea salt, it is thus accelerated still more by sal ammoniac. When I said that the other salts accomplished nothing, I did not mean to imply that they might not have had an effect later on. I was referring to their effect during the time that was sufficient for the sal ammoniac and the sea salt to be effective.

11. In another experiment I used tartar in place of the aforementioned salts.

12. In another vitriol.

The conclusion derived from all the experiments in which I used salts was that sal ammoniac and sea salt were in this instance far superior to the others and that sal ammoniac had the advantage over sea salt.

13. In my investigations concerning the conversion of iron into steel I had found one substance that made of iron a harder steel than any other steel obtained but also a more intractable one. This was burned pigeon dung reduced to charcoal. Its application seemed very promising to me, and I tried it several times. When used alone, it had as much effect as soot moistened with urine and mixed with half its weight of sea salt.

14. I therefore believed that, in order to combine speed and effectiveness in soaking, all that had to be done was to use this

dung moistened with urine and mixed with sal ammoniac or sea salt. Experiments showed that it hardened iron very fast, and I doubt if one could do any better.

15. Instead of soot I also used powdered mineral [373] coal mixed with sea salt. In this I was led again by my experiences in converting iron into steel. It hardened well, and I am not sure if it was not more effective than soot.

It now remains to discuss a heat treatment which is different from the one given steel products in order to increase their hardness as quenched—a treatment used, on the contrary, to soften them. When steel which has been quenched very hard is put back in the fire and is given a degree of heat similar to the one it had when it was plunged into water, it loses the hardness it has acquired, it becomes soft again, and it can be worked with the file. To heat it thus is called "annealing." But besides this degree of heat, besides the anneal that completely voids the effect of quenching, there are an infinite number of treatments at intermediate degrees of heat which will take only part of its hardness away from the steel and will restore part of its toughness. [This is called "tempering."]

As we cannot quench a steel tool at exactly the degree of heat desired, it may happen that, in trying to give it only just the necessary hardness, we give it too little. The general practice is to quench tools of fine steel into cold water after they have been heated to a color approximating cherry-red. Products for which this is appropriate are left with the resulting hardness; from those which ought not to have so much hardness but ought to have more body, some hardness is abstracted. More or less is [374] taken away from them, depending on the use to which they are to be put and on the quality of the steel of which they are made. Of two chisels of which one is meant to cut iron cold and the other to cut wood, more hardness will be taken away by tempering from the chisel that will only have to cut wood.

A thorough examination of everything concerning the different types of tempering, the way of adjusting them to different types of products and to products made of different steels, could, again, be made the subject of a rather long treatise. But again, as in the case of quenching, I shall confine my discussion to the most general concepts.

We know from the color of a steel whether it is hot enough to be quenched; likewise, we know from its color whether it is sufficiently softened, whether it has been tempered to the point desired. The piece that is to be tempered must be put on the charcoal in such a way that it is possible to observe the different colors it will take on in succession. Let us suppose that it has been put there; but let us also suppose that this workpiece, this arbitrary piece of steel, before being quenched has at least been cleaned by the file, so that its color is white, as white as clean iron and steel are; let us further suppose that the charcoal on which it has been placed is not burning brightly, so that it can heat the steel only slowly. If then we watch the changes that will occur on its surface, we shall first see the white color of the [375] steel become paler; it will assume a shade of the palest yellow; this shade will become stronger by degrees until the yellow finally becomes what the artisans call the color of gold, a color which nicely cleaned steel actually attains. As the steel continues to become hotter and hotter, the gold color will start to disappear; it will become mixed with a light tint of purple; at the end, everything that was golden will become purple. The purple will take on continuously darker shadings; it will become violet. The violet will then change into a beautiful deep blue; this blue will become imperceptibly diluted; it will become light blue and then the very lightest blue. At the end the last color we can still see will be the color of water, which is, so to say, the last degree of blue. No new color can be perceived between this one and the first shade of red, which increased heat will impart to the steel.

If steel, which is thus being colored, is heated uniformly over its entire extent, one of the colors or one of the shades of the colors I have just described will be observed all over the steel. But, if it is heated non-uniformly, the colors will be differently distributed like the degrees of heat. Suppose it is heated at one end and that the remainder of the piece is heated entirely by the heat of this end, which advances very gradually. Then we will soon observe on the steel the entire sequence of colors and of all [376] their shades. As the pale yellow, which will be the shade that is farthest away from the end, advances, there will be a change in each of the colors that precede it [*sic*].

When the steel has been well cleaned and certain precautions (which I need not explain here) have been taken in heating it, its colors are equal in beauty and vividness to the most brilliant colors encountered in paintings. Furthermore, we know that they are permanent if desired. When a spot that has acquired a certain color is not heated any further, it will keep this color. Everybody has seen violet or blue steel. Steel is given these colors to make the most beautiful products even more beautiful, and this is especially true of those that are made to look golden. The first time we see steel thus colored we are inclined to believe that the color has been applied with the brush; at least we cannot imagine that a light degree of heat has been enough to produce it.

By the way, these colors are not comparable to the different shades of red which a more violent heating conveys upon our metal. The latter penetrate the steel throughout. The steel is red inside, or rather its condition inside is such as to give us the impression that it is red, as on the outside. But the blue, the violet, the gold color of which I have just spoken are only on the surface of the steel. Whether the steel is cooled slowly or rapidly after it has been given one of these beautiful colors, its surface will always preserve this color; [377] but, if the very outside layer is removed with the file and the piece of steel is broken, nothing but its natural white color will be found under the outermost surface and all over the inside. The property of being thus colored by different degrees of heat is not restricted to steel; it shares it with iron; but iron does not acquire such beautiful and such vivid colors as steel and acquires them less easily.

In looking for the reason for these different colors which appear on the surface of our steel, we must again turn to the sulfurous parts of this metal. And, if we could not turn to them, we would have to look elsewhere for sulfurs that could produce this effect. A mild degree of heat causes the sulfurs to rise; it conducts them to the surface, and they give the surface different colors, depending on how many of them collect there.* But only a moderate heat can tint the surface of the steel through the sulfurs it conducts there, for, if the heat were greater, it would burn these inflammable substances; it would not let them linger at the surface.

It has been observed that steel which has been colored rusts less rapidly than steel which has remained white; but I have made no systematic investigation of this subject. However, people who are afraid that their firearms might rust give their barrels the color of water. It is well known that oil prevents the rusting of this metal; the thin layer of oily [378] or sulfurous substances that color it must therefore also protect it against rust, at least to a certain extent.

The spots called "roses," which are found inside of steel, owe their origin to the same substances, which upon stronger heating, and in steel containing more of these materials, have been driven toward the center of the bar, in the same way as they are driven to the surface in tempering. Or we may assume that the heat, which has set these sulfurs in motion, has burned those closest to the surface; but, because it has less effect upon the ones farther inside, they are still left there.

We should have no doubt, by the way, that the sulfurous substances that color our steel originate in the steel itself, that they do not come from the charcoal on which it is heated—that it is not smoke that attaches itself to its surface. A fact I must relate before I return to the subject of tempering removes all uncertainty. If a steel tool has been heated and quenched in water and is then withdrawn at once, it is still hot, especially inside. The

* Robert Hooke had given almost exactly this explanation in his *Micrographia* (1665 ed.): "The action of the heat does by degrees loosen the parts of the Steel that were before stretched or set atilt as it were, and stayed open by each other, whereby they become relaxed and set at liberty, whence some of the more brittle interjacent parts are thrust out and melted into a thin skin on the surface of the Steel, which from no color increases to a deep Purple, and so onward by these *gradations* or consecutions, *White, Yellow, Orange, Minium, Scarlet, Purple, Blew, Watchet,* &c. and the parts wherein are more conveniently, and proportionately mixt" (p. 52).

water only has had time to cool its surface thoroughly. When it comes out of the water, the heat which its interior still holds spreads out gradually until its surface becomes heated; when it has been heated to a certain degree, it appears pale yellow, then golden, violet, and blue. In other words, when steel is quickly withdrawn from the water, it runs through the whole scale of colors which it could have been given by [379] heating it on charcoal. The colors this steel takes in the air can therefore come only from matters that are part of its own substance.

But let us go back to tempering, about which I could say nothing very definite until we had become familiar with the succession of different colors taken on by steel as it is heated. It is evident that tempering sets the sulfurs of steel in motion, and it is natural to conclude therefrom that, as this tempering brings some of them to the surface of the steel, it puts others in condition to be reabsorbed by the metal. The thing that is certain and which is the basis of the expected effect of tempering is that it alters the grain. Assume that a steel has been quenched at a degree of heat which has given it a [coarse] white grain or a mixed grain; assume that this piece of steel has been broken in two, that one of the pieces has been put aside, and that the other one has been tempered until it has become light blue or water-colored. After it has cooled, it shall be broken. On comparing its fracture with that of the piece that was put aside, it will be found that the fracture of the tempered piece has a finer grain. It will be noticed even more clearly that the grain of the latter is duller than that of the other fracture. Thus, the steel has been put back in a state resembling that in which it would have been if it had been quenched less hot—that is, at the degree of heat which results in the kind of grain it has after tempering.

There are two different ways of tempering a tool just as I have shown that there are two ways of [380] giving color to steel. The first is to quench the tool and let it get quite cold, or almost so, in the water in which it has been quenched. It is then placed on burning charcoal and there heated to the proper degree. The second is to withdraw the steel from the water immediately after it has been plunged into it. The colors are then allowed to appear on its surface; it is, so to say, allowed to temper itself.

When its surface has reached the shade of color that is right for tempering, the tool is quenched a second time and left in the water until it is quite cold. For instance, if the cutting edge of a tool is supposed to stay very hard, one will let it become golden and then quench it immediately, because there is reason to fear that it might be tempered too much, soften too much, if its color were allowed to reach violet. Another tool, in which more body is desired, will be allowed to become blue, when it will be quenched to prevent it from reaching the color of water. There are others which will be allowed to take any color they can reach in this way without quenching them a second time; this is done when there is no reason to fear that they may become softened too much by the heat the quench has left them.

There is a limit, however, beyond which tempering must not be carried, or it would deprive the steel of all the hardness it was given by the quench. To reach this limit, it is not necessary to heat the steel to anything like the degree of heat it had when it was quenched. [381] Steel that has been quenched white or almost white will be completely softened if it is allowed to take on the first shades of red after it has been put back in the fire. Since the hardening of steel depends on sulfurs that are frozen between its molecules, the reason for this is easy to understand. Steel readily absorbs sulfurs and retains those it has absorbed. As soon as the heat is strong enough to melt those that have frozen between its molecules, they will re-enter the molecules, a reaction which does not require that the steel become as hot as it was when they were driven out of the molecules. The natural tendency of steel is to favor their entry and to oppose their departure.

When a tool is tempered at the forge, it is not always easy to observe the color it has reached. It is rarely light enough around the forge, and the surface of the tool is often scaled, which prevents the colors from showing up distinctly. In order to judge, therefore, if a tool has been sufficiently tempered, one must under such circumstances (which are the usual ones) employ certain expedients. There are tools that are rubbed with oil before they are tempered; when the oil burns, it is an indication that the steel has been heated long enough. Other tools are rubbed with a piece of dry wood after they have been heated for a little while, and it is possible to judge from the way in which the wood chars if the tool has been tempered too much or too little. But these are precisely such details as I intended not to discuss, as they are the concern of different arts.

We have [382] come far, and much time has passed, since we started to discuss the art of converting wrought iron into steel. After I had explained everything that is directly concerned with it, I believed I ought to explain some of its ramifications. It is hoped that I have not included too much; there still is a great deal that could be added.

PART II

The Art of Making Cast
Iron Malleable

[385]

OR

*The Art of Producing Cast-Iron
Work with the Finish
of Wrought Iron*

*The First Memoir, on the Different Kinds of Cast
Iron and Their Properties; on the Method of
Increasing the Purity of These Irons; and on
the Reason Why Many Articles Which
Can Be Made of Wrought Iron Are
Not Being Made of Cast Iron*

THE MOST obvious characteristic that distinguishes metals from minerals and rocks is that the metals can be drawn out under the hammer—that they are malleable. However, although iron has this property, although it has acquired, one might say, the principal characteristic of the metals, [386] it differs from other metals in that it cannot be melted by the intensity of the fire of our furnaces. All wrought iron, all iron in the form of bars, can at most be reduced to a kind of paste soft enough to fall in drops. This is the material we call iron made melting-hot. However, it then cannot be made to become liquid like lead, tin, copper, gold, and silver. We do succeed in melting it but only by the addition of fluxes which, in a way, put it back again in its original state, in the state in which it was immediately after we obtained it from the ore. By being thus re-melted, it loses its malleability and toughness; it once more becomes almost as hard and as brittle as it was before refining. In addition, most of the fluxes make it very spongy.

To fashion articles out of iron that was forged into bars, we are therefore forced to work this metal with hammer, file, chisel, and graver—or with other similar tools; and, if we except the hammer, the fashioning by these tools is almost always done cold. However, as iron is then quite hard, pieces that have elaborate and beautiful ornaments necessarily will take considerable time. There is a key of this kind which kept a skilful artisan occupied for several months. When the workpieces are big, the difficulty increases for another reason. We start by forging a mass of iron made up of several bars. From this, [387] the shape for which we have a design or model can be created as from a block of marble. This mass, being made of different bars which are welded upon each other, is not always of such uniform texture, of such uniform solidity, as a block of marble with which I just compared it. Cracks or fissures or badly joined spots often remain in the interior, and these defective spots are sometimes not discovered until after a lot of metal has been removed with the chisel. It is only too common that such defects make all the preceding work in vain; one is forced to abandon the piece and to forge a new one, running the same risk once more. Our artisans call this "preparing the bloom," and it sometimes happens to them that they have to make two or three of these bad blooms before they succeed in obtaining a mass of iron that is worthy of being employed. But the price of articles of this kind reflects even better the time they require. In Paris those interested in well-executed ironwork are familiar with the striker or, to use the term of the locksmith, with the knocker at the carriage entrance of the Hôtel de la Ferté, rue de Richelieu. It cost 700 *livres* in a year in which everything had its ordinary value. More than this is sometimes paid for well-chased sword hilts, which are eulogistically called steel hilts, although they are usually only simple iron. But in this case it is not the material that makes the article expensive. It is true that such exorbitantly priced pieces of ironwork are rare, and it would indeed be [388] regrettable if there were more than a limited number in existence. These are non-essential products, and they consume too much time which could be better employed. But it would be nice if we could make them at a fair price, and it would have its advantages, especially in connection with the decorative features of large buildings and private homes, if beautiful pieces of this metal could be cheaply made. Ordinarily, railings for balconies, fences, grilled doors, and the rails of staircases are only mediocre work. Nothing is used for this purpose that is well filed, carefully worked, and polished. Thus, if we find such workmanship unacceptable, we are forced to give up the use of iron. Copper is used instead, which, although more expensive, sells at a much lower price after it has been fabricated. The only items of any size that are made of iron are bars or rods, which have been rolled or twisted, and at most some ornaments made of embossed sheet. These always take a long time to finish, and they are rarely good enough under close inspection. It is difficult to name many large pieces of solid iron, here in the Kingdom, which are well executed, such as the famous doors of the Château de Maison near Poissy. These are magnificent; however, hardly anybody but a sovereign, or those who administer his finances, can afford to have something like them made. It is reliably said that these doors, which consist of only three panels, once cost 69,000 *écus*. At how much would they sell today? Nowadays one does not dare undertake [389] large and beautiful work of wrought iron because of the excessive amounts it would cost.

The price of articles made of copper alloys, or even of gold or silver, has been considerably reduced by the ease with which they can be cast in molds and dressed after they have been removed from the molds. Without this possibility we would be without our superb statues, our famous pieces of bronze, and an infinity of more ordinary but more necessary articles made of brass. It is true that iron, before having attained the state of being wrought iron, iron as it is obtained from the ore—in short, the iron called "cast iron"—is cast in molds. We owe to this method of casting a number of products which are, however, of no great beauty and whose value is only proportional to their weight—such as chimney backs, stoves, pots, iron kettles, flower vases, pipes to conduct water, cannon, etc. But nothing of any real value is made of this material, and the uses to which it can be put are very limited. However, I dare give the promise that within a short while we shall make of this same cast iron articles as beautiful, as finished, as if they were wrought iron or even steel, and that this will require such small investment that there will be no hesitation in starting the enterprise. But before I reveal this secret and before I even indicate the extent of the usefulness which this development will have for a large number of the arts, it seems advisable to give some information on the different kinds [390] of cast iron and of their properties and to explain the difficulties that have, in the past, prevented the production of the articles for which without any doubt cast iron will be used in the future.

It is known, and my preceding memoirs should have made it additionally clear, that the material that flows out of the furnace immediately after iron ore has been smelted is what we call "pig iron" and that this is a non-malleable iron. It is characterized by being hard and brittle. When this material has been cast into a final product, it is usually called "cast iron." Cannon made of it are called "iron cannon" or "cast-iron cannon"; pipes that conduct water are "iron pipes" or "cast-iron pipes." It no longer retains the name of "pig iron" unless it has been cast into pigs or into some other shape which it is not intended to keep. I, too, shall call it "pig iron" only before it has been cast into a mold.*

In general, cast irons can be and are divided into two classes according to the color observed in their fracture. One class consists of white irons (Pl. 11, Figs. 1–4) and the other of gray irons (Figs. 5, 7). Sometimes, a difference in the ore plays a part in causing this difference in color; more often, it is caused by the way in which the furnace has been heated and charged.

When cast irons are divided into white irons and gray irons, we are using only two of the terms which describe the different colors they can have. Some of the gray irons can be almost [391] black, between the white and the gray irons there are shades of every possible variety, and the white irons can have many different shades of white. There is one kind that could constitute a separate class. In Champagne it is called "speckled" [or *mottled*] iron. It is white but has gray or blackish spots, which resemble in some way the speckles of trout (Fig. 6).

White irons are purer than gray irons—they contain more iron. This has been explained before, but I shall give additional proof for this statement, which is that in the forge more wrought iron can be made from a given weight of white iron than from the same weight of gray iron. There is more foreign

* This has not been strictly adhered to in the translation, since "cast iron" is the more generic term in present usage.

matter in gray iron and, perhaps, particularly more earthy matter, more vitrified matter, more of what is called "slag"* in the furnaces in which iron ore is smelted.

The fracture of white iron seems of a compact texture; no grains are evident. On careful inspection it would seem to be made up of platelets which are, however, very closely pressed together, which leave no spaces between them as the platelets of wrought iron do. The fractures of white irons sometimes show radiations—that is, we observe something resembling radii directed approximately toward the center (Figs. 3, 4). This is similar to what is seen in certain reguli of antimony,† but here the radii are not so pronounced. It will be observed, [392] however, and elsewhere it will be necessary to remember this remark, that the white of the whitest cast irons is not the same as that of the wrought irons with platelets or as that of steel quenched melting-hot; the white of the latter is brilliant, but this is a dull white. The white of cast iron compared to the brilliant white of certain wrought irons is as the white of matte silver compared to the white of burnished silver. The fracture of gray irons is more spongy than that of white irons; it comes closer to the fracture of quenched steel. It often is granular, but the grains are big, not well-rounded, and not well-detached from each other. Some of them, and these frequently are the ones that belong neither to the very gray nor to the very white kind, have a band (extending from the skin that envelopes them) which is composed of grains very similar in color and shape to those of quenched steel. These irons are rather favored for conversion into steel.

If both classes of cast iron are examined under the microscope,

* This is an interesting paragraph. The difference is now known to be due to silicon content, which ranges from 2 per cent or more in a gray iron to as little as 0.5 per cent in a white iron. The total carbon content is slightly less in a white iron, but the amount in the form of graphite greatly less, a fact which is responsible for the change in appearance of the fracture. On making wrought iron, the silicon would, of course, appear as slag, as Réaumur observed. Somewhat later (p. 268) Réaumur remarks that the loss in weight amounts to about one-fourteenth—considerably more than would be due to silicon and carbon alone.

† Réaumur discussed and illustrated the structure of antimony at some length in his paper in *Mém. Acad. Sci.*, 1724, pp. 307–16.

the very white irons will always show a compact texture. There may be some interspersed flat platelets, which are, however, much smaller than those of steel. They cannot be seen through the same lens that brings out those of which the grains of a steel are composed which has been quenched at a low degree of heat. Gray irons when viewed under the microscope seem to have such a spongy texture that everything seems to be a mass of some kind of crystallization (Fig. 5) or, if you wish, a thicket, some sort [393] of chemical vegetation made up of an infinite number of interlaced branches (Fig. 8) but each composed of little platelets arranged one on top of another (Fig. 9). If one places under the focus of the microscope grains of both kinds as small as the grains of an extremely fine sand, they appear more transparent than the most crystalline sand.* Their transparence, and especially the vividness of their color, resembles more closely the transparence and brilliance of the diamond. In spite of the vividness of the color which the grains of the different cast irons thus have, the color of the gray irons can be distinguished from that of the white ones. The gray ones are more like polished steel and the white ones like polished silver.

But a more important statement about cast irons, and one which concerns most closely the use to which we presently want to put them, is that we may accept as a rule, to which I know no exception, that they are the harder the whiter they are. When they are very white, there is no file or chisel that can bite into them, whereas there are gray irons, and particularly those that are extremely brown bordering on black (Fig. 7), which yield to the file. I have found some that can be filed quite well, and in general I have found them increasingly easy to file as their color becomes darker.

Thus, almost all the iron-smelting furnaces from which cast iron is tapped into molds (to make chimney backs, pots, [394] kettles, or cannon), all these furnaces produce only gray iron, either because the ores that are being smelted naturally yield this kind of iron or because the irons are made that way by the process employed in smelting the ores. It is the general custom

* Réaumur must be confusing specular reflection from the metal surface with internal reflections in the sand or diamond.

[262]

never to pour into molds the white irons of the tall blast furnaces. The reason is not that they do not satisfactorily take the
desired shape. But articles made of cast iron, even if they are
intended to be left quite rough, usually must be worked over a
little after they have been removed from the mold. It is at least
necessary to knock off the casting gates; and as the artisans do
not always succeed in breaking them off sufficiently close, the
worst unevenness must be removed; the castings must be
dressed. The file or rasp is passed over most kettles; cannon must
be bored smooth; and, if these products were made of white
iron, one would work on them with the tools without accom-
plishing anything.

But, although I have said that there are gray irons that can
be worked quite passably with the file, it should not be believed
that any of these irons are suitable for the production of articles
which must be carefully finished with the file or must be
scraped and polished. The file cuts into them; but it would be
almost impossible to dress them with the chisel or graver.
These tools would bite into cast iron; the trouble is that they
would often bite into it more than desired. Iron, brass, and any
other metal which is scraped, which is dressed, must cut like
wood, or even more cleanly. In cutting metals, as in cutting
wood, [395] the chips lifted must be exactly only what the tool
finds in its path. Our gray irons, however, do not yield to the
tool in this way; they yield as the parts of a piece of sandstone
would yield; they spall. The chisel does not cut off slices; it
removes lumps. It does not cut through the grain; it breaks off
pieces composed of several grains. It would be useless, therefore,
to try to make something neatly finished out of gray iron.

The file might be a little more successful than the chisel, but
that is not enough. If there were areas that could be worked
with the file, there would be others to which the file could do
nothing. There is a non-uniformity in hardness, because white
iron is sometimes intermixed with gray iron. Furthermore, even
if we succeeded in scraping, filing, and polishing an article
made of gray iron, it would never be as white nor as shining as
good wrought iron. The color of such articles would always be
too dark and too dull.

Finally, any cast-iron article made of gray iron as it comes out of the furnace would always have the great fault of cast iron of being excessively brittle, of not being able to sustain the blows of the hammer, either cold or hot, although there is an infinite number of circumstances where that is required, as when different pieces are fitted together and attached to each other.

In order to produce cast-iron articles that have the whiteness and brilliance of the beautiful work made of wrought [396] iron, it is therefore necessary to make them of white iron. It fills the molds perfectly. Some interested persons have had it cast for the purpose of making medals, the lids of snuffboxes, and other delicate pieces. And when these pieces are skilfully molded and cast, they sometimes come out of the molds so clean and reproduce even the finest designs so well that there is no need to work them over. Such results will be possible if the molds for these small pieces are made with as much care as those in which glass is given so exactly the impressions on engraved gem stones. But it would be useless to attempt something like that on a large scale; it would result in failure. Even if a large piece came out of the mold quite perfect, its gates would still have to be removed, it would have to be dressed, and it would also have to be made less brittle. However, we know at least that white iron casts very well, although it is not usually used for casting.

It is easy to obtain white iron, and iron as white as we wish it to be. It is good to know this and on what it depends, for it is this iron that we shall use from now on. There are some irons which are so white that it is no exaggeration to say that the color of their fracture is hardly inferior to that of silver. Gray irons, and even the grayest ones, can be changed into this beautiful iron; and this does not require much skill. White iron is cast iron which is naturally more highly refined, which (as I said before) naturally contains [397] more metallic parts and fewer foreign parts; and we have also seen elsewhere in passing that in general all that is necessary to refine cast iron is to remelt it. The expressions "to refine iron" and "to make it whiter" can therefore be considered to be synonymous. The more often it is melted, the more highly refined it becomes. Remelting consequently can change the grayest irons and even the black ones into white irons, if desired. Iron that is white when it comes from the furnace into which the ore has been charged thus becomes more so, and becomes sufficiently so, when it is melted a second time. Irons that are only gray, not blackish, are also changed into sufficiently white irons by a second melting; but black irons will have to be remelted more than once.

What is accomplished by repeated melting can also be done by keeping the remelted iron molten, or liquid, for a longer time and by removing from time to time all the slag that floats on top. But iron that is to be refined must always become completely molten; it must be given the highest degree of fluidity it can possibly attain.

The firing of all ore-smelting furnaces must be interrupted each year for some time in order to make repairs. The first time after the fire has been relighted, after the first charge has been smelted, nothing but gray or brown iron is obtained from the same ores which thereafter [398] will give white iron. The reason seems to be that, when the ore is smelted the first time, the furnace has not yet acquired the degree of heat which it will reach later. This alone might be sufficient reason; but a second factor contributes to this, the examination of which would, however, lead too far. I mean that before the ore is smelted a larger quantity of charcoal, relative to the quantity of ore, is charged into the furnace [in this case]. And it is one of the principles recognized by the smelters of ore that, the more charcoal is charged relative to the same amount of ore, the grayer will be the iron.

Nothing, however, contributes more to refining cast iron, to making it white, than casting it after it has been smelted and, especially, casting it very thin. I became convinced of this after observing very many times a fact that at first seemed strange to me. When I had gray irons remelted and cast into molds where they had to assume certain shapes, and some accident prevented a piece from coming out right in the mold, it occurred to me to break this piece, and I then made the observation I wish to relate: In the same piece I found iron of different colors. At some places it was almost as gray as when it was charged into the furnace, and at others it was very white. But the important phenomenon I observed was that the places where it was gray were generally the thickest sections. If we break the gates of a moderately [399] refined iron, in which some gray iron has been left (Fig. 10), the rims and especially the areas where the gates are the least thick will be white. (We call "gates" the material that has filled the channels through which the material passed that has filled the molds.) I have often seen that all the gates were white, the surface and everything close to it was also white, and so were all the leaves and other thin ornaments; but everything that was thicker was gray. Finally, it seemed undeniable that iron cast into thin shapes always became white. However, it sometimes happens that of corresponding locations in a casting, although they are sections of equal thickness, some will be white and others gray—that the white iron has collected on one side, for instance, and the gray iron on the other (Fig. 11).

In order to explain this fact and to prove at the same time that, when iron is made whiter, it is refined, I shall describe a process which I mentioned in the ninth memoir of *The Art of Converting Wrought Iron into Steel*. In refining pig iron that is to be converted into steel, the practice used in some provinces of the Kingdom, as for instance Nivernais, is to melt a certain quantity of iron, say, 200 or 300 pounds. When the iron is molten, the bottom of the furnace is tapped; the iron is made to flow out, and it is roughly cast on the ground itself, where it forms a cake of irregular shape, $1\frac{1}{2}$ or 2 inches thick. When this iron has cooled, it is found to be covered with a layer of foreign matter, which can easily be separated [400] from it. The cake of iron is covered by a thinner cake of blackish, vitrified matter. This blackish matter is some kind of scoria called "slag"; it is a vitrified earth mixed with some ferruginous parts. Glass is lighter than iron. When the molten iron was tapped, the glass rose to its surface from all sides—or at least that which could rise before the mass had cooled. The iron, after having been purged of this vitrified earthy part, is purer and whiter. If, instead of being cast into a thin cake, this iron is tapped into a vessel when it issues from the furnace, an equally large amount of vitrified matter cannot be expected to separate therefrom.

This matter is neither light nor fluid enough to rise quickly. The mass of iron in the vessel will rarely be covered by a layer of slag that is thicker than the thin cake, or at least it will never be thick enough to compensate for the larger area of the other one.

The application of this fact and of this argument to our iron made into a casting is so natural that it is unnecessary to argue further why the gates, as well as everything that is near the surface and everything that is thin, are white, whereas the thick sections stay gray. It is clear why any iron cast thin becomes more refined, becomes whiter, than when it is cast thick. However, it should not be thought that, to verify this explanation completely [401], a layer of vitrified matter must be found in the molds. If the layer covering a piece of the thickness of several inches amounts to only a few lines, the layer covering a piece that is only several lines thick will amount to only some fractions of a line. It will be hardly enough to wet the grains of sand or clay of which the mold is made and to fill their interstices. It may also be that there are certain parts, more volatile than the earthy matter, which disengage themselves from the thin iron and from the entire surface of the iron; for instance, some sulfurs and salts may issue therefrom either because they leave the metal entirely or because some of them pass from the metallic parts into the spaces left between them [cf. Part I, Mem. 7].

However, white iron and gray iron are sometimes found irregularly mixed in the same piece, and this will generally happen when the entire material was not very uniformly and very thoroughly melted. Everything that has been melted to a certain degree will be white, while the remainder will stay gray. Iron that is still gray can be incompletely mixed with white iron by the movement to which the crucible is subjected, by the bubbling of the more thoroughly molten material, and by several other similar causes.

Finally, the longer the iron is held liquid, the better will the slag, the purely earthy matter, rise to the surface. The iron is given an additional opportunity to be purged of it if the slag is removed as soon as it has come to the top. If this step [402] is taken, the iron will become as white as one could wish it to be.

Furthermore, if in order to refine gray iron, it is melted in a crucible as will be explained in the following memoir, it will be found that it does not lose much of its weight by changing from gray or brown to white. I once weighed out 9 pounds of very brown iron and had it melted in a crucible and poured into a mold. It became very white. After having weighed it in this second condition, I found a decrease of less than 10 ounces, which is not even one-fourteenth of its original weight. Even this one-fourteenth must not be considered to be solely due to the earthy matter or other foreign matters, for many particles of iron remain mixed with the slag that is removed.

It is, then, sufficiently clear that white irons are more completely refined than gray irons, and in a general way it is also clear what is involved in making irons as white as we want them to be. This is one of the requisites in our attempt to perfect the art, and it was necessary to discuss it. But it does not constitute the difficulty that has actually held back the art, which consists in managing somehow that this iron after it has been cast into a mold, that iron castings, can be worked, filed, scraped, dressed, etc. In a word, the problem is to make white iron tractable, to eliminate some of its hardness, its rigidity—to achieve its softening. The art of producing well-finished iron castings is, therefore, precisely nothing but the art of softening cast iron.

Two ways [403] of softening cast iron are conceivable—either to soften the iron while it is in the molten state, to change it so that the articles produced from it can be dressed, or to cast highly refined iron, mold it into articles that will have all the hardness and rigidity natural to this iron, and thereafter soften it and make it tractable. It makes no difference in which of the two conditions the iron is made softer, provided that it becomes suitable for our purpose. In a word, it was the secret of how to soften it in this respect that we did not possess.

If we believe the stories told by our artisans, this is a secret that was lost and found several times. They claim that everything made of iron that is really great and amazing, such as the fixtures on the doors of Notre-Dame, is actually cast iron. A more reliable claim, and one that is rather recent, is that one individual in France has had something that came very close to the real secret of softening cast iron. Approximately twenty years ago he even undertook to start an enterprise at Cosne and another one at Paris, in the suburb of Saint Marceau. He founded a company which was to furnish the funds and which, as a matter of fact, according to what I have heard, made considerable progress. The company had some beautiful patterns made which were then cast in iron. The man had several of the iron castings softened; but the enterprise failed, and the man himself [404] disappeared, and no one knows what has become of him.* He apparently had started too precipitately, before

* In the 1762 edition Réaumur states that the factory at Cosne which was engaged in softening iron belonged to Le Sieur d'Haudimont, who had both the secret and the funds to develop it. A legal process served on him by his associates stopped the work, and d'Haudimont died before it was settled, the establishment ceasing with him. A son of d'Haudimont came to see Réaumur, bringing architectural castings made by the method, but he was unable to give information other than that the process consisted of covering the castings with a certain compound and exposing them to fire. Réaumur thought he might have been extremely polite and have wished Réaumur to have the pleasure of rediscovering the secret! Later in the same edition it is said that iron cannons had been annealed to lessen their hardness in both Normandy and in Dauphiné. Réaumur believed, however, that the heat treatment there used was more like the tempering of steel and was quite inadequate to produce the more basic changes of his method. The possible anticipation of the invention in England by Prince Rupert about 1670 is suggested by A. R. Hall (*Ballistics in the Seventeenth Century* [Cambridge, 1952]). All that is known is that the Prince used a glasshouse for the annealing, and it is somewhat unlikely that his castings were of white iron to begin with.

The annealing of cast iron has been practiced in Japan for several centuries with precisely the same aim as that which motivated Réaumur, the making of a material with a surface that would lend itself to intricate surface treatment in the same way as wrought iron. J. J. Rein (*The Industries of Japan* [London, 1889]) says: "It is a peculiar decarburizing process, by which the surface of the kettle or pot receives a structure like to that of soft iron or steel, and then can be treated in the same way as in the *zogan* work on forged iron." *Zogan* involves fine chiseling and inlaying with gold and other soft decorative metals. The pots or vases were heated by being surrounded with charcoal in simple cylindrical furnaces. The charcoal was ignited and allowed to burn out. The operation was repeated as many as ten times, until a test with a file showed that the proper surface had been obtained. It is unlikely, but not impossible, that Réaumur had heard of the oriental process.

being sure enough of his secret, before having developed it to the necessary degree of perfection. I have seen articles produced by this foundry which were passably softened; but men who are familiar with this enterprise have assured me that chance played too great a part in the results obtained. Sometimes, after much wood had been burned, it was found that the castings were just as hard as they had been at the start. More often only parts of them had become softened; there remained hard, intractable spots, which made it necessary to discard the rest. Often, finally, the castings came out of the furnace disfigured by scale, which came loose. I have encountered all these difficulties in my own work. They are no less capable than the basis of the secret itself to stop those who are not guided by principles.

Even though this secret knowledge was imperfect, I have long regretted its loss. The man has taken it with him. My plan to describe all the arts working with iron, and the wish I heard so often expressed to possess this secret, further convinced me of the importance it must have. It means progress when we learn that what we are trying to do is not absolutely impossible. I therefore searched for this secret as one of the items that I believed ought to be of foremost usefulness. I hope that we [405] shall derive from it the profit I expect, that soon we shall no longer have to fear the possibility of losing it again, and that an effort will be made to perfect it at the same time as we try to use it.

The method of softening cast iron which I wish to make known today is the method of softening it after it has been cast into the shape which it is meant to keep. I have made many attempts to soften it while it was still molten, and elsewhere I may describe some of them. They seem to indicate that this method is not as promising by far as the other method; as a matter of fact, they give the impression that not much can be expected therefrom. However, why should we worry about softening cast iron in two different conditions as long as we know one method that is very easy and very cheap.

The Second Memoir, Dealing with the Different [408]
Methods of Melting Cast Iron and with the
Special Precautions That Must Be Observed
in Pouring the Molten Iron into
Molds and in Removing the
Castings from the Molds

THE ART OF producing iron castings which are as well finished as wrought-iron work is requires that the metal be first melted and case into molds. Afterward it is necessary to soften the castings that have been removed from the molds; in other words, they must be put in a condition in which they can be worked with tools, in which they are tractable. It then remains to dress them, which is the task of the scrapers, who will do this work on iron as they do it on brass, gold, and silver, provided their tools can bite into this metal as they bite into the others. Here we are only concerned with the softening of cast iron; there are enough artisans who know how to accomplish the rest. We can, therefore, also dispense with going into details concerning the art of casting iron into molds. Treating this subject would make it necessary to describe in its entirety the art of the foundryman, which is a large enough field by itself to require a long treatise. If nothing were to be [409] omitted, I should have to explain how patterns are made and what materials are used for them; how molds are made of clay, sand, or wax; why certain castings must be molded in sand and others in clay, and why still others require wax; how the different molds must be dried; the different methods of molding pieces of different shape, and how cores are made; how parts that have not come out right are repaired. Finally, I should arrive at the different methods of melting the iron and at the special attention this metal requires if it is to be cast into a mold. It is only this part of the art of the foundryman with which I shall deal at present, so that those who wish to have cast-iron ware made will know how to go about it, what they will be able to do themselves, and to whom they must turn for the rest.

All the methods of melting iron can be reduced to two general processes—melting it in crucibles, where it is made liquid solely by the heat that passes through the crucible walls, and melting it by exposing it to the direct action of the fire, that is, by surrounding it by flame and coals. There are, however, several ways of making this metal liquid either when it is inclosed in a crucible [410] or when it is placed directly among burning coals.

The common brass founders, those whom I have mentioned several times before, and whose furnace I had illustrated on Plate 2, melt iron as they melt brass, in similar crucibles and in the same furnace (Pl. 12, *c*). The iron stays in the furnace a little longer before it becomes liquid, but the difference in time it not considerable enough to make the process more expensive. The iron melts faster when it is broken into smaller pieces. But it is possible to melt very big pieces in this furnace, and one can use crucibles holding up to 30 or 40 pounds of molten metal.

The ordinary furnace of these founders does not occupy much space, but it is built to be stationary. Smaller ones can be made, or even furnaces of the same size, which are easily movable and which will prove convenient on many occasions. I actually have one of this kind (*f A*) at my home in the country. A few times I have had it placed in the middle of the gardens. Whereas the ordinary furnace is made of a great number of bricks placed one upon another, this one is built of only four or five pieces, which when assembled make up the unit (*D* to *I*). Imagine the ordinary furnace cut at different levels—that is, divided by parallel planes into several sections. Each one of the "pieces" I mentioned is one of these sections; but the section is not [411] assembled of many bricks; it is made of crucible clay, and it does not take much work to make it. All that is necessary is to mold out of clay a square block (*L*) of suitable thickness, whose height on the outside will depend on the size which the furnace shall have. A square opening, of a cross-section as required by the inside of the furnace, is subsequently scooped out of the inside of this piece of clay. Several similar pieces placed one upon another make up the entire furnace. Only one of the pieces will be different from the others—the one which serves as the base, which forms the ashpit (*E*). This piece is provided with a flange all around, except at the corners. This flange is meant to support the iron plate on which the crucible will stand. In order to use this furnace, one needs a bent pipe, which will receive the wind from the bellows of a forge and usually conducts it under the iron plate of this furnace. If, in addition to the movable furnace, a movable forge, a forge on wheels (*i k*), is also available, the furnace can be moved where desired. The thinner the pieces of which this furnace is made, the easier it will be to move it. Every time its location is changed, all the joints must be luted with a sandy clay.

If iron is to be melted for experimental purposes or to cast small pieces in molds, an ordinary forge is sufficient as a furnace. In less than half an hour, 1 or 2 pounds of this metal will become thoroughly liquid. [412] This is only a question of intensifying the wind of the bellows and of being careful to keep the crucible well surrounded by charcoal. In such a case I still prefer the use of cylindrical crucibles. I always take one that is larger than would be required to hold the quantity of metal which I wish to melt in it, because I like to lay it down in the forge at an angle of about 45 degrees or more; a little more or less does not matter here. When it is lying down, it is less likely to be upset; it is easier to put in the iron and to see what is happening to the iron in the crucible—whether it is molten and whether sufficiently so; furthermore, it is then easier to turn the crucible.

This method of melting, as simple as it is, is very good if it is intended to cast small pieces that have many fine designs. The reason is that the iron is made perfectly liquid and is consequently in a condition easily to fill the smallest hollow spaces of the mold. Even if a furnace is used in which the heat is more intense, equally perfect, equally uniform liquefaction is not obtained, because, in proportion to the size of the furnace, a larger quantity of iron is also being melted at one time. Not all the material contained in a large crucible is exposed equally to the heat. During the very time it is being melted this material may be compared to an iron bar which has been brought to red heat in the midst of a fire and whose center has always received a lower [413] degree of heat than the layers nearest the surface. This unequal distribution of heat among different locations of the same melt seems to be sufficiently proved by a single observation—namely, that part of this melt, if it cools in the crucible, will become white and another part gray. Since we know that more thoroughly melted iron becomes correspondingly whiter, the part that stays gray must, then, have been melted less thoroughly than the rest.

It is possible in the forge to melt a larger quantity of iron at a time if a larger crucible is used and this is put inside a baffle which will hold the charcoal together. I have had one made for this purpose which is almost as good as a furnace (M). However, compared with the effect produced, the consumption of charcoal is a little greater than in the foundry furnace.

Before charging pig iron or cast iron in the crucible, one could have it heated on charcoal to either white or red heat, and one would then be always that much ahead. As soon as the crucible contains a certain quantity of molten iron, care must be taken never to add more iron unless it has been preheated, or else the iron that is already liquid would be cooled too much.

Everything that can be said about the different ways in which iron can be melted in a crucible is contained in the preceding paragraphs. It now remains to discuss the methods of melting it by exposing it to the direct action of the fire. [414] I do not know if it could be done in reverberatory furnaces similar to those in which bronze is melted on a large scale, as for casting cannon* and bells. I have not experimented with them, but certain intelligent persons, who are familiar with the operation of these furnaces, are of the opinion that their heat is not sufficiently forceful to liquefy iron. This may be true of these furnaces in the state they are at present; but, as it is easily possible

* Cannon were cast directly from blast furnaces. Saint Rémy (1696) mentions the practice at Périgord, where furnaces 24 feet high gave enough iron to cast an eight-pounder weighing 1,950 pounds, but as many as four furnaces were tapped simultaneously for larger pieces.

to increase their activity, it might perhaps be possible to increase it to such an extent that iron can be cast from them like bronze. However, there are enough other furnaces that can take their place. All those in which the hotness of the fire is urged by bellows can be adapted to melting iron.

As the wind of an ordinary forge melts iron contained in a crucible, there should be no doubt that this same iron will melt still faster if placed directly amid the charcoal of this forge. But, since we are concerned not only with melting the iron but also with having it run easily into the molds after it is molten, an ordinary forge, not changed in any way, would be impractical.

I have spoken of the fineries (Mem. 9) in which cast iron is refined before it is used for conversion into steel. There, two bellows moved by water power drive the wind against the iron and make it liquid. It drops into a box, or into a large crucible, where [415] it stays liquid until it is tapped. Some of these crucibles hold more than 200 or 300 pounds of iron. I have said before that in some provinces of the Kingdom this iron is tapped from the bottom of the crucible. I believe that it would not be difficult to arrange these fineries, or crucibles, in such a way that the metal will be conducted into prepared molds or so that these molds will be in a position to receive the metal as it comes out of the crucible and that the metal would therefore be cast hotter. I suggest this idea only to those who own iron forges, so that they may investigate whether they could undertake the casting of white iron into molds without great expense.

Furnaces constructed according to the same principle as those in which iron ore is smelted, but smaller, and in which the heat would be still more intense would be most suitable for melting a large quantity of iron at a time. In order to increase their intensity over that of the ore-smelting furnaces, all that would be necessary is to introduce continuously a larger quantity of air compared with the capacity of the furnace.

Although almost all brass founders, even the less skilful ones, are now able to melt iron in their furnaces, they almost never do, because the castings, which are necessarily left in the condition in which they come from the mold, have found only [416] a very limited market. However, there is one kind of foundryman who daily melts iron and melts no other metal at all. There are only few of these. I am not sure whether there ever were more than two or three at a time in Paris, and I believe that at present there is only one. Some of these foundrymen travel through the country. They appear successively in different provinces. They make iron weights and plates needed for certain purposes. They sometimes cast kettles, and sometimes they repair them. If the leg of an iron kettle has broken off, they cast a new leg in its place. As their method of melting iron is comparatively uncommon and not well known but may become very useful in the future, the main purpose of this memoir is to describe it exactly as it is practiced today, so that it can be used either in the present state of development or after it has been perfected.

Cast iron is not very expensive. However, in order to make it even cheaper, there are men who travel through the villages to buy up old broken pieces, which they then sell to our foundrymen. In the country this kind of merchandise is not paid for in ordinary currency. Around Paris one buys all this old iron for apples. A man, scales in hand, leads a horse loaded with rather low-grade fruit and pays for the iron he is given by an equal [417] weight of these apples. (The trade in old clothes, which are so necessary in papermaking, also has its own special currency. The ragman gives the peasants pins in exchange.) For the time being, there should be a sufficient supply of cast iron in Paris, as old kettles, broken chimney backs, and especially water pipe will furnish a great deal. I have never seen it bring more than 1 *sol* a pound, and sometimes it can be had for less than 2 *liards*. Perhaps it will become more expensive when it becomes known that there is a demand for it; now it is almost useless. But it will always be easy to obtain it cheaply at the smelters where iron ore is smelted. There it will be cast into thin plates which are easier to break into small pieces than ordinary pig iron.

But let us come back to the furnace of which I wish to speak at present (Pl. 13, *a b*). As I said before, it resembles the ore-smelting furnace but is smaller, and it differs in two points from those which I suggested might be constructed after its pattern.

First, the furnace of our foundrymen is still smaller than this new furnace ought to be, and, second, the new one ought to be stationary, whereas the one which I shall describe is destroyed, or at least knocked down, every time molten metal is tapped and is rebuilt again every time it is to be used for melting. It consists of two parts—of something like a [418] crucible (*AA BB*) and of a stack shaped like a truncated cone (*F G H I*), which is set upon the crucible.* First I shall describe these two parts, and all the others, when they are as simply made as our foundrymen use them. Then I shall tell how they can be made more substantial, how they can be assembled more skilfully. It is good to know what could be done more cheaply, for there are occasions when stability is of no importance.

The crucible is called the "ladle" by the artisans, and their method of melting is called "ladle melting." The crucible partly consists of an old pot or an old cast-iron kettle, depending on its intended size (*ABBA LMML*); or, rather, this old pot or kettle serves to support the actual crucible, which is made of a layer of sandy clay about $1\frac{1}{2}$ inches thick, which lines the inside of the vessel of which I am speaking. For reasons of stability (and this is how I have had it made), this lining must be made of the same grades of clay of which crucibles are made and must be prepared in the same way; for, if it is made of too easily melting clay, it has to be patched too often. The clay may extend above the rim of the vessel which supports it (*B C*); and, where it does this, the clay alone is provided with a semicircular opening (*D*), which will receive part of the tuyère into which the bellows must drive the wind. (This opening could be in the rim of the vessel itself.)

The second part of the furnace (*F G H I*), the cone-shaped stack, is constructed to be set on the crucible. Its base rests on this crucible, and its diameter [419] is consequently more or less determined by that of the crucible which was chosen. On the outside it is also made of cast iron. Our artisans often make it of several kettles without bottoms, which are stacked one upon another; but it is more convenient to make it out of sheet iron.

---

* Biringuccio (1540) had described furnaces somewhat of this type but with lower superstructure.

It is given a height of approximately 15 or 16 inches, but it is safe to make it even higher. On the inside it is lined with clay like that used for the crucible in such a way that the opening on top will be a little narrower than that at the bottom. I shall give no definite measurements because they can all be varied widely. But if these furnaces are to be used as they have actually been constructed, the plans will give the dimensions and serve as a guide.

I should not forget to mention that the stack has an opening similar to that in the ladle or crucible. This is placed directly above the other one, and the two together form the hole which will receive the tuyère (*O*).

By joining these two pieces, one obtains the whole furnace. The heat of the fire is urged by means of two bellows, each of which will keep one man busy (Figs. 1, 2). The power to operate these bellows can be supplied more efficiently than shown in the illustration which I had made. But I have said before, and I repeat, that it is my intention to describe first what is actually practiced. Furthermore, [420] these are problems that are in no way restricted to our art and on which the industry can go to work. In this case the bellows are stationary, and the location of the furnace is determined by their location. What is more important is that they must be inclined in such a way that the wind is directed toward the bottom of the crucible—not at the exact center of the bottom but at least right at the lower end of the wall which is opposite the tuyère.

The floor under the ends or, to use the term of the art, under the nozzles of the bellows, this floor and even a piece extending a little beyond this spot is hollowed out to be a little deeper than the rest of the workshop. This hollow is filled with the kind of charcoal powder that is always found at the bottom of heaps of charcoal, and is known as breeze, and with previously crushed slag of the kind that is removed from above iron. The ladle or crucible is set in the middle of this heap of powder. It is easy quickly to scoop out a hole which will receive it, for it is as easy to dig into these cinders as into sand.

I must point out, however, that the crucible is not placed directly on the bottom of the hole. This crucible will soon receive the molten metal, and, when it is full, it must be carried over the molds, where the metal is cast. In order to be then able to lift it, it is placed into a certain openwork cradle the bowl of which is made of several strips of iron (*T V X Y, 1, 2*); it has a handle, which is several feet long, and furthermore [421] another handle, a bail, which looks a little like that of a kettle.

The time has not yet come to explain the purpose of the two handles. For the present let us just think of this cradle, imbedded in the powder or breeze, and of the crucible or ladle, set in the cradle. This will be at such a distance from the bellows that their ends are about half an inch inside the opening which was provided to receive the tuyère. We shall also assume that the tuyère has been put in its place. It usually is made of cast iron and is always wider where it is outside the furnace, at the opening that receives the ends of the bellows, than where it is inside the furnace.

Let us, at last, place the stack upon the crucible and surround the crucible and also the bottom of the stack with breeze, so that the flame cannot escape from the furnace through the joints between our two pieces. Even if they have been luted with clay, everything will then be only that much tighter. After this is done, our furnace is set up and ready to receive the fire. Some pieces of lighted charcoal are charged through its upper opening, and unlighted ones are thrown on top of these and quickly set afire by the wind of the bellows; then, finally, the furnace is filled up with charcoal.

When all the charcoal is burning and the charcoal that has descended has later been replaced by new charcoal, and when the furnace is finally hot enough, the first charge of iron that is to be melted is brought over. [422] Every time iron is charged, the furnace must be full of charcoal up to the top. (This is the only place through which it can be charged, with charcoal as well as with iron.)

The iron is broken into pieces approximately as large as *écus*, for they must be molten when they reach the crucible, and pieces that are too large might not melt while they make this journey.

When the last charge of charcoal has descended 2 or 3 inches, it is advisable to introduce an iron rod into the furnace through its upper opening. By poking with this rod, the charcoal is made to lie better and to descend faster. There will then be less empty space between the pieces, but on top there will now be a larger empty space. This is filled with a new charge of charcoal, on top of which a new charge of iron is spread. Each charge of iron is only as thick as the pieces of iron are, and the width, or surface, of this layer is the same as that of the entire upper opening of the furnace. As long as it is considered advisable to keep the fire burning and to melt more iron, the operations just described are repeated.

But during all this time one has to keep watch at the tuyère. The nozzles, or ends, of the bellows do not fill it completely. There is enough space left to observe as through a tube what goes on inside the furnace at a certain distance above the crucible. This is not a large field of observation, but it suffices on occasion [423] to see a very amusing spectacle. One recognizes the iron, which, after having elongated, comes off in drops. From time to time a new drop falls into the space one can observe. But what the artisans really attempt to observe is whether the light of the tuyère is very brilliant, very white, or, as they say, whether it resembles the moon, which is an expression that gives a very good idea of the color of the fire in the furnace opposite the tuyère when the bellows has raised it to the intensity it must have. On the other hand, if the color is reddish, it is a bad sign. It is an even worse sign when the tuyère becomes dirty, when something black is seen there. It means that it is becoming stopped up, and the artisan must continually be on the alert to prevent this occurrence. He does this by passing a small rod of red-hot iron or even a small stick of wood through the tuyère into the furnace. By this means he removes the materials that have started to attach themselves to the inside end, that have begun to stop it up and would gradually close it until the wind could pass no longer. Vitrified matter that has become stuck on the tuyère or a piece of badly melted iron that has come in contact with it may be the cause of this accident, for nothing that happens to be exactly at the end of the tuyère will continue to melt, and matter that has become liquid would even cool if it should rise up to this height. As long as the wind is in the tuyère, and at the [424] moment when it comes out of it, it is cold and therefore cools whatever it encounters before it has encountered the charcoal. Unless constant, concentrated attention is paid to keeping this tuyère open, the charcoal may have been burned in vain.

Finally, after all the iron that was to be melted has been fed into the furnace in a number of operations, the artisan gets ready to pour the iron into the molds. He looks to see if no more pieces of iron lie unmelted on the charcoal. If none can be seen, he feels with an iron rod whether some are left which are not visible; and, if that should be the case, he lets them descend into the crucible. He then stirs the material it contains, so that the iron that has just come down can become liquid. When everything seems to be molten, he stops working the bellows, removes the clay from the furnace, takes away all the breeze with which it had been surrounded, and knocks the stack off.

Now the crucible is uncovered, and the metal is ready to be cast. The molds have been prepared to receive it, and it is necessary to raise the crucible and to carry it over these molds. The customary method of lifting the crucible out of its hole is to pass an iron bar under the handle of the cradle into which we have seen it placed, and the only reason for having two handles on this cradle-like piece is to make it easier to pull the crucible back and tilt it. After the iron bar has been passed [425] under the bail, two men grasp this bar, each at one end, and carry the crucible to the molds. A third man then takes hold of the long handle of the cradle, by means of which he inclines the crucible and pours the molten iron into a mold.

M. Cusin, an ambitious artisan of the suburb of Saint Antoine, uses a less strenuous method of carrying the crucible. A few feet away from the furnace he has installed an upright post, which is several inches square in cross-section (Pl. 13, *f*). The upper end of this post is provided with a lever (*g g*), the shorter end of which is long enough to extend to just opposite the furnace. The lever turns freely on the post that supports it. It passes through a ring which is part of the head of an iron pin. This pin is almost an inch in diameter. It is set vertically into the post and rests in a hole in which it turns easily (*9, 10, 11*). A chain ending in a hook is fastened to the shorter end of the lever. When the crucible is to be lifted, the bail of the cradle is fastened to this hook; and, to make it easier to lift the whole assembly, the other end is loaded with a weight, which is increased as much as is necessary. Thus, the lever alone carries the crucible. By turning the lever, the crucible is brought over the molds. Care has been taken to place them approximately upon the half-circle which is described by the end carrying the crucible. [426] At the moment when the crucible has been brought over a mold, a man grasps the handle of the cradle and tilts the crucible (*3, 4*).

I shall not stop to explain the making of the molds and their differences; this is one of the principal details concerning the art of the foundryman. The molds illustrated on Plate 13 are simply held closed with weights, and there are cases where they must be locked in a clamp, like those shown on Plate 12.

When the crucible was lifted from its original position, the molten iron was still covered by charcoal and liquid scoria— that means, by vitrified matter or slag which had formed from the iron as it became refined and also from the ashes of the charcoal as they were reduced to a glass. The artisan first removes the charcoal, using any tool whatsoever, such as an iron bar or some kind of rake. He then tries to pull off all the vitrified matter that floats on the iron. As long as it is liquid, it is not easy to remove it without also removing some molten iron, but a simple expedient overcomes this difficulty as follows.

With a wet cloth attached to the end of a stick, one man sprinkles the contents of the crucible with water. Immediately, another man uses a stick or any other tool to push everything that has any solidity over the rim of the crucible. Only the vitrified matter will have become solidified, for it cools more [427] easily than iron, and the water has fallen directly upon it. This same process of sprinkling water and removing from the crucible everything the stick can pull off is repeated seven or eight times. The surface of the iron will then be very clean, very open, and hereafter nothing remains but to pour the metal into the molds.

The small amount of water with which the surface of the iron is repeatedly wetted seems to contribute to refining it thoroughly. As the metal is agitated in lifting off the dross or slag that has solidified, new slag can come to the surface, from where it can always be removed. This operation can be repeated as long as the iron does not seem to lose its fluidity, but beware lest the metal thicken and lose some of its liquidity.

The furnace which I have described is built very crudely, but it nevertheless gives an idea of the way in which it could be improved. It is easily seen that the crucible can be placed more solidly than in a cast-iron kettle. I had one built of wrought-iron bars where the spaces between the bars were occupied by good sheet iron (Pl. 14).

The iron will melt better the higher the stack, and we will have a safer and more stable structure if the stack is made of sheet iron rather than of pieces of kettle, which always fit poorly upon each other. This shell of sheet iron only serves to give support to the clay with which it is lined on the inside. [428] To give the clay still better support and to prevent large pieces of clay from detaching themselves—and also to make it easier to replace any clay that may have broken off—the stack will be pierced with nails, the heads being on the outside, while the points penetrate horizontally inside. The closer these nails are to each other, the more firmly the clay will be held.

Instead of nails I have had iron rods put into one of my furnaces, the two ends of which were bent (*H0 H2 H3*). These rods, which are quite as long as the stack, are spaced only an inch apart. The clay is held in place between them and covers them by at least an inch.

In the furnace I have described the crucible was sunk in the ground. I have had one built in a completely different location. My crucible is in the air—its bottom is more than 14 or 15 inches above the ground. It is held in this position by two trunnions, which are supported by two uprights of a wooden structure (Figs. 1, 2). I shall not go into details concerning the characteristics of this furnace. The Plate and the accompanying explanations will give sufficient information. Improvements can be thought of to make it even more convenient.

My principal purpose was to eliminate the necessity of knocking the stack down every time iron is to be cast. Because of this practice, the furnace becomes cold. It is not easy to re-erect it immediately. [429] Each time it is to be used for melting, it is necessary to start anew, with new expense. One receives no return at all, or very little return, from the charcoal that was burned before. Instead of carrying the crucible over the molds, in the new arrangement the molds are carried under the crucible. The crucible is tilted, and its contents can be poured without moving it from its place and without taking off the stack. In a way the stack and the crucible are one, or at least they are held together by iron bars as firmly as if they were one. Furthermore, to tilt the crucible, two iron poles are used, which are attached to or locked into a hoop which encircles the stack toward its top. One man grasps one of these poles and a second man the other (Fig. 2, *l l*). By pulling the top of the stack downward, they tilt the crucible, which pours its contents into the molds which receive the metal. If several molds are held in a clamp, an artisan advances or retracts, inclines or restraightens, the clamp as each of the molds is filled. He is careful to have the opening of the next one ready for the metal that is flowing out. It is also possible to place the molds on a little cart, of which one man will hold the pole; this increases the ease with which they can be moved and tilted in the way that seems most suitable.

Because it is not as easy to cast the metal issuing from this large crucible into the opening of a mold as to cast the metal from a small crucible held by tongs, it [430] will be found convenient (as I had it done) to use a small funnel made of baked clay (*X*), or of wrought iron or cast brass if a more durable one is preferred. This funnel is placed upon the opening of the mold. It is supported by a piece of iron (*Z2*) which in the middle forms a sort of collar large enough to let the funnel slide in only a little way. Near its two ends, this piece of iron is bent at right angles. The distance of these two bent parts from each other is such that it exactly equals the width of the frames which make the mold. It is not expensive to have such pieces in all the sizes of one's frames; but, by means of screws, the same piece can be adapted for use with frames of different widths. Before the funnel is put in place, the precaution of heating it should be observed. It also should be placed in such a way that there remains some space between the end of its tube and the hole, or sprue, of the mold, so that the mold can be filled without leaving any metal in the funnel.

In Plate 14, which illustrates it, the new furnace is placed on a wooden framework (*a a b c d*) whose four corner posts have wheels. I had this done so that it could be moved at will; but this feature is by no means necessary. The framework which will hold the furnace can be stationary, and the furnace may even be supported on one side by a bracket fastened in a wall.

Instead of [431] one bellows, which in this case is also mounted on the wooden frame carrying the furnace, two bellows may be used. This can be done in any way desired and will only increase the activity of the furnace. If a furnace is to be constructed which is capable of containing more molten iron, the size of the bellows must be increased, and more power and speed must be used in moving them. And remember that a single bellows moved twice as fast is worth two bellows, each of the size of the single one, moved half as fast.

When the crucible is sunk in the ground, it is placed more favorably as far as conservation of heat is concerned than when it is suspended in the air. In order to remedy the disadvantage of the second arrangement, the case, the sheet-iron shell (*P P*) forming the outside walls of the crucible, must be given more depth and diameter than the crucible requires. A second, less deep shell, whose diameter equals that of the outer shell only at the rim, is then placed inside the first one. This inner shell is subsequently coated with clay, and it will be the actual crucible. An empty space remains between the two. The outer shell has three or four openings large enough to admit burning charcoal, which will be placed inside the empty space to heat the bottom and the outside walls of the actual crucible.

Something [432] just as good as the second shell could be constructed by arranging several bars of iron in such a way that one end of each bar touches the upper rim of the sheet-iron shell, while the other end joins with the ends of all the others around the same point. They will inclose something like a cone, form something like a cone-shaped cage (*Q Q R*), which can be coated inside with the layer of clay that must become the crucible.

Avoid trying to make the crucible too substantial by making this layer of clay too thick. It would be difficult to heat it, and the iron that would touch the bottom might solidify. Make it an inch thick or a little more, and it will be thick enough.

At the very bottom of the stack (*D*), approximately opposite the opening for the tuyère, another opening should be left without fail. It will depend on the use to which it is put what size it should be given. Each time iron is ready to be poured, a poker with a bent end will be passed through this opening, a sort of rake, with which the charcoal and especially all the slag, all the vitrified matter which floats on the molten metal, are removed.

The large furnaces of which I have just given some idea are needed to cast into molds pieces of such size that the crucibles of the ordinary foundry furnaces could not hold the metal they would require. However, small pieces, [433] delicate pieces, will be cast more successfully if the iron is melted in ordinary crucibles. I do not mean to say that the metal is not liquefied as perfectly in the large furnaces—it is liquefied even better—but it is not so easy to conduct it into small molds. Furthermore, the weight of iron lost is greater when the fire acts directly upon the iron than when it acts upon it only through the walls of a crucible.

In making the crude cast-iron work we have produced so far, there are two methods of filling the molds with molten iron. In order to cast cannon, water pipe, and chimney backs, inclined channels are built between the large molds and the furnace. The metal flows through them as soon as an opening has been made in the furnace. In order to cast kettles and pots, as much metal as is needed is removed from the furnace itself with a large iron ladle and carried over the molds. But white iron, the more refined cast iron, if transported such a distance before being poured into the mold, would rarely be fluid enough to fill the impressions left by the patterns of thin and delicate pieces— at least unless the ladles in which the liquid iron is carried were preheated thoroughly and the molds were placed very close to the furnace.

Consequently, one of the items that must be attended to most carefully [434] will be to make the iron very liquid and to conserve its fluidity up to the moment when it enters the molds. Be sure, however, to obtain this fluidity by the heat of the fire alone. Do not add fluxes to succeed better, at least for the ordinary work. The fluxes that help to make the metal melt better convey upon it properties that oppose the softening to which it is to be subjected. In an experiment in which I had several pieces of cast iron softened, there were some which I had placed more favorably than any of the others and which I hoped to soften better than the rest. However, while I succeeded perfectly with all the others, these were less satisfactory. I tried unhappily to analyze the cause of a result that was so contrary to my expectations, until the foundryman confessed to me that, to melt his iron more perfectly and faster, he had thrown sulfur into the crucible.

Nevertheless, I do not mean to exclude fluxes under all circumstances. Later I may relate some of my observations concerning cases where they can be employed. But no foundryman should add them to ordinary iron, to iron that he does not wish to make more difficult to soften.

Our foundrymen know that the molds in which they are to cast metal should be very dry. It is important to dry them thoroughly, but an attempt should also be made to have them [435] as hot as possible when they are ready to receive the molten iron. There is no doubt that, the hotter they are, the less the metal will thicken in flowing into them, and the better it will be able to fill the molds perfectly. It would be impossible, therefore, to make them too hot, provided that in heating them certain precautions are observed which prevent the formation of fissures or cracks inside. The frames of sand molds are made of wood and therefore little suited to being exposed to a hot fire, but I can see no reason why such frames could not be made of iron. No great supply of such iron frames would be required. It would be enough to have them available for the casting of the finest pieces—those which require greater fluidity of the iron.

Even after the iron has been poured into the molds, it frequently still needs the attention of the foundryman. We know that cast iron is extremely brittle; but we must learn that it is so brittle that it breaks by itself in the molds without being jolted. When pieces are removed from the molds which otherwise have come out very well, they are often discovered to be broken almost clear through. Sometimes there are only small cracks which, however, always weaken them and usually make them useless. This accident happens almost exclusively with thin castings, and it happens particularly to those which are thin and large. Well-refined cast iron is almost as brittle as glass, and it cracks in the same way when it is [436] cooled too suddenly. We therefore must try to prevent this accident by an expedient similar to the one that keeps pieces of glass intact. I mean that, as soon as such pieces have been made, they are carried into furnaces called *lehrs*. The heat in these furnaces preserves the heat of the glass for some time; it lets it decrease only little by little. Glass which is cooled so gradually keeps the shape it has been given. By using a corresponding precaution, it will surely be possible to prevent the cracking of cast-iron work. In a factory, an oven similar to those of bread or pastry bakers can be purchased (Pl. 12, *q*). It will be heated by wood, as they are, and will be kept hot as long as any casting is done. As soon as the metal has been cast, the mold will be opened, the piece will be withdrawn still red-hot, placed into the oven without losing a minute, and there cool very gradually.

Without incurring the expense of building an oven, I have saved the finest, the most delicate pieces by a method that can be adopted by everybody. It consists of lighting a heap of charcoal very close to the molds (*p*). Then, as soon as the iron has been poured, I have the mold opened, have the piece withdrawn, and have it plunged at once into the heap of charcoal.

The avarice of the foundryman is often the reason why thin

pieces break in the molds. Although he has only small pieces to cast, he exposes them as much to the danger of breaking as if [437] they were considerably larger and as thin. I mean that, to save the trouble of preparing many frames, he fills a few with the largest possible number of impressions, which are all connected. These impressions of different pieces, or of duplicates of the same piece, endanger each piece almost as much as if it were nearly as large as the frame, and more than if it were, by itself, as large as all the other pieces together. This is the case because he pours the metal which must fill the different impressions through only one and the same opening of the frame (Pl. 12, *N*). Consequently, all the pieces that have been molded are connected by runners, by something like channels, by the gates (*P*). As everything else, these gates are filled with metal that freezes. All the pieces of the mold are joined together, or constitute a single piece with parts cut out (*Q R S T V X Y*). Now, then, it is easy to see why a piece should be the more likely to break the larger it is, for it breaks only because not all the parts decrease in volume, or shrink, in the same proportion. If there are some that cannot contract like the others, there will be a crack. A body made of an extremely brittle material such as glass, when exposed to the air, would break in cooling for this reason alone. But a body made of a somewhat less brittle material, such as our cast iron, can break in the molds under circumstances which would not cause it to break [438] in air that only has the degree of heat of the molds. In order to shrink, the parts of the pieces that are inclosed in the mold must overcome the resistance of the opposing sand by which they are constricted. This constriction is greater, and more important relative to the casting, as the casting has more surface and less thickness.

It seldom happens that heavy castings crack in the molds, because thicker castings cool more slowly and also have more strength to overcome the constriction. Furthermore, the resistance by the sand is less in proportion to their volume. This resistance increases with increasing surface.

If a foundryman absolutely insists upon filling his frames very full, he should at least increase the number of the openings through which the molten metal is poured. He then would no longer be forced to open so many connecting channels.

When he has patterns made for new castings, he should avoid having a heavy, very bulging section very close to a thin one of considerable extent. Otherwise he will find that in the iron casting produced from this pattern the thin part will be in danger of cracking in the mold for the reasons given in the foregoing, or it will be otherwise unsatisfactory. In cases where the casting absolutely requires that very heavy, very bulging parts are close to thin parts, [439] it will be the safest to place cores into the bulging ones, which will make them hollow. The shape of the casting will not be changed thereby, and those parts which otherwise would have been much too heavy will now be only of a thickness proportional to that of the thin parts with which they are connected, and there will no longer be quite so much danger that there will be empty spaces left in the thin ones.

It has happened that pieces which I had not cooled in a low heat cracked several hours and even a day after they had been completely cold. This also happens sometimes with glass. In order to protect the pieces of glass on which he had reproduced the impressions on engraved gems, M. Hombert had them ground all around, and he claimed that they were then no longer imperiled. Our iron castings would be spoiled if they were ground; we could at most do that with their gates. But it seems to me that this accident happens so seldom that it is not very important to find a remedy therefor; and I doubt, moreover, that castings which have cooled surrounded by charcoal after they were withdrawn from the mold are subject to it.

A last warning which I shall give the foundryman is to make the gates, the channels which conduct the metal into the hollow spaces of the molds, as thin as possible, to make the gates and vents only just large enough to have the metal flow easily, to [440] decrease the depth and compensate this by increasing the width. It would be a nuisance if we had to soften with the casting all the gates that are connected with it (Pl. 12, *R S T*), and the gates must therefore be broken off; but, when they are as thick or almost as thick as some parts of the casting, it will often happen that, when the gate is struck with the hammer, one of the thin parts breaks off. When the gates are weak, this is not likely to happen.

If the gates are heavy and it is absolutely necessary to knock them off, the safest thing to do, according to my experience, is to place the casting in the forge and let it become red-hot, especially at the place where it is to be broken. It will then be placed on the anvil; the part that is to be separated from the rest must lie absolutely flat; a chisel is set upon it and struck with the hammer as if it were to cut wrought iron but always more lightly.

The Third Memoir, Outlining Exploratory Tests on Different Substances Considered for Use in Softening Cast Iron and Describing Those Which, According to These Tests, Seem To Be Best Suited

ET US ASSUME that by the known processes of the art well-refined white iron has been melted and cast into molds and that it has filled the impressions perfectly. In other words, that we have, or that we can have, well-made iron castings, but that it remains to soften them, to take away some of their rigidity and especially some of their hardness, so that they can be dressed. This secret has seemed to me of such importance that I searched for it for a long time—indeed, even before I thought of the secret of converting iron into steel. There was no doubt that the action of the fire had to be used in order to effect in cast iron a change such as I envisioned. But I had convinced myself that it could not be expected from the action of the fire alone. I knew that the chimney backs of large kitchens keep their hardness, although they stay for many years in a place [451] where they are heated considerably and repeatedly. I believed, therefore, that cast iron that was to be softened had to be inclosed in crucibles and surrounded by substances which, with the aid of the fire, would produce this effect.

After a number of trials, some of which made me believe that I was making good progress, I temporarily abandoned this project in order to pursue my work on the conversion of iron into steel, which, in a way, was the material of the time. Every day one heard of people who claimed to be in possession of the secret and who failed to realize the hopes they raised. I said that I abandoned my experiments with cast iron in favor of my work on the conversion of iron into steel. I should have said that I thought that I had abandoned them. In reality I continued them by working on the conversion of iron into steel without knowing it at first, however. Later I found that I had progressed a good way toward softening cast iron. I found that I could dispense with many of the complex experiments which would have confronted me before I could have reached the simple expedients that suffice in this case, when I thought about all I had proved in the foregoing concerning the composition of steel, its true nature, the fundamental difference between steel and iron, the nature of cast iron as I have described it, and especially when I turned my attention to the method of reclaiming steels which have the defect of being difficult to forge or, what amounts to the same, to the method [452] of reconverting steel into iron, which is described in the eighth memoir.

In any physical science, experimentation and theory must be mutually complementary. Those who want only experiment and those who want only theory are equally far from advancement, especially in applied physics. All my reflections and all my experiments about the nature of iron and steel had shown me that, by converting wrought iron into steel, it was brought closer again to the state in which it had been originally; that, one might say, the more it became steel, the closer it was once again to becoming cast iron; that steels which were penetrated too much by salts and sulfurs shared with cast iron the characteristic of being hard to forge and of being more easily softened by fire than ordinary steel and wrought iron are. I believed to be justified by these theories and experiments in concluding (Mem. 9) that well-refined, very pure cast iron is a kind of steel but the most intractable of all. Steel that is difficult to forge becomes steel that bears the hammer well if it is deprived of its excess sulfurs and salts. Cast iron always contains more sulfurs than ordinary steel of any kind.

What could be more natural than to go further with these conclusions—to believe that, if cast iron is absolutely incapable of being worked with the hammer and is at the same time so very hard, this must be because it is excessively full of sulfurs and salts and that this is also the reason [453] why it melts more easily and is softened more easily by the fire than wrought iron and steel are? I had no trouble to believe that the sulfurs were capable of augmenting the hardness of a metal to this extent. I have spoken before of the great hardness of certain pyrites, which are neither metal nor stone, although they are often and quite improperly given the latter designation.* They are almost nothing but sulfurs and salts. When they are reduced to a powder and placed on charcoal, they burn almost entirely; they flame like common sulfur and give off the same odor. However, these same pyrites are so hard, as I have said before, that they were formerly used in wheel-lock harquebuses for the same purpose as flints are today used in muskets.

When I believed that it was sufficiently established that the hardness of cast iron was caused by the sulfurs and salts it contained, it seemed to me that the secret of softening, or of malleablizing, cast iron consisted only in taking part of its sulfurs away from it and that the process by which this could be done must be fundamentally identical with the one I had used to correct the defectiveness of steels that were hard to forge. It seemed most likely that the same processes and the same substances which removed superfluous sulfurs from intractable steels, which could even reconvert these steels into iron, would have a somewhat similar effect on cast irons; that they would also cause them to be in a state approaching [454] that of wrought iron. We have seen that the substances producing this change in steels are earthy substances of the most alkaline kind and that those which act upon the steel the fastest are bone ash and chalk reduced to a fine powder.

Almost sure of the success of my experiments, I inclosed very thin pieces of white cast iron in crucibles. In some they were packed in bone ash and in others in chalk. I exposed these crucibles to the fire for some hours and then removed the iron. When I tested it, I found everything I had hoped for—that the pieces, as hard and resistant as they had been to the file, had softened to the point where they could be filed like wrought iron.

Nevertheless, I had set my expectations a little too high. I soon had a new example of one of those many experiences which show that conclusions drawn from small-scale experiments are

* Firestone.

not always reliable when applied to large-scale operation. I had iron castings of a reasonable size cast into molds. They were more than 1 inch or more than 1½ inches thick and were full of ornamental designs. I completely surrounded them by bone ash and placed them into a furnace where they could be heated without being exposed to the direct action of the flame—a furnace similar to our steelmaking furnaces. They were exposed to the heat for more than two days, and that was not too much for their thickness. When I withdrew them from the furnace, [455] I found that I had badly miscalculated. I do not mean that the castings had not been softened as much as I had expected. They were easy to work, but they had a defect which did not accord well with my hopes for commercial application. The outer layers had completely come off as scale, and the thin leaves and delicate features on the pattern, which had come out well on the piece as cast, had come off with it. It would have been possible to work these pieces, but it would have cost very much time to repair so much damage. To soften cast iron in this way is not good enough, and it would be practically useless for delicate pieces.

The same principles that led me to discover how to make cast iron easy to work also led me to discover the cause of this adversity and made me hope to find a remedy. Earthy, alkaline substances absorb, or imbibe, some of the sulfurs with which cast iron is penetrated, but during long exposure to the fire they remove too much of them from the layers next to the surface. They deprive the outer layers of the iron of all the unctuous matter they contain, the matter that holds their parts together. These parts therefore become disconnected and finally detach themselves in the form of friable scale, similar to the scale that falls off iron when it is forged under the hammer or iron that has been overheated. This scale will be of increasing thickness and [456] amount as the action of the fire lasts longer. Nothing like this happens to pieces of cast iron which are exposed to the fire only for a few hours, a fact which explains the success of my first experiments.

It occurred to me that one would have to add to these over-absorbent substances (which return to the iron nothing which they have once absorbed) some other substance which would moderate their effect—which, even if it could not return to the iron as much as had been taken away from it, would at least furnish enough oily parts to moisten that which had become too dry. One would have to do something almost equivalent to what is practiced in a forge when iron is heated which must be treated especially carefully, whose surface must be preserved. Although the fire is meant to act forcefully on such iron, the iron is nevertheless repeatedly sprinkled with sand or fine clay in order to protect its surface against the direct action of the fire.

Even though this reasoning may be questioned, it made me decide to mix very finely powdered charcoal with chalk or powder made of calcined bones. My experiments in converting iron into steel had amply proved to me that, regardless of how long powdered charcoal is exposed to the fire, it does not become consumed, provided that no air is admitted, so that it would always be in condition to exert upon the cast iron the effect which I expected from it. I therefore mixed it [457] with bone ash or chalk in different proportions, in order to discover which would be the most suitable mixture. The result of these experiments was as favorable as could be desired. With this expedient I succeeded in softening cast iron, and I could keep it in the fire as long as it was necessary without having trouble with scale.

Although I found the effect of the afore-mentioned mixture most reliable and satisfactory, and although it seemed to soften the iron perfectly and at the same time prevent scaling, I nevertheless wished to find out whether there might not be other mixtures which would act faster or more strongly. However, none of the experiments which I believed ought to be tried was of any help to me, and I shall recount only the principal ones, only those which seem most promising.

I tried the effect of different salts, especially alkaline salts, such as soda, potash, etc. I also tried sea salt. I packed pieces of cast iron in these different salts and let the salts occupy the entire space of the crucible. Used alone, they never caused any appreciable softening, but they did cause scaling. Furthermore, the cost of the operation would be considerably increased if nothing but a salt were employed, regardless of which kind.

But I believed that I ought to find out whether there was one that would make my compound more [458] active. To a mixture of two parts of bone ash or chalk and one part of charcoal I added in each test the following salts—of each one part. I mean that I took, for instance, two parts of bone ash, one part of charcoal, and one part of sea salt. In another test I used glass salt, in another vitriol, in another alum, in another potash, in another soda, in another pearlash, and in another saltpeter concentrated by tartar. I also used tartar. None of the salts mentioned seemed to have bad effects, but, if they helped to accelerate the softening of the iron, it was not very noticeable. However, the irons that were packed in mixtures which included alkaline salts were softened a little more and a little faster than the others, and mixtures containing pearlash seemed to be better than the rest. I believe that alkaline salts can be added successfully to the mixture if the duration of firing is to be shortened. But one can manage perfectly well without them.

I also tried out what effect antimony, verdigris, and corrosive sublimate might have. Indeed, I was especially anxious to use the last-named substance, as I had heard that it had been successfully employed in softening cast irons. However, it retarded rather than accelerated the effect of the substances with which it was mixed. The antimony ruined the grain of the cast iron and [459] prevented softening. It did more than that. The effect of an entire furnace run, comprising a large number of castings, was checked by a little antimony which I had used in the mixture in which the iron of one small crucible was packed. This small crucible was placed in the large crucible together with all the large castings. Although I had been careful to lute this small crucible, almost all the castings which surrounded it remained hard, and some of them also scaled rather considerably. The verdigris did no harm, and it may have done some good.

I substituted powdered leather charcoal for an equal weight of wood charcoal. This is successfully used, especially in soaking iron in pack-hardening; but I was unable to recognize whether in this instance this powder had any advantage over ordinary charcoal powder.

There was no reason to believe that oily substances would be helpful in the operation; but, since one must be extremely cautious in making assumptions, even the most likely ones, and it is always wise to confirm them by new proof, I moistened earthy matters with molten suet. This caused them to be less effective than when they were used alone.

In order to ascertain whether our powders of calcined bones or chalk should rightly be preferred to other neutral or alkaline substances, I used [460] the same amounts by weight as in my other experiments of quicklime, slaked lime, potter's earth reduced to a fine powder, and crushed glass. The lime softened the cast iron, but it did not give it as much body as the other two substances. The potter's earth, or clay, softened it pretty well, but it caused more scaling. Gypsum, or transparent plaster, is of all the substances the one to be feared most because of scaling.

So that, after having examined the different substances which I thought might be suitable for the purposes of our operation, I had found nothing that was better than calcined bones or chalk.

Our new art seems to be especially apt to furnish examples of the difference between operations on a small scale and those on a large scale. I told of one example when I discussed the accident for which I discovered a remedy in the use of powdered charcoal. Another occurrence furnished a new and more unusual one. It is only too common that those who seem to reveal secrets to the public keep to themselves the part that is of the greatest importance. They give like a miser; they only wish to give the impression that they are sharing because they wish to show that they possess; but they guard the master-stroke, certain tricks, certain essential information. The information I wish to reveal, if kept hidden, would deprive us of the knowledge which assures us of the success of our art. In my trials on a small scale, chalk reduced to a powder was on a par with bone ash. I [461] could discover no difference in their effects. In my first trials on a large scale I used bone ash. The results were all that could be desired. When, subsequently, I wished to make another experiment on a large scale, and I found that my supply of bone ash was insufficient, I used chalk without hesitation. This experiment made me realize that bone ash has such

great advantage over chalk that it is surprising that this discovery should have escaped me during the trials on a small
scale. During an exposure of almost twice the duration, to the
same degree of heat, the chalk produced not quite the same effect
as the bone ash. Although this difference is important enough,
bone ash has another, even more considerable, advantage. It
never fails to soften cast iron, whereas there is one circumstance,
which is difficult to avoid, under which chalk effects no softening and even restores to the iron the hardness which it had taken
away, a fact which is even more surprising. This happens when
the fire acts too strongly, when it is urged to a degree of intensity which I shall define later on. Even though the castings
are not removed from the furnace until after they have been
there for more than the necessary time, they will be found to
be as hard as when they were put in. I have observed even more
—pieces which I placed into the furnace already softened came
out very hard.* However, this happens rarely except in a uniformly very hot furnace. Often, too, a somewhat large piece
does not acquire an even degree of heat throughout, and, if some
of the castings or some portions of these castings [462] have
been heated beyond the proper degree, they remain hard either
entirely or in part, and what had been softened even becomes
hard again. It must have been some substance similar to chalk
that made the outcome of the softening which was tried at
Cosne and at the suburb of Saint Marceau so uncertain [see p.
269]. This must have been one of the adverse factors that, combined with scale formation which occurred under certain circumstances, ruined these enterprises and caused a great deal of
wasted expense. Calcined bone always softens without fail, and
it softens the faster the higher one heats the cast iron which is
packed in it.

Chalk works well, therefore, only when it is used to soften

* This is hard to understand, unless perhaps the distinction comes from the
fact that malleabilization in chalk (as indeed in any non-oxidizing compound) would leave the carbon still in place as graphite, and heating (or reheating) above the transition temperature would cause enough carbon to return into solid solution and give considerable hardening on rapid cooling.
The superficial absence of carbon after malleablizing in an oxidizing medium
would prevent such hardening.

thin pieces or when large pieces are given a very gentle fire—
when they are heated to be only cherry-red. It follows that this
substance, in addition to requiring a much longer time than
bone ash does in order to soften cast iron, is always dangerous
to use because, after having produced a favorable effect, it may
completely destroy its own effect. But why would this chalk,
which softens on a small scale and at moderate heat, fail to
soften and would even reharden when the heat is more violent?
Why would the same thing fail to happen with bone ash? This
phenomenon is strange enough [463] to justify an attempt to
explain it, and our principles shall once more provide the explanation. They have shown that cast iron is softened as it becomes deprived of its sulfurous and saline parts. Progressive
softening requires that more sulfurs and more salts continue to
leave it and that those which have been driven out by the fire
do not return; other substances must absorb these sulfurs and
salts and must not permit them to escape. This is what powdered
bone ash always does. Most of the salts contained in bones are
volatile and have been removed during calcination. Their sulfurs have been burned, and the ash seizes everything that issues
from the iron and has room for it. Chalk is, indeed, an absorbent
matter; but it is not equally denuded of sulfurs and salts. Its
sulfurs and salts are fixed, and, being fixed, they remain as long
as the chalk is not heated beyond a certain degree. In this condition it even absorbs those which are removed from the iron.
During this whole time, as long as the same degree of heat is
maintained, it contributes toward the softening of cast iron;
but when it becomes hotter, when the heat has enough force
to carry away its salts and sulfurs in spite of their being fixed,
then the chalk no longer absorbs those of the iron and will even
supply it with more whenever none are expelled from the iron
by the fire. Consequently, it then no longer softens it but may
even help to reharden it; and that is what actually happens
whenever [464] cast iron that had been softened by chalk, or
iron that had started to become softened, is later found to have
been rehardened by this same chalk. The acids, the salts of
chalk, are probably vitriolic and therefore very difficult to remove. They dissociate themselves only at a very great heat. Our

experiments in connection with the conversion of wrought iron into steel (Mem. 1) have shown, indeed, that salts cannot be introduced into iron except when assisted by oily or sulfurous substances, that they need this vehicle. Possibly chalk cannot provide enough of these parts, but those which escape from the cast iron can re-enter after having absorbed salts from the chalk. There is nothing to prevent this kind of circulation. Cast iron and wrought iron contain very different quantities of sulfurous matter.

It is possible, however, that not all chalks have the same adverse effect. There may be some that are less charged with salts and others whose salts are more fixed and can, therefore, be separated from them only by a more violent fire. But I have found none among those which I tried out later in small-scale operation that did not reharden iron which had already become softened if this iron was heated enough to become almost melting-hot.

As there are so many objections to chalk, which was the best of all the earthy substances which I have tried in my attempts to bring about softening, and other kinds of calcines were still less successful, bone ash seems to be the right [465] substance to use; and the reason why a reliable method for softening cast iron has so far been lacking is that nobody had thought of employing it.

Indeed, as soon as the problem had been reduced to using those substances which were the most salt-free, as soon as I was guided by this principle, bone ash was of all the substances known to me the one that seemed most promising. The salts of bones, like those of all animal matter, are volatile; they can be removed by calcination. After calcination, bones contain no fixed salts or almost none, but the different kinds of other ashes do. Bones contain no salts of the nature of mineral salts, but the different kinds of clay do. When cupels are to be prepared, which of all the different kinds of crucibles are those which must be made of the most insipid, the most salt-free, clay, bone ash is used.

Although bone ash is the material that must be used in preference to all the others which I have tried out in my experiments, it is evident that we must not forget to moderate its effect by mixing it with powdered charcoal. But as the latter may retard the softening or does at least not further it as much as bone ash, I have investigated (as I mentioned before) how the mixture was to be proportioned. Sometimes I added only one-sixth, sometimes only one-fourth, and sometimes [466] only one-third. If long firing is not required, these amounts suffice. A still more general rule is that, the better the crucibles are closed, the less it is necessary to use powdered charcoal. The safest is, however, to add one part to every two parts of the other substance. After all, a little more charcoal is not able to retard the operation. Even if powdered charcoal by itself does not help much in softening cast iron, it can be relied upon not to harden it. After rather prolonged exposure to the fire, I have taken cast iron from a crucible where it had been packed only in this powder, and it seemed to me that it had become a little softer. Leather charcoal alone also produced this same effect— after rather prolonged firing it had produced a slight softening.

Furthermore, it seems to me that powdered charcoal helped in giving the cast iron more body. Perhaps it prevents that the softening takes place too suddenly, and this consideration alone would justify the use of a little larger portion of charcoal.

Even though the softening of cast iron caused by charcoal powder alone is very inconsiderable, it may seem strange that any softening occurs when we recall that we have seen elsewhere that this powder alone can convert iron into steel, can supply it with sufficient sulfurs and salts to change its nature. How does it happen, then, that it does not increase the hardness of cast iron, that it removes [467] sulfurs from it instead of supplying it therewith? The answer to this problem is again the same as the explanation I proposed for the different ways in which chalk acts at different degrees of heat. I believe that the sulfurs of wrought iron are much more firmly fixed than the sulfurs of steel and also more firmly than those of cast iron. Wrought iron contains fewer of them, and it is more intimately penetrated by them. The sulfurs of charcoal are emitted more easily than those of wrought iron. The iron soaks them up when it is surrounded by this charcoal. Conversely, cast iron, which is surcharged with sulfurs, which in a way is a kind of pyrites but more metallic than the ordinary kind, releases the sulfurs sooner, or in larger amounts, than the charcoal releases those it contains.

It is to be concluded from these experiments that the best thing to do in softening cast iron is to rely on bone ash and charcoal. There is no reason to fear that the price of these substances will make the work too expensive. It would be hard to find anything cheaper. There is no reason to worry about the amount of bones needed, for city dumps will supply more than enough. Can you think of anything easier than a job consisting of collecting something that costs nothing? Furthermore, it seems rather pleasant to me to realize that something which was useless so far has become of great usefulness. If collecting the required bones should seem too much trouble, the men who [468] have no other work than to collect rags for paper mills can add this to their occupation. They may even find more bones on the streets than rags. The butcher trade will also furnish bones in abundance.

The quantity of bones needed will not even be as large as one might think. After enough of a supply to fill a crucible or furnace has once been obtained, all that has to be additionally collected will be the amounts needed to replace what is lost; for something is lost of all materials that are handled and rehandled. But there will be no noticeable loss in the fire. I have employed the same material several times without noticing a measurable difference in its effect. It is possible, however, that, in being used, it may absorb too much of the salts. By calcining it once more and then leaching, one would rid it again of any salts it might have absorbed from the iron and of the alkaline salts of the charcoal which will have been reduced to ashes. Part of the charcoal is always burned in each operation, but this can be replaced by adding a little fresh charcoal at one's discretion. It was shown in the experiments with the salts that the alkaline salts which the charcoal will leave are not objectionable. But, if the mixture is made up of one part of charcoal to two parts of bone ash, it can safely be used three or four times without the addition of fresh charcoal.

In making cupels, we look for certain kinds of bones, such as the bones of sheep's feet [469] or calves' heads. I well believe that there are certain bones which are better than others, but I have used indiscriminately all those which were brought to me without worrying from which animal or from which part of an animal they came. I have found all of them very good. In the case of work on a large scale we often must choose what is easiest rather than what is best. However, our art would profit from experiments made to find out which kinds of bones are most effective. Perhaps they would be found among those which are most easily obtained; and, if the best were of a rare kind, we could save them for work that requires the greatest care. But such experiments would take a long time and would be difficult to follow through, so that they will necessarily have to be made as we gradually become more accustomed to soften cast iron.

I have said nothing so far about the method of calcining bones, and there is indeed very little to be said, for all it amounts to is to let them burn until they become easily friable and very white. They can be placed in any kiln or furnace, where a fire will be maintained until they are sufficiently calcined, which does not take long but varies of course in proportion to the amount of bones which are calcined at one time. There is no reason to be afraid of burning them too much. I believe to have noticed that bone ash which I used to soften cast iron was more effective during a second [470] furnace run than during the first, and the reason for this may be that the calcination of these bones was still continued during the entire duration of the first furnace run. I should give warning, however, that it is impossible to burn these bones without causing a disagreeable odor.

After the bones have been thoroughly calcined, they are pulverized. The powder to which they are reduced cannot be too fine, but it is not necessary to make it extremely fine. I often have used some as coarse as sand, but it is more effective when it is finer. When it is too coarse, it sometimes happens that small spots on the iron castings, corresponding in size to the coarsest grains of the bone ash, become scaled. Sometimes, the casting is spotted all over by such grains, which means that the bone ash and the charcoal powder were not very well mixed.

The amount of bone ash to be used at one time is left very much to individual choice. This process is not like the process of making steel—a little more cannot spoil anything. However, the amount used is sufficient if it prevents the castings in the same crucible from touching each other and keeps them a little apart.

In addition to the different substances which I have tried out according to the foregoing, I believed I should also try some that are obtained from animals and therefore might be somewhat analogous to bone ash. Shells are, one might say, the bones of certain [471] aquatic and terrestrial animals. I had oyster shells calcined, the shells of fresh-water mussels, and those of garden snails, and in each of these different calcines I packed the iron of a different crucible. As ordinary lime is able to produce some softening, it seemed easy to assume that iron would also become softened in these calcines. And it did.

Still another kind of fish bone which I believed I ought to try out was the shell of the cuttlefish. Goldsmiths are very familiar with cuttlebone, and so are jewel-setters and diamond-cutters. All these people make use of it in molding small objects. When calcined, these bones also softened the iron. But the iron scales just as it does in true bone ash when any one of these different calcines is used unless its effect is moderated by an addition of charcoal. Most of these substances would be easy to obtain at the seashore, where one could cheaply prepare large quantities. But are they better than the calcine of ordinary bones? Are they even as good? After my experience with the effect of chalk it would be unwise to make a decision before trials have been made on a large scale. I do not believe, however, that I myself can be expected to make all these experiments on a large scale. Only in a factory that has regular work can test runs of this kind be undertaken without being too expensive.

Since I wished to try at least on a small scale all the materials that I imagined might be [472] suitable, I also used eggshells after they had been calcined. They had about the same effect as the previous materials, but it would not be so easy to obtain them.

I have made still another test, with which I shall conclude

this memoir. I have used iron itself to soften cast iron. Remember that, when I described the furnace for the conversion of iron into steel, I said that I had the crucibles, the vessels in which the iron is inclosed, made of plates; and that I said that these plates must be made of clay in order to resist a violent fire but that they could be made of cast iron if only a moderately hot fire was to be employed. In many cases I have used only cast-iron plates. After they had been exposed to the fire for one or more days and the fire had completely burned out, the surface of every plate upon which the fire had acted was covered by a rather thick layer of powder which had a very beautiful red color and sometimes a red verging on violet. This layer consisted of the parts of iron that had been burned. In other words, the chemist knows that this powder is what he calls "saffron of Mars," and a saffron of Mars* made without any addition. I have had these plates brushed and all the powder removed and collected. What I just said about it (and the place of its origin) sufficiently proves that it is nothing but burned iron which has been deprived of its [473] oily part. As this powder is far from containing the quantity of oily and saline parts that it can contain, I thought it would be very suitable for softening cast iron which is imbedded in it, and I therefore packed cast iron in this powder. It softened it perfectly, and it has seemed to me that it softened it much faster than any of the other materials did. In an attempt to confirm this matter, I placed some of this powder (that is, very pure saffron of Mars) on the bottom of a cylindrical crucible. In the same crucible I placed a second layer consisting of this saffron mixed with bone ash; and higher up I placed a layer of pure bone ash. This crucible was kept in the fire for some time. When it was withdrawn, I found that the cast iron which had been softened best in this crucible was that which had been packed in the saffron of Mars alone. The mixture of this powder and bone ash had had less effect but more than bone ash alone.

In factories in which only cast-iron plates are used large amounts of this powder could be collected. It could also be

---

* Saffron of Mars, also known as *crocus martis*, was usually made by roasting iron sulfide or by igniting the nitrate, sulfate, or acetate of iron. Apothecaries also made it by rusting iron filings in the morning dew.

made very cheaply. (Its volume per unit weight is very different from that of iron.) But, even so, it hardly seems as if it would be suitable for work on a large scale; all one can expect is that it will be used in softening some small castings. However, the crucible in which it is contained must not be exposed to a violent fire, or [474] the powder would become a compact mass that clings to the cast iron. It is true that a few taps will make it come loose, but this would entail the risk that some small part of the casting might also break off. If the fire in the furnace has been violent, this powder is no longer found on the surface of the plates; the grains will then unite and form a spongy scale in such large amounts that it is surprising that the thickness of the iron has not noticeably diminished at the places where the scale has fallen off; for the pieces of scale, if placed one upon another, would be thicker than the plate. The explanation is that their texture is very spongy, even much more so than it seems.

The Fourth Memoir, Dealing with the
Furnaces Which Should Be Used
in Softening Cast Iron

S OUR IRON castings must be packed in fine powders to be softened, it follows that they must be inclosed in crucibles, as I have always indicated heretofore. But from this fact alone it does not necessarily follow that the crucibles must be luted as well as those in which we placed our bars to convert them into steel. In order to make steel, we must force sulfurs and salts to penetrate into the iron; in order to soften cast iron, we must, conversely, remove the excess amount of these substances present in the iron. It would seem, therefore, as if in the latter instance evaporation might be nothing to be afraid of but something that might be rather desirable. Actually, however, the crucibles in which the cast iron is placed, or the compartments used in their stead, must be luted just as in making steel, although for different reasons. We found that a mixture of powdered charcoal and bone ash was required. If air had access to the crucible, the charcoal would burn. Furthermore, it is a general rule that any iron that is heated for [476] a long time in a place to which air is freely admitted is subject to scaling.

Nevertheless, I wished to see if the softening would not be accomplished faster when the sulfurs and salts were free to sublimate. I took a long, slender crucible and filled it with layers of bone ash and layers of cast iron approximately halfway up. There I placed a clay partition which prevented interaction between this half and the other. I filled the second one, like the first half, with layers of bone ash and layers of cast iron and left the crucible open, so that the sulfurs and salts of the material in the upper half of the crucible were free to evaporate. After exposure to the fire for as long as I thought necessary, I compared the pieces of cast iron from the lower half with those from the upper half. The differences I found were not great enough to make me regret that the presence of charcoal powder prohibited leaving the crucibles open.

The same reasons that led me to give my new steel furnace the shape I have previously discussed (Mem. 4, pp. 75 ff.) are also valid in softening cast iron. In one as in the other of these operations we must be equally careful to use the heat efficiently, to reduce the consumption of fuel. In both, metal is heated in crucibles closed tightly against the flame. And the factor which is more than any others of the same importance in softening cast iron as it is in converting [477] wrought iron into steel is the ability to observe what happens in the crucibles, to know how the workpieces are faring which have been charged at different levels. This is accomplished through those windows, those large openings, which go from the inside of the crucible to the outside and for which we have stoppers which are taken out and put back in again at will. In order to make it easier to withdraw test bars through these openings, we can cut out part of the furnace wall on the outside at the level where these openings are and thus provide a setback in the wall which can be as deep as desired.

To soften cast iron, we therefore shall use the same furnaces we have used to convert iron into steel. Although their construction is described in a very long memoir, I purposely have reserved certain particulars for the present memoir, which will serve as a supplement to the other. What I have saved, however, concerns cast iron more than steel. For steel I preferred furnaces in which the heat is urged by the blast of bellows, whereas it would be better in the present instance to use only furnaces in which the air is not forced. I do not mean that bellows would not be effective; but, if they are to be used, care must be taken to moderate their blast, for in the present operation the heat must not be so great as in the former. Wrought-iron bars can stand [478] a degree of heat that would melt our iron castings. However, the openings through which we can look into the crucibles enable us to know how great the heat is and to judge whether it is time to reduce it.

For the conversion of iron into steel I suggested to build furnaces which could be charged from the side, so that during the second furnace run the heat which the furnace has acquired during the first run can be utilized—and I have had this done for softening cast iron (Pl. 15, Figs. 2, 3). An additional reason decided me to make use of this arrangement. I shall explain in a moment that the furnaces used to anneal cast iron must be made higher by one-third or even by one-half than the steel-making furnaces, and for that reason the inconvenience in charging from above would be much increased.

I am assuming throughout that it is still clear what I mean by the crucibles of my furnaces and how they are located. In order to charge from the side, all that is necessary is to leave each crucible open on one side, from its bottom, or almost from the bottom, up to the top. If the furnace has three crucibles, the large opening of the center crucible will be on one side of the furnace (Fig. 2, *C D E*), and the openings of the other two crucibles, of the end crucibles, will be on the opposite side (Fig. 3, *I K, L M*).

As one crucible is being charged, part of its opening is closed. For this purpose we [479] shall have five to six pieces of fired clay (Figs. 5, 6), of crucible clay, made so that they fit upon each other and into the opening that has been left in the crucible. Together, these pieces will form something like a small connecting wall (Fig. 4) which can be easily set up or taken down in a minute. Two iron bars go through each one of the pieces, and where they extend out of the piece they end in knobs (Fig. 5, *P P*). They will serve as two handles which make it possible to pull out the piece into which they are built. Each of these pieces will also have a square opening, which has a stopper of the same shape (Fig. 6, *Q*); and these are the windows through which we can see what happens at different levels of the furnace and through which we can remove test bars.

When I first proposed this arrangement (Mem. 4), I did not fail to warn that, as it weakens the body of the furnace, we must remember further to strengthen it by ties to prevent the furnace from opening up. In addition to horizontally placed ties, other iron bars must be placed vertically. The ends of these are bent around and will be anchored in the masonry (Fig. 2,

K K). The horizontal ties will be fastened to the vertical bars either by rivets or by screws and nuts.

But the main thing is that a vertical bar must be placed almost flush with each side of the opening of the crucible on the outside and that the horizontal ties (Fig. 2, *I H, H I*) are well connected with these [480] bars. This is made necessary by the following: In order to make charging easier, the horizontal ties are cut at each of the openings, for it would be inconvenient if the parts of the ties that pass over the openings were in the artisan's way when he wishes to charge. It is essential that these parts can be taken out and placed back again. Of the hundred possible ways in which this can be done, it suffices to describe one. Near the openings of the crucibles each tie rod will end in a larger knob than the rest of them do, and this knob will be pierced to form something like a ring (Fig. 2, *H H*). Into each of two rings that are placed equally high on the furnace and on both sides of the edge of the opening of a crucible the bent end of a rod or bar of iron will be inserted. When this piece is in place, the tie will be complete. The two ends of this piece will have holes through which keys are put which keep the pieces in their place and which will also help to tighten them more (Fig. 7). These pieces can be taken out and put back in again at will. When they are in position, the furnace will be closed as tightly as if every tie consisted of one piece. These connecting links can be fastened with screws or, as I said before, in many other ways.

If the air that enters the furnace is not driven by bellows, the number of openings of the ashpit should be increased. We shall then have four, one at the middle of each side (Figs. 1, 2, 3, *A*). There will be a door in the form of a stopper for each of these openings, and these stopper doors will take the place of registers. [481] Depending on whether they are in or out, smaller or larger quantities of air will enter the furnace.

Furthermore, the air can be made to enter with a greater rush and in larger amounts; it can be made to produce an effect similar to the one the bellows make it produce, but less dangerous, by installing ducts which bring the air in from afar. We are familiar with that arrangement, a sort of blower, which is used in some fireplaces. It is described in the *Mechanics of the Fire* by the ingenious M. Gauger.* In these fireplaces all one has to do in order to urge the fire is to open a small adjustable register, which is on a level with the hearth. As soon as the hole is open, the wind rushes out of it with greater speed than it would come out of a bellows, the working of which would be a great deal of trouble. All the mechanics involved in this simple blower consists in the way one connects this hole with the air outside. To have something like it in our furnace, we shall have to place the bottom of its ashpit below the level of the ground around the furnace; and, starting at each of the openings that admit the air, we shall have to dig a trench in the ground (Fig. 1, *A A A A*), which will form something like a tunnel, which becomes increasingly wider farther away from the furnace. After these four channels have been dug, they will be covered up by boards, and the boards in turn will be covered with earth. The longer [482] these air ducts will be and the wider the mouthpieces, the more air will be introduced into the furnace.†

Nevertheless, there is no reason to be afraid of its effect, which can be moderated at will. The quantity of air entering through each of the ducts can be reduced as desired, or its passage through one of them can be completely shut off. This is done by installing above each one, wherever it seems most convenient, something like a door, which can be lowered down to the bottom of the channel or raised to its upper rim. The same thing can be accomplished by any other arrangement one might choose. These ducts will stand up better if they are lined with rocks or burned-clay tile on the inside.

This furnace, which will be fired exclusively with wood and

* Nicholas Gauger, *La Méchanique du feu* (Paris, 1713); English trans. (London, 1716).

† These ducts to the outer air were often found in eighteenth-century furnaces (see, e.g., William Lewis, *Commercium philosophico-technicum* [London, 1763], p. 24) but served no useful function whatever. In a domestic fire, to which Gauger first applied it, it was useful to give a concentrated draft and to avoid cooling of the room. It is odd that Réaumur should adopt this part of domestic fireplace design and not the chimney stack, which would have been far more useful.

is designed to anneal cast iron, can, or, rather, must, be at least one-third or one-half higher than those used for the conversion of iron into steel, for which I have given the dimensions. The flame of wood and the flame of charcoal rise to very different heights. Furthermore, since in this case the heat is not the result of the same large, continually introduced quantity of air, the reasons for keeping the furnace lower when bellows were used are no longer valid. The top part of this furnace, though higher, will therefore have sufficient heat; furthermore, it can be charged with the smallest castings. If we [483] give the body of the furnace greater height, it will be found more convenient to excavate for part of the bottom—that means, to place the bottom below the level of the ground around it. This will make it easier to look into the furnace from above, and this arrangement fits in very well with the plans for our air ducts, which also require that the furnace stands free.

As long as we use wood fire, there are no objections to making the crucibles of cast-iron plates. The reader will recall, or ought to recall, the position of these plates; and I further assume that he has not forgotten that I stated in the fourth memoir that, the larger the furnace, the thicker must be these plates. However, their thickness should hardly exceed an inch. As they are used, they become thinner and thinner. At the end of each furnace run the side on which the fire has acted will be covered by a rather thick layer of a red powder; this is a saffron of Mars which one will do well to collect. It has the properties of ordinary saffron of Mars and has been formed without the addition of sulfurs. It can be used for the same purposes as it is used in medicine and for some others which I have talked about before. The plates become thinner by the amounts that come off to form this powder and also by the scale that forms. But, in spite of the powder and the scale, they last a long time. The thinner they become, the more subject they are to [484] warping. In order to prevent warping to such an extent that they become so distorted that the shape and the proportions of the crucibles and of the fireboxes would be changed, care must be taken to reverse them after each furnace run. The side that was inside the crucible must become the outside. The fire will then straighten them out, and later it will even make them convex at the side where they were concave.

If we want to be even more certain that their shape is preserved nearly flat without having to turn them so often, the following precautions will be helpful. I assume that they are made of gray or black iron in which holes can be drilled, as one can drill them in the iron of which stoves are made; but, even if they are not made of cast iron of this quality, it will always be possible to do what I shall describe (Fig. 9) after the plates have been in service for two furnace runs. After having divided their height into any desired number of parts (three or four will be enough), draw parallel lines through the divisions and drill in each dividing line two or three holes several lines in diameter. Through each of these holes put an eyebolt. This bolt will have a head with a square hole in it which can hold a $\frac{3}{4}$-inch merchant bar or some other piece of thinner iron. The head of each bolt will be on that side of the plate which will be inside the crucible, and the end goes all the way through to the other side, upon which it will be firmly riveted. Through all the bolt heads [485] on the same horizontal line pass a square bar which is almost as long as the plate is wide. It is clear that these bars spaced at intervals will keep the plate from warping. But to be even more certain of the effectiveness of the bars, to make sure that after they have been installed they do not yield to the stress of the plate, the bars of the two plates are connected by some arrangement, which is easy. I assume that the cross-bars are placed at corresponding heights on both plates. We shall use pieces of nailrod, or of heavier iron, the two ends of which are bent around. Their length between the two bends will equal the distance from one plate to the other. Each one of the hooks will be engaged in one of two bars equally high. The number of these links connecting each pair of bars will depend on individual choice. It would also be possible to join one end of such a connecting bar firmly with one of the bars and have the other end enter into a hole drilled in the other bar. All these arrangements can be varied according to the ingeniousness of the artisan. We shall leave the choice to him. For instance, he may use cotters, if he considers it advisable, to hold the ends of the hooks.

With these precautions, the plates will be firmly held in place. The elongation of the bars and connecting rods will not let them expand to the point where they become warped; and the space which these bars occupy in the crucible is not large enough to deserve consideration.

A single [486] plate will hardly be enough for the entire height of the furnace if we make the furnace as high as we can— and, indeed, as we must—to make efficient use of the heat. We therefore shall arrange to have two or more, one on top of the other; but then, to be quite certain that the flame cannot enter, the edge of one of the plates will have to be shaped so that it has a groove into which the edge of the other one fits (Fig. 8, *bb*). Clay, applied on the side that is inside the crucible, will close the joints well enough to be used as a substitute for the groove.

These plates will last longer if the side that is exposed to the flame is coated with lute. It is true that it will be difficult to make the lute stick to the plate unless the plate is pierced with rather closely spaced nails, which will help to hold the lute. If instead of cast-iron plates we used plates of thick sheet iron, it would be easier to apply the nails. Sheet iron is more easily pierced, but it is also more expensive than cast iron.

In the fourth memoir on the conversion of iron into steel I weighed the advantage of using plates, and especially of using thin plates. It is, indeed, considerable as long as we are forced to let the furnace cool down before it is recharged and as long as it is charged from above. But when it is charged from the side and when it is still very hot, which can easily be done by following the explanations at the beginning of this memoir, [487] it is no longer so important to use such thin partitions to form the crucibles nor to have partitions that can be so easily taken out. We shall build something like small walls, approximately $1\frac{1}{2}$ inches thick. They will be made either of small brick of this thickness or even of a single piece of clay. But this clay and the clay used for the brick must always be clay prepared like that used for ordinary crucibles in the way I have described so many times before. These partitions, these little walls, can be made by people who do not have to be especially skilful in handling clay, particularly if a tolerably even wooden board of the height and width of the partition is available. The wooden board will be placed upright in the furnace; it will serve as a guide in applying the clay evenly and making it stand up quite vertically. But the ends of every one of the partitions are locked in the body of the wall, in grooves or slots resembling those which hold the plates.

In order to make these partitions more rigid, in order to reduce the danger of warpage, we can use some arrangement similar to that suggested for the iron plates. For instance, on the inside of the crucible the partitions could have one or two places (extending from top to bottom) where they are thicker than elsewhere. Something like columns will be formed there. In order to make them even more rigid, each column will have two or three projections. Every one of these projecting parts will have [488] a hole that goes all the way through in a vertical direction. When the columns of each partition or plate are opposite those of the next partition, and the projecting parts of one are at the same height as the projecting parts of the other one opposite from it, the plates will mutually support each other if one end of an iron rod is inserted in one of the projections and the other end in the other one.

Another, more simple way of bracing the plates, which I have found satisfactory, is to place a third plate of clay or cast iron in each firebox—I mean between the plates of two different crucibles. The width of this one will be perpendicular to the widths of the others (Figs. 1, 2, 3, *F*) and will be as wide as the space between the two others. This will be something like a partition dividing each firebox into two equal parts. However, it will not go down to the floor of the firebox, to the bottom of the furnace. If its lower end reaches to within a foot or within 9–10 inches of the bottom, it will be near enough. In order to keep this plate more firmly in position, we shall, in making the other plates, arrange to have slots cut into them where this third plate must be joined to them. They will be made thicker at these locations by as much as is needed to make these slots. If it were to be feared that the plate of one of the small crucibles might be pushed inside the crucible by the stress exerted upon it by the plate of the center [489] crucible through the plate that is in contact with both of them, this could be avoided without fail by placing in each of the end crucibles, in a similar way, another small plate like the one in the firebox (Fig. 1, *F G;* Fig. 3, *G*).

Finally, we shall proportion the size of the crucibles of each furnace to the amount and dimensions of the castings that are to be charged in it. I have never had any intention to give detailed dimensions for design. As the capacity is increased, the necessary time of firing becomes greater; but it must always be remembered that, in order to use the wood economically, neither the fireboxes nor the chimneys should be made much larger.

It is a known fact that for heating purposes there is a great difference among different kinds of wood; but in this case we must also realize that in our furnaces there is a great difference between very dry wood and the same wood when it is wet. The people who work in glassworks have had the same experience. They place their wood in the same shed where the furnace is located, and these sheds are usually designed so that the wood can be laid directly above the furnace, where it is piled up on a sort of lattice floor. The degree of heat which wood acquires when it burns will be tempered by the parts of the water which wet wood contains. If the burning parts that rise are mixed with a greater quantity of water vapor, the latter may quench the [490] heat of some of the former and will reduce the heat of all the others.

If somebody would like to soften articles of cast iron on a small scale, either because of curiosity or for some other reason, this can be done like the trials in converting iron into steel. He can use the fire of a forge or of any small furnace in which iron can be given a considerable degree of heat without melting it, however. Some castings can be softened in two or three hours in this way. The crucibles used must be of a size and shape best suited for the pieces that are to be inclosed in them.

The way in which the castings are arranged in the furnace requires no explanation. I have said elsewhere that, although it would be impossible to use too much of our mixture of bone ash and powdered charcoal, all that is actually necessary is what is needed for satisfactory separation of the pieces from each other. It also would be superfluous to point out that the thickest pieces, and those which must be softened the most, must be placed where the heat is most intense. But I am warning that any sand which may have stayed on a piece when it was removed from the mold must be carefully brushed off. The spots where sand has been left will not soften or will soften much less than the rest; and, furthermore, if the sand starts to melt, it will form a crust which will spread far beyond the place where it has been. If it does not make the piece harder, it will cover it with a substance that will often be hard to remove.

After [491] having carefully tried out whether more pro-longed but more moderate heating produces better results in softening than violent heat, I became convinced that the heat cannot be too great, provided it does not reach such a degree that it melts the castings. But I can give no general rules concerning the length of firing necessary to soften the castings. It must be greater when the articles are thicker; but not all of them must be softened to the same extent. In order to ascertain whether the thickest pieces have reached the desired condition and to find out whether the heat is neither too weak nor too strong, we must be careful when we charge the furnace to place pieces of different thicknesses of the whitest, the most thoroughly re-fined cast iron on a level with every opening. These can easily be taken out and will inform us about the condition of the others. It is not necessary that they have the shape of commer-cial castings; on the contrary, it is important that they have a simple shape, for they can then be more easily lifted out with-out disturbing anything inside the furnace. Of all the shapes one might give them the most convenient will be to make them round. I have them cast into small cylinders, or rods (Pl. 16, *A B C*), each of which is at least half as long as the furnace; and I have them made of different diameters. The diameter of some will be [492] almost equal to the thickness of the heaviest pieces that must be softened to the core. The small ones show whether the thin castings are in any danger of melting. This is especially evident from the fins that are left on these rods. When the rods are removed from the mold, they have all along each side, diametrically opposite each other, a little thin leaf of metal which has been cast in the empty spaces which are almost always left by the two parts of the mold, even if they have been fitted upon another very carefully. Surely there is nothing thinner in the furnace than these little fins and, consequently, nothing that is in greater danger of melting.

The Fifth Memoir, Dealing with the Precautions Necessary in Annealing Cast Iron; with the Changes Produced in the Iron by Different Degrees of Softening; How One Can Restore to Cast Iron the Hardness That Has Been Taken Away from It; and How, and to What Extent, Wrought Iron Can Be Softened

WHILE THE furnace is being filled with castings that are to be softened, while it is being charged, cast-iron test bars (Pl. 16, *A B C*) are placed level with each of the openings that can be closed by easily removable stoppers. Among these bars there are some whose diameter is approximately the same as the thickness of the heaviest pieces and others that are thinner. These different test bars will show what effect the anneal has on the castings. But, in order to appraise this effect, we must be familiar with the successive changes produced by this anneal in the iron that is being softened, for then we shall only have to observe on the fractures of the bars which we remove whether the changes [497] that indicate softening have taken place. We also must know to what extent the different kinds of cast iron can be softened.

When a piece of cast iron has been withdrawn from the furnace and has cooled, it is possible by merely inspecting the outside to judge whether it has been partially softened or not at all. Iron that has cooled in the mold in which it was cast has a bluish color—it is slate blue. If the iron has preserved this color or if it has again become blue in the furnace after this shade had been replaced by a sort of rust color, it has not been softened at all. The first way of investigating whether it has been softened is to test it with the file, which rarely cuts into iron that has this bluish color. But if the color is dark, of a brown resembling coffee or even blacker, we can assume with confidence that the surface has become softened.

Cast iron that looks brown on the surface thus has become iron that can be worked with the file, at least near the surface, where it has been softened. Let us break it to study the discernible changes that have taken place on the inside; but let us start by breaking a piece which has not been softened through to the center (*E*). We shall observe that the entire fracture has changed color. If the iron was white, it now will be less white. If it was gray, it will have become more brown, or almost black. Iron that was black will have become deep black. [498] No element of doubt is left in such a comparison of colors if a piece is cut off from each test bar and put aside before the bar is placed in the furnace. This change in color extends to the center of a piece before any considerable softening has taken place at the center. Often it precedes softening by a long time. As soon as the thinnest surface layer, a layer thinner than paper, has become softened, everything else has changed color in the way I have just described.

But the most remarkable change in the iron that is being softened is the change in texture. The texture of white iron, which was compact, where grains were not discernible, where at most a few platelets could be distinguished even under the microscope, gradually disappears. First, a band composed of grains (*E*) appears all around the rim; and, wherever this iron has acquired grains, it has been softened. Very gradually the grains extend and reach the center (*F*). When the entire inside has become granular through to the center, the cast iron has become softened to the center. It can be worked with the file wherever it has become granular. But at first the grains are only scattered where the iron begins to be softened; they occur apart from each other. As the softening progresses, the quantity of grains increases at each location, and they become more closely pressed together (*G*). Also, as the softening continues, the color of the cast iron becomes darker. That of white iron, and even of the whitest iron, [499] becomes grayer than ordinary steel, grayer even than the kind of steel that is most difficult to work. But one strange thing is to be noted—that in the midst of these grains there are spots with a scattering of larger and very black grains. The entire texture is dotted with them (*K K L*).

Let us follow the changes a little longer. The fire, or anneal, has given our iron a darker color. If this anneal is continued, a white, brilliant band forms around the rim. Its color is brighter than that of steel; in short, it resembles the color of the white wrought irons with platelets. This band is likewise composed of platelets, which leave empty spaces between them as the platelets of the iron of our second classification do [p. 112]. Thus, this band is truly a band of wrought iron which should be malleable like ordinary iron.

Finally, when the anneal is continued still longer, the white band becomes wider (*K K*). The whole inside again takes on lighter and lighter shades and then becomes white. But what is still more remarkable is the change in texture which continues to take place. There are cast irons whose fracture becomes exactly like that of the irons with platelets of the first and second classifications. It would be impossible by comparing the fracture of these irons with the fracture of our cast irons to say which are the cast irons. Both kinds of iron show very large, very brilliant platelets [500] mixed with smaller ones. If one of them is whiter and more brilliant, it is the fracture of our cast irons. Other cast irons, after having been annealed for a long time, resemble the granular irons in their fracture (*M*). They look less white and less brilliant than the fracture of the other cast irons but always at least as white as the wrought irons which they resemble, and they have, indeed, been returned to the nature of wrought iron.

Let us take a little more time to study the changes which have taken place in our white irons as they have changed in texture and color. Until now, we have not spoken respectfully enough of our cast-iron products, at least if steel deserves more respect than iron. They are, if you wish, steel products; they are similar to products made of ordinary steel. And it is more difficult, or at least it takes longer, to convert them back into common iron. It is a necessary consequence of all we have learned of the nature of steel, soft iron, and cast iron that our cast irons, in becoming softened, must become steel resembling ordinary steel. They are, indeed, steel as soon as their color has become dull gray and their fracture seems to be composed of grains (*F G*). When these irons, after they have become workable by the file, are heated and quenched like ordinary steel, they are also hardened by quenching. When they come out of the water, the file no longer cuts into them; and, when [501] they are subsequently heated over charcoal, they again become workable by the file as ordinary steels do. In other words, our cast iron is then transformed into a true steel; it is the same as common steel.

But this new steel ought not to be more durable than the other steel. It should be possible to reverse the process, to reconvert it into iron (cf. Mem. 8 on steel), to render it incapable of being quench-hardened, by continuing to deplete it of its sulfurs or, what amounts to the same, by continuing to anneal it. And this is indeed what actually happens. As soon as the gray band composed of grains has become white and consists of platelets, it is wrought iron. If it is quenched in this condition, we shall observe exactly what we observed in our steels that had been softened by soaking and had a band of iron around the rim. After quenching, the file will cut into the first surface layer, which is iron, but it will not cut beyond the place where the band of iron stops. If, after having hardened the center of our piece of cast iron by quenching, we place the piece on a bed of charcoal and let it become red-hot and then allow it to cool slowly, it will again become workable by the file like ordinary unquenched steel.

If the iron casting is thick, it is possible, therefore, by annealing, to have iron in all its possible states in the same fracture. The surface could be soft iron, next will be steel, and the center—if it has not yet been softened—will have remained cast iron.

The result [502] is that, if a cast-iron product is softened only to a certain point, it becomes a steel product; that, if the anneal is continued, it becomes steel enveloped in a layer of iron;

and a still more prolonged softening turns it completely into wrought iron.

I shall review the uses we can make of cast iron in these different conditions in different products, although in most cases it will not be necessary to go beyond the conversion into steel, so that our cast-iron products really become steel products. Since this new name would add nothing to their value, let us keep the old one.

Our cast iron, placed into the furnace white, has there first become dull gray; then it has taken on brown hues of increasing intensity while it has become continuingly more softened. After it has become brown or gray up to a certain point, and has softened all the while, it has then started to show shades of white, which have become increasingly white; and, finally, it has become whiter than it ever was before.

Obviously, we shall ask why iron that begins to soften becomes less and less white, and we shall be even more interested to know why it becomes white again after it has become gray or brown to a certain point. It seems to me that the most probable explanation of the underlying reason for this cycle is as follows: When the cast iron [503] is first exposed to the anneal, its texture is uniform, all its parts are about equally penetrated by sulfurs and salts; neither grains nor platelets are discernible, and so it appears white. After the fire has acted upon this iron for a certain time, the iron appears granulated. The sulfurs and salts that have evaporated have found more convenient passages in some directions than in others, and, by finding their way out, they have divided the mass of iron into particles. It is this sort of breaking-up that produces the grain structure which then appears. The fact alone that the iron has become granular is reason enough to make it appear less white than it appeared before. But, in addition to this, each of its grains has become more spongy. Furthermore, the sulfurs which earlier had penetrated its parts and are now on their way out—the sulfurs which have left the elementary parts—can also cause a change in the color. There is enough reason, therefore, for the iron to turn brown, and become browner and browner, as soon as we have caused it to become granular and have also made each of its grains more spongy.

I mentioned in passing as a strange phenomenon that at certain places there seemed to be a scattering of very black grains (L). These black grains can serve to demonstrate what causes the brown color of the rest. I have studied them under the microscope, but then I no longer found grains at those places. I realized that what I had taken [504] for black grains were holes much larger than those found elsewhere,* and it follows that smaller holes, which are closer together, will color our cast iron only brown or dark.

It is much more difficult to understand what causes the iron to become white again. However, the difficulty would be greater if, after it has turned white once more, it were of the same whiteness as before and had the same texture. But it will be noted that the last white is sparkling and brilliant, whereas the first was matte. Furthermore, whereas the first texture was uniform, the last is very non-uniform. We find in it either grains with empty spaces between them or platelets separated from each other by even larger empty spaces, and nothing like it could be seen when it was first exposed to the fire. The spaces left between the grains and platelets, which were not there before, are surely not the locations abandoned by the sulfurs and salts, for these were not present in such accumulations. But it must be realized that the grains which were spongy after the sulfurs had been driven out have later become more compact. The parts of the metal, which had reached a state approaching that of fusion, have come in contact with each other and have adhered to each other. For this reason there is subsequently no longer so much empty space within every grain and every platelet, but there are larger spaces between the grains and [505] platelets. But the grains that can be distinguished by themselves have become whiter because their texture has become closer, and they are of a more sparkling and brilliant white than before, because the metallic parts are no longer mixed with so much foreign matter.

Once, when I first started to soften cast iron on a large scale (the same time when I had the trouble with scale formation),

* The black spots referred to are probably areas of flaky graphite in a mottled fracture of the original casting and do not result from annealing.

something happened which seems worthwhile reporting but which would have been difficult to explain without the earlier observations of which I have just spoken. Among the castings in the furnace there were several large knockers for carriage gates (*QQ 00 PP*). These knockers were heavy, as one would expect from their size and thickness. When I withdrew them from the furnace, I was very much surprised to find them light. Although they had been solid when I put them in, they had now become hollow. They now were nothing more than hollow shapes (*R S T*); their inside was entirely empty, but their contours on the outside had been preserved; they had only lost a few decorative leaves, which had come off with the scale. On close inspection, I noticed several small holes (*T*) through which the material forming the inside had run out after it had become liquid. It is not astonishing that these knockers had become light, since part of the substance of which they were made had run off. But it was obvious that it was the substance occupying [506] the inside and even the very core that had become liquid, while the outer layers had remained solid. It is against the rules that melting should start at the inside. The only heat that the inner layers possess is the heat that they receive from the outer layers. They can at most have as much heat as the outside, but they cannot have more. To solve this problem, it was enough, however, to remember that wrought iron cannot be melted by ordinary fire and to realize that the heat in our furnace was not violent enough to liquefy cast iron until after the knockers had been softened to a certain depth, that is, had been converted into forgeable iron or steel to a certain depth. An increase in heat would then be without effect, and the knockers therefore kept their shape on the outside. On the inside, they were cast iron, which was contained in a sort of crucible made of non-melting iron and closed on all sides. The cast iron became molten in this crucible, and, where the crucible was the thinnest and the weakest, the molten iron softened its walls and forced them to yield. It opened passages for itself through which it flowed into the furnace or into the crucible that held all the castings. I found this cast iron at the bottom of the furnace as a shapeless mass.

Perhaps we can make profitable use of this observation by making certain cast-iron products lighter which otherwise would be too heavy. [507] If, after having converted their outer layers into steel or wrought iron, we urge the fire more violently, their inside will melt rather fast. This will not even have to lead to surface scaling if charcoal powder is mixed with the bone ash. I had used bone ash alone when the previously described accident happened.

In order to make sure that this experience was not the result of one particular chance happening or, more correctly speaking, of the coincidence of causes which are difficult to reproduce, I tried to change full cylinders into hollow tubes. For this experiment, I used pieces of the same irons ($X\,Y$) which I employed as test bars. I placed these pieces in small crucibles where they were surrounded by the compound used in softening. These crucibles were exposed to the fire of a common forge and completely covered with charcoal. I first gave them a moderate fire as required for softening. When I estimated that this fire had produced enough of an effect, that it had changed the state of the first layers of our cylinders from the state of being cast iron, I increased the fire as far as it was necessary to melt cast iron. The iron occupying the inside of our cylinders actually did become liquid and, being liquid, ran out of the cylinder, which was changed into a cylindrical tube (Z) in accordance with the purpose of the operation.

However, [508] this experiment made gropingly, one might say, did not always succeed.* Sometimes, I used the hot fire too late—at a time when the cylinders had been softened through to the center—and then they stayed solid. Sometimes I used the hot fire too soon, and then everything became liquid, because the softened layer, which had become common iron, was too thin and therefore was too weak a vessel to hold the molten metal. But if you are looking for an infallible way to succeed, withdraw from the furnace some of the test bars placed there.

* It is surprising that this experiment ever succeeded, for the production of the unmelted surface shell would be a result of decarburization which could hardly occur when there was an excess of charcoal in the packing mixture, as recommended by Réaumur.

Break them and observe on their fracture to what depth they have been softened. If this depth seems sufficient, give the companion pieces a violent fire as I have just explained, and they will become hollow. The expedient I am suggesting for these bars can be used generally with all classes of castings. Feeding heads can be left on the castings which, when fractured, will indicate the condition of the casting. However, the thicker the pieces, the more assurance there is that the operation will have the desired effect. This in itself is a fortunate circumstance, for we will naturally wish to use it only on heavy pieces. Before changing the subject let me add that we can make it easier for the substance that will melt at the inside of a piece to flow out and make this liquid material come out wherever we wish. Both can be accomplished by coating the chosen spot with a thin layer of sand or [509] any material that is less suited than our compounds are to contribute to the softening of cast iron (Y).

Among the articles that can be made of cast iron there are some that have to be softened only on the outside. They are the castings which require nothing more than being worked with the file, chisel, or graver, castings which are intended for applications that involve little strain or, when they are very heavy, applications for which their heaviness gives them sufficient strength; for cast iron, although naturally brittle, can be strong because of its bulk alone. Anvils which can stand the blows of the heaviest hammers can actually be made of cast iron without any other preparation. (Similarly it is possible to batter bulky bodies of glass without breaking them.) It would be useless to anneal for a long time pieces that require only such superficial softening.

Other iron castings must be softened through to the center. Examples of these are all castings that must be pierced from one side to the other by a drill and all those in which screw threads are to be cut. By long annealing it is always possible to bring them to this point if desired.

Finally, there are other castings that not only require softening but must be made less brittle; they must become tough up to a certain degree. This is what I shall here call "acquiring body," as I did when I discussed steel. Castings that must be given some sort of flexibility have to [510] be flexible either hot or cold. As castings are used only to avoid the trouble of forging, the toughness required of iron castings in order to be hot-workable is not such that they can be forged as a whole or such that we can entirely change their shape. That would mean wasting the advantages of our art. But there are cases where a piece, to be fitted into the place where one intends to use it, or to be assembled with another, must be bent, or straightened, or flattened out somewhere. Floral ornaments, or others, which are to be placed into a grillwork often need such adjustment. Cast-iron products which have been softened to the center can be heated cherry-red and will then withstand bending and flattening, provided they are carefully handled.

Although castings have been softened, it is possible that they have become softened only to some extent, so that, if they were given a welding heat, they would break under the hammer and would be found to be full of cracks. Softening first makes steel of them; but they start by becoming intractable steel, the kind of steel that is most difficult to forge. At the end, one succeeds in converting them into steel of a quality similar to the quality of ordinary steel, or even into something of the nature of wrought iron, if the softening is further continued.

However, I have encountered some that, even after they had been changed to the condition of wrought iron, could sometimes be forged only like steels that are difficult to work, [511] which is not astonishing, for there are ordinary irons that are difficult to forge. The parts of our iron which owes its condition to having been softened are separated from each other; there are empty spaces between them. These are part of the spaces that had been occupied by the salts and sulfurs which have been driven out. If we heat this iron to a high degree and want to forge it drastically, we spread open parts that are not well united. Some of them become detached, and cracks form. By repeated heating we succeed in reuniting these severed locations, just as two different pieces of iron can be welded together. But, I repeat, our cast-iron products are not meant to be shaped by the hammer. Iron is not cast into molds unless we wish to avoid the trouble of forging. The most that should be necessary is some slight adjustment, and it is easy to put cast iron in condition for that.

Nevertheless, I have changed cast iron by softening so that it could be hot-worked just like wrought-iron bars, and, after having been forged, it had neither splits nor cracks. But, in order to bring it to this point, the anneal must be continued much longer than would be necessary to give cast iron sufficient softness to be cut by the chisel or the file.

More can be accomplished if the pieces are thin. When the anneal is repeated often enough after such pieces have been converted to the state of wrought iron, they can be made to acquire a toughness which, when they are cold, [512] surpasses that of some wrought irons. I have frequently softened thin pieces so well—for instance, sword hilts and lids of snuffboxes —that I could bend them upon themselves by the blows of a hammer. There are many pieces which have no such toughness, although they are made of different kinds of wrought iron. More prolonged annealing will also give a degree of flexibility or body to thick pieces, especially if they are made of certain kinds of cast iron.

In addition to the advantage of body which cast iron acquires after more prolonged annealing than would be needed for working by the file, it acquires another one. Our observations have shown that iron that has started to become soft, or has even become quite easily workable by the file, has a dark, gray color but that, if annealing is continued, this color becomes lighter and is followed at the end by the whitest, most sparkling color iron can have. When iron is withdrawn from the furnace during the first stage of softening, it is evident that the cleaned castings, even if they are polished very carefully, will not be as white as when the iron is withdrawn during the second stage. However, if the castings that are to be softened need only be dressed after being softened—that is, if it is not necessary to drill them or to remove thick layers—it will never be necessary for the anneal to make the whole inside of the iron white. We are [513] then interested in the surface, and we know well enough that fortunately the softening and consequently the shades of white begin there.

We have assumed so far that all our castings were made of white iron. Castings of gray or even black iron, which are workable with the file without any additional softening, might be expected to have still greater softness after annealing. At most one might be afraid that, since they are already brown and will become more so by the first anneal, they would become irons of an ugly color. That is not their worst fault, however. These castings, which are already workable by the file before they have been annealed, are indeed more easily worked after the anneal. But, regardless of how much they are softened, they will never have as much body as castings of white iron. Do not expect that gray irons become hot-forgeable after repeated softening, and still less that they acquire a degree of toughness that would permit cold bending, as white irons do. We know that they differ from white irons because their metallic parts are mixed with more earthy parts or more vitrified parts. Annealing does not remove these earthy substances. Melting is the method that is so effective in this respect. When gray irons have been resoftened, when their sulfurs have been removed, they are more easily worked by the file than they were before. The file cuts glass well. But these earthy or vitrified parts, which are always [514] rigid, always inflexible, which are absolutely non-forgeable by nature, prevent the metallic parts from being sufficiently interconnected to be pliable or forgeable. However, if one continues the anneal of these irons for a certain time, their naturally brown or even black color, which has become even deeper at the beginning of the anneal, becomes lighter and then changes to white. But this color has never seemed as white to me, nor as sparkling, as the white reached by naturally purer irons.

Moreover, not all cast irons will be capable of acquiring the same degree of flexibility, even though they may have the same color after annealing. There are some that will be much superior to the rest in this respect. There are wrought irons that are incomparably much more flexible than others, and it is probable that those cast irons from which the most pliable wrought irons are made will also yield the cast iron with the most body. I have encountered cast irons which became so flexible that I was surprised. There exists no wrought iron that can be better bent than the pieces of cast iron of which I wish to speak. Unfortunately, I did not know from which furnace they had come, and a series of experiments will therefore still have to be made in order to find the irons from different countries that are given more body than others by annealing. These are experiments [515] which will necessarily be made as our art expands. Actually it is to be expected that they will be the irons from which fibrous wrought iron is obtained.

I have said that at present most of the iron that is immediately cast into molds when it comes from the furnace where the ore is smelted is gray iron. But if in the future iron is to be cast into molds immediately upon coming from the furnace, ores must be chosen which yield the whitest kind of iron, and it will have to be made still whiter and as liquid as possible. The quality of the ores has at least some effect, and possibly an important effect, on the color of cast iron. In some of our provinces, as in Berry, almost all iron is white; and in others, as in Nivernais, almost all iron is gray. Gray irons can become white, depending on the precautions taken in melting. But it is very probable that those which are naturally white will yield castings that have more body.

Thus, by paying some attention to the above, we shall be able to cast the irons obtained in the first smelting of the ore. Particularly, we shall use these irons to cast large pieces, those which require more metal than can be held by the crucibles or the other furnaces I have described in the [516] second memoir on this art. Moreover, this will constitute a saving. Finally, we know that castings, even if made of the grayest irons, can attain a beautiful color and a condition in which they can be polished, provided they are annealed as long as is necessary.

I have stated elsewhere that wrought iron which is converted into steel increases in weight. Cast iron which is converted into steel or into wrought iron should then, conversely, lose some of its weight. I weighed some cast iron very accurately before annealing it and weighed it a second time after it had been annealed. Indeed, its weight had not increased during the operation, and it seemed to me that it had even decreased somewhat, although very little, so that it was difficult to determine it exactly.

I have made a distinction among different degrees of softening which are suitable for different kinds of castings. It is almost impossible, however, to discuss in detail the length of firing required, for this always involves the thickness of the castings. To give some idea of the costs, I should say that, when a furnace with crucibles of the same size as in the furnace shown on Plates 3 and 4 is fired by wood, one cartload of wood should soften almost all the castings to the point where they can be easily dressed, regardless of the size of these castings and even though they were 1½ inches thick at some spots, which constitutes heavy iron [517] castings. The whole furnace, however, should not be filled with such heavy pieces. Much thinner ones must be placed at the locations where the heat is less intense. This cartload of wood must be burned in three days and two nights at the most and preferably within a shorter time. If it takes longer, the heat will not be strong enough. If the furnace has the same dimensions as the one in Plate 15, approximately two cartloads of wood will be burned. The operation will take less time and will soften the iron to a greater depth if charcoal is used instead of wood and if its heat is urged by a bellows. But more attention must then be paid to how hot the castings become, as they could melt. Provided they do not melt, they cannot be too strongly heated. A check can be kept on the degree of heat, as on the effect of the operation, by means of test bars which I have discussed in sufficient detail before.

When I say that it is impossible to heat too strongly, I assume that the castings which are to be softened are surrounded by bone ash. If we were forced to use chalk, clay, or some other alkaline matter derived from the earth, we should have to be very careful to maintain only a moderate heat in the crucibles. If these materials were of the same nature as the one whose strange effect I have described, the one which returned its original hardness to softened [518] cast iron, we would gain little by increasing the fire. Under such circumstances one should make it a rule to keep the castings in the crucibles at a cherry-red color; but the annealing time will thereby be very considerably prolonged.

Even though we are very careful in locating the pieces where it is best for them depending on their thickness, it will often happen that some will not be sufficiently softened because they are themselves of very unequal thickness in different places. Some sections can be softened in ten to twelve hours, but others require several days, and such different sections can occur in the same casting. The remedy is simple; it means to set such castings aside, to save them for a second furnace run and recharge them, as one generally recharges all pieces that have not become sufficiently tractable.

It is a fact that the first furnace run, the one that would have consumed only one cartload of wood, does not cause sufficient softening in thick castings which must be softened to the center in order that they can be drilled, nor in those of the thin castings which must be softened to the point where they can be bent cold. They will have to be annealed a second and a third time until they have reached the desired condition. It would constitute a greater saving if one were to use different furnace runs for castings that require different [519] degrees of softening. By not letting them become cold, and continuing the fire until they are softened to the core, one would make more efficient use of the acquired heat. We do not have to fear, as we did when we were dealing with steel, that continued heating would damage iron that has been softened to the desired degree. (If there is a limit beyond which it is inadvisable to continue, it would be after repeating the anneal too many times.) But it would be a pity to consume wood only to produce an unnecessary effect. It would be advisable, therefore, to have two or three or even a larger number of furnaces, the price of which will not be very high. Which one should be used would depend on the kind of castings that are to be softened. The small furnaces would always be used for all the thin castings.

Although I cannot go into close details concerning the cost of softening cast iron, it may be advisable to give a rough idea to allay any fear that softened cast iron will cost more to dress than the other metals and that this has to be added to the cost

of annealing. In order to give an idea of the savings, I shall discuss only two castings of the same kind which I had made for
my own information. The first is the knocker on the door of the
Hôtel de la Ferté (Pl. 17, Fig. 1), which I mentioned in the first
memoir. I had a pattern made of it. The cost of the pattern
should not be entered in the [520] calculation, since it adds very
little. As the same pattern serves to produce an endless number
of similar castings, its cost will have to be distributed over all
of them. Owning the pattern for this knocker, I had several of
them cast and then softened and dressed. These knockers, which
were very beautiful and had a very good finish, cost me less than
20 *livres* each, whereas the original had cost 700 *livres*. I had
the pattern of another knocker made of lead (Fig. 3). I showed
it to different artisans to find out what they would charge to
make it of wrought iron. Some of them set the price for making
it at 1,500 *livres*, and none stayed under 1,000. Several of these
knockers, which were very beautiful and very well finished,
cost me only 25 *livres* each when cast in iron. However, it would
be wrong to believe that the first castings will sell so cheaply.
The makers will wish to make their first pieces pay. As long as
there are few artisans, they will keep the prices high; but, as
the number of artisans increases, they will reduce them.

I have nothing to add concerning the method of crushing the
charcoal and mixing it with the bone ash. The practice differs
in no way from that discussed in connection with the compounds used in making steel. I could only repeat what I have
said so often concerning the necessity of luting all the joints
carefully. The flame is able to prevent softening and, what is
more, to reharden with time anything that [521] has been softened. It gives back to the iron what has first been taken away
from it.

The following is an example which must not be forgotten. In
annealing my castings, I often used cast-iron plates [for crucible
walls]. That side of these plates which was in contact with the
compounds should have been softened after the operation was
completed, and it was, which is according to the rules. It is
equally according to the rules that the side turned toward the
fire stayed hard. During the next furnace run, when each plate

was reversed, so that the side which had been outside of the crucible became the inside, it was the turn of this side to become softened, and it did. But the side that had been softened before, the one upon which the flame now acted, regained its original hardness. The drill could no longer pierce it, which means that, every time one reverses the plates, one side is softened and the side which had been softened before is rehardened—at least in the beginning.

The side of the plates that is exposed to the fire would also re-harden if these plates were wrought iron. Any burned iron, any iron that has been turned into scale or is about to be turned into scale, acquires a hardness that makes it almost proof to the file and the drill—that is, a hardness approaching that of glass. Burned iron is vitrified iron, at least in part.

So that when by some accident the surface of iron castings has become a little burned, if it has scaled, the scale will always be [522] hard. But if one removes the scale, the iron underneath will often be easily workable by the file. The scale can some-times make one believe that the iron has not been softened at all, although it has been softened very well. This happens when the conditions are such that this scale, this portion of the sec-tion that has been burned, has not come loose from the iron at all. It sometimes seems to adhere so well that one would not suspect that part of this iron can easily be detached from the rest. If then we try the casting with the file, it will be resistant. But, if we gently tap upon this casting with the peen of a ham-mer, the burned part, the scaled part, will come off in small particles. By successively tapping the whole casting in a similar way, one can cause the thin, burned shell to come off, and under it the iron will yield to the file.

If cast iron, when it is withdrawn from the annealing furnace where it has stayed long enough to become softened, has a bluish color or appears sprinkled with small brilliants—in short, if it has not acquired the coffee-brown color I spoke of at the beginning of this memoir—it is undoubtedly burned at the surface. It is covered by a hard scale which can be made to fall off by tapping it with a hammer.

Objects made of iron or steel cannot be too soft while they

are worked with the file or the graver. But it is often desirable
to harden them when the file, the chisel, [523] and the graver
are no longer required to cut them. Unless they were hardened,
it would be impossible to give them a high, brilliant polish.
With metals, as with gems, the height of the polish always depends on the degree of hardness. In addition, these objects
would not stay well polished unless they were hard. An extremely well-finished key, like those imported from England,
would soon lose its luster if we neglected to have it quenched
before giving it its final polish. Steel is quenched the harder the
more carefully it is to be polished. When the result of the anneal
has been to convert our cast iron only into steel, there is no
doubt that it can be quenched like steel. And, when the result
has been to cover the steel with only a thin layer of soft iron,
the piece can still be quenched if this layer of wrought iron is
removed in working. But if the anneal has resulted in making it
too thoroughly wrought iron, if it has become soft iron either
entirely or too deeply, it can no longer be hardened by ordinary
quenching, as I have said before.

I have found, however, that it can be rehardened to any desired extent by pack-hardening it. There is no steel with a hardness greater than that of cast iron so treated. Subsequently it
can be polished as perfectly as desired. Furthermore, [524] it
takes less time to pack-harden cast iron than wrought iron.

We have seen that, in order to pack-harden a piece, it is
heated, surrounded by substances which are capable of converting it into steel, which supply it with sulfurs and salts. It is
sufficient to soak it rather briefly in order to condition the piece
in such a way that it hardens when quenched in cold water.
But I purposely used a very long soaking period on iron castings
which had been softened to the point where they had acquired
a white grain. While they soaked, they were packed in the same
compound I have described for use in converting iron into steel.
After soaking, the cast iron, which I had not quenched in water,
had regained a large part of its original hardness. There were
spots which the file could no longer cut, but other spots were
merely less soft, and the white color which they had had before
had again become more brown. Apparently we could in this

way fully restore its old hardness to a piece of softened iron by continuing the experiment still further. In order to soften cast iron, we take something away from it, and by this operation we restore it. But, unless the soaking is done in a very hot fire and for a very long time, it will not increase the hardness, although it will give body.

Although cast iron is the subject of our new art, I must tell that this art can also be [525] usefully applied to wrought iron. An endless number of products require much softer wrought iron than that which we produce. When very complicated wards are to be made for a lock, the iron is never flexible enough to please the artisan. Regardless of how much care he uses in selecting his iron, how cautiously he bends it, it breaks. Extremely soft sheet iron is needed for an endless number of products. The same anneal that we have used for cast iron can produce considerable softening in wrought iron, provided the sections are not thick. I believe that there would be a demand for iron thus softened, and it would give additional work to the men who will soften cast iron.

It is very important, however, not to continue the annealing of wrought iron for as long as one anneals cast iron. In this case, too much of an anneal would be harmful. After I had kept a piece of sheet iron in the fire for a certain time, I found it as flexible as a thin piece of pasteboard. I have withdrawn from the furnace iron wire which could be bent, rebent, and twisted as if it were made of lead. However, I annealed a piece of the same sheet, and one of the same iron wire, which broke much more easily than they would have in their normal condition. This happened when the duration of the anneal was longer continued. If some of its sulfurs and salts are taken away from common iron, it again becomes softer. This is what is accomplished by a short anneal. But, if the treatment is continued too long, too many of these same parts are removed from the iron. Its [metallic] parts are then no longer firmly connected; [526] it is in the same condition as iron that has been burned in the forge or as the scale which comes loose from iron while it is being hammered on the anvil. If the metallic parts are mixed with an excessive amount of sulfurs and salts, the iron is stiff and brittle; but, if it contains too little of these same substances, its parts are no longer tied together—they come off in thin flakes or scale, or it crumbles. The surface of any bar that has been heated and forged almost always furnishes an example of the first condition, and iron that has been heated strongly and reduced to saffron of Mars furnishes an example of the second condition. Fatty clay can serve as an illustration of something rather similar. When this clay is overslaked with water, its parts are no longer holding together—it is mud, or in a condition approaching mud. If it has soaked up water only to a certain limit, it can be shaped. It has not only consistency; it has plasticity or flexibility at the same time. But if it is deprived of water to a certain extent, if it becomes too dry, it at once becomes friable. The water in the clay corresponds to the oily parts in our metal. This idea could be further developed, but with reference to wrought iron I shall only add that, depending on its quality, it will be able to stand annealing for longer or shorter periods, that differences in section size must also be taken into consideration, and that the best results will be obtained with thin iron.

The Sixth Memoir, Where the Different Products That Can Be Made of Cast Iron Are Reviewed; Where the Precautions Are Discussed with Which Some of These Should Be Cast and Annealed; and Where Information Is Also Given on Which Products Should Not Be Made of This Kind of Iron

THE PRODUCTION of more beautiful work, without sacrifice of quality and at lower cost, is the route to progress along which we must endeavor to guide the arts; and it seems as if from the start our new art had an advantage in this respect over those by which iron work has been produced in the past. There are few of these arts to which the new art cannot become useful, and, the more we become aware of the innumerable applications which can be found for it, the more convinced we shall become of this fact. Some of these applications will be discussed hereafter. Perhaps it will be thought that I am glad of this opportunity to make my researches seem more valuable. Be assured that I shall be satisfied with my work only to the extent as it becomes useful to the public; and, in order to make it more [530] useful, I ought at least to point out the advantages that can be derived from it and advise not to overlook them.

The art of the locksmith* is, of all the arts which use iron,

* *L'Art de serrurerie.* Although the *Encyclopédie* defines *serrurier* as "the artisan who produces all sorts of ironwork, particularly locks," *serrurerie* is explained as the art whose position among the arts is closest to the art of building. It is part architecture and part sculpture and produces a great variety of work "for the adornment of churches, palaces, parks, and homes." It is evident that Réaumur here uses the word in this sense, and interesting that neither the French nor the English language has a name for the architect or sculptor in iron.

the one that produces this metal in the greatest number of different shapes and for the greatest number of possible applications. But even locksmiths do not dare undertake the processing
of this metal beyond a certain point, especially in the case of
large pieces. I have said before that grillwork and railings for
balconies and staircases now are of mediocre workmanship.
Anybody who asks for ornamental leaves or flowers can have
them done only in thin sheet. If ornaments of a more solid nature are required, copper must be used, to the great regret of our
locksmiths, who are always very much annoyed when they
have to abandon their favorite metal. When they have produced
something beautiful of pure iron, they believe that even gilding
would spoil it or that the ironwork would then be mistaken for
brass; for in most of the large grillwork in churches anything
golden is almost always an inset made of brass. Once the patterns for grilles and balcony railings and for the floral ornaments that are to be used with them have been made, work of
this type can be duplicated as often as desired. People who have
patterns for ornamental flowers which are to be cast in brass
have already begun.

Patterns for grillwork and railings for balconies and stairs
will be expensive but not as expensive as one might think. Such
work is composed of a [531] limited number of pieces which are
repeated. Only one pattern is necessary for each of these pieces,
which will be assembled after they have been softened. Balcony
railings, for instance, are simply assembled from repetitions of
the same panel, and only a small number of different pieces are
used in each panel. It would be possible to cast the entire panel,
but making the mold would be much more difficult, defects
would occur much more frequently, and larger furnaces would
be required for annealing. It will be satisfactory, therefore, to
cast it in parts. The main upright supports could be balusters or
could have any other elaborate shape instead of being made of
plain bars as nowadays. The capitals of pilasters or columns and
their bases, which now are sometimes made of brass or are too
thin if made of iron, will be cast with all the thickness that is
suitable.

The heavy pieces which will be part of this kind of ironwork have enough strength as they are. It will not be necessary to anneal them in order to give them body. They will be sufficiently annealed when their outer layers can be worked with the file and cut with the chisel. If there is any reason to drill them, they must be annealed further; but the annealing time can be shortened by arranging to have the pieces cast with holes. If these holes must have screw threads, it will be possible to cut them into the holes of the casting, even though the piece has not been softened to the middle, because part of the section that [532] surrounds the hole will have been softened. Two other types of ironwork will serve to give additional hints on how to be economical with the duration of the anneal.

Nowadays, the strikers, or knockers, on carriage gates or on other entrances are almost devoid of ornamentation but cost as much as quite ornate cast-iron door knockers will cost in the future. The spot that will become part of the hinge is one of those which is most subject to strain and must be drilled. In order to avoid annealing for a longer time than the body of the knocker requires, I put at this spot (Pl. 17, Fig. 2, *AA*) in the mold a piece of wrought iron (*BBC*) of the required shape, size, and thickness. When the molten iron is poured into the mold, it will envelop part of the wrought iron and fit itself exactly to this iron, which will then be as solidly united with the cast iron as if it were also cast iron; but it has the advantage that it can be drilled without having to be annealed.

Today, grates for fireplaces would be very expensive if they were somewhat ornate. There are some in Paris that cost very much. In the future they will be made as cheaply as everything else. If I speak of them at all, it is mainly to say that in annealing some grates which I had cast I used a trick which it would be wise to remember. The upright part of the grate is screwed into the base, and the end of the upsight part must therefore be threaded. I placed in the mold a piece of wrought iron, into the end of which screw threads had been cut (Fig. 5, *L*). This adds nothing to the cost of fabrication [533] and means work saved in the anneal.

After describing these two special cases, let me now make a general observation which will be useful in connection with many iron castings. This is that, if heavy pieces are to be cast and if these heavy pieces must have body (that is, will be subject to strain), and if the expense of long annealing is to be avoided, all that is necessary is to place into the mold pieces of wrought iron of a size that is proportioned to the mass of the casting and to the strength desired. Sometimes, an iron wire will be enough which is only as thick as a finger; sometimes, an iron bar will be used. The cast iron will unite well with the wrought iron; they will become one body.

By the way, this practice is not used exclusively in the iron foundry. Foundrymen use it for many castings made of brass which would break too easily unless they were supported by iron. The large buckles on the thorough braces of coaches are often reinforced inside with iron. Large bronze statues sometimes contain several thousand pounds of iron to give the whole mass strength. The eagles on lecterns, and other similar pieces, owe a large part of their strength to iron.

However, I must not forget an important warning: If parts of the pieces of wrought iron which are used in a casting project outside, like the legs of the staple [534] in the door knockers (Pl. 17, 2), these parts, being wrought iron, could become brittle during a long anneal, even more brittle than cast iron is. The remarks at the end of the preceding memoir would let us foresee this. Wrought iron that is annealed too much dries out. In order to meet this undesirable occurrence, such parts will be carefully packed in substances that can furnish more oily parts than our annealing compound does. Powdered charcoal will have this effect, and anything that is pure wrought iron should therefore be covered with it. Such pieces are made a little wet, and, after they have been moistened, they are plunged in charcoal powder. They will take up enough from it to become proof against the effect of the anneal. In order better to safeguard this powder for them, it can be covered by a layer of sandy clay thinned to the consistence of paste or by foundry sand. Or else one could charge these pieces in the furnace like the rest and, when they are in place, put charcoal powder all around the parts that are wrought iron.

But let us return once more to the products of the locksmith.

Nowadays, the housings of locks or, to use the term of the art, the casings, even in the most luxurious living quarters, are simple and unadorned. If they are to have any beauty, they must be made of brass, although it is always disagreeable to touch this metal. In the future it will be possible to make the most ornate, the most elaborate, casings of cast iron.

From now [535] on, escutcheons, large and small bolts, hinges —in other words, any ironwork pieces that are not subject to strain—can be made most artistically and yet will cost hardly more than the plain ones do today. Keys such as we now import from England will be made cheaply. When they are cast, their bits will be left blank (Fig. 7, *O*). They will be notched later to fit the shape of the ward with which the key is to be used (Fig. 8). These keys are castings which will have to be annealed very well, so that the bit has body and the shank can be drilled. In this connection I cannot help mentioning an objection that has been raised. (At least it proves that there is nothing which cannot be attacked from some angle, and all the more when the desire to contest has nothing to do with the objection.) Some otherwise clear-thinking magistrates have considered the possibility of casting keys to be a very bad thing and a dangerous invention. Being unfamiliar with the practices of the art, they could not understand that it would be easier for people who wish to use a key for dishonest purposes to have one forged than to have it cast in iron; that immediately after it has been forged any kind of ward could be cut out, whereas it takes time and equipment to anneal keys made of cast iron; that a key and its bit can be rough-forged in less than half an hour. Furthermore, [536] it has always been permissible to cast keys of brass which will easily open a lock, but to my knowledge our crooks have not yet made use of this expedient.

Let me add here some more advice which concerns more than one type of casting. If a minor accident happens to a piece which was difficult to cast, if there is a place (Fig. 4, *E*) where the metal has not completely filled the mold, we can file and scrape, in other words, dress, the casting, without worrying about this defect. It can be repaired later by making of wrought iron a small piece (*F G*) just like that which should have been cast.

A tail will be left on this small piece into which screw threads (*G*) will be cut, and a screw hole will be bored where the piece must be placed. If this is skilfully done, the place where the piece has been added will be unrecognizable.

There is still another method of repairing spots that have not come out right in the mold. The trouble is never that there is too much metal; there is always too little—cavities or blow-holes may have to be filled up. This can be done by pouring a few drops of molten iron into the cavities. But, in order that the iron which is cast on unites perfectly with the rest, that it becomes one with it, the places into which one wishes to pour iron must be heated as hot as it can be done. The area around these places, the area to which the iron is not supposed to weld, will be covered with clay.

In the future, sword furbishers will have sword hilts cast [537] and will be able to complete in a few days work that so far occupied them for several months. They already have their patterns, for they can use the same as those which they have now cast in brass or silver. It is true that these swords will no longer cost almost as much as if they were made of solid gold, as they did before, but there will be more demand for them. The hilt and the pommel will easily become more than soft enough, but the arms of the cross-guard, being long and thin, must be annealed repeatedly, or they would be too likely to break.

Belt buckles, buckles for shoes, boxes, watch keys, watch clamps, and an endless number of trinkets will no longer occupy our artisans for as long as very large pieces. Provided we have the patterns, these things can be quickly made.

From now on, the diamond polishers' wheels and the rolls used to flatten out, or laminate, gold or silver wire can be made of cast iron; but at present they are very expensive to make.

I believe that the art of the spurmaker will also benefit. The cheeks of most bridles are not subject to much strain and can be made by casting. They are among the most difficult objects to forge. I had several of them cast, which came out very well. If somebody would like to have them cast with ornaments, they only have to be ordered; it will be possible to have them decorated all over. Snaffles will be even more successful.

An art [538] which will benefit from the softening of cast iron by saving much time, and which will be enabled to produce the most beautiful work, is the art of the gunsmith. Gunlocks will be excellent when made of cast iron. I had several of them cast as an experiment. Whether they are left plain or made elaborately ornate will be decided by the artisan. But, when they are given ornaments, these will be neither so scanty nor so expensive as they are today. Instead of some designs in light intaglio, with which the finest ones are now adorned, they can have ornaments in relief in the same style as used for the most beautiful sword hilts. If intaglio ornaments are desired, they will be made like those of the most beautiful seals. However, the cock and the hammer should not be made of cast iron for reasons I shall explain elsewhere. But the stock plate (the piece that covers the end of the stock) can be made of it just as well as any other piece, and so can lock plates, ramrod holders, and the ornamental pieces which are placed near the screws which hold the lock. If the trigger guards are made of cast iron, they must be softened considerably, like all pieces that are long and thin. In brief, the new art could save the arsenals of His Majesty very considerable sums. A very ingenious and very useful suggestion has been made—that is, to make all the pieces of the muskets of our troops of the same dimensions.* A musket with a broken barrel becomes useless because the lock, or the pieces of the lock, cannot be fitted into another [539] musket. But, when all the pieces are of the same dimensions, the pieces of one musket can be substituted for those of another. A few broken pieces will no

---

* This attempt to manufacture guns with interchangeable parts took place in 1717. It is referred to, with no further information except that it was a failure, in the standard histories of the subject (e.g., see Chas. H. Fitch, "Report on the Manufactures of Interchangeable Mechanisms," Appendix to *United States Tenth Census Report* [Washington, D.C., 1880]; J. W. Roe, *English and American Tool Builders* [New Haven, Conn., 1916]). In 1785 Thomas Jefferson reported seeing a French mechanic named Le Blanc who was making "every part of [muskets] so exactly alike, that what belongs to any one may be used for every other musket in the magazine." As is well known, it was left for Eli Whitney first to achieve, in 1798, the benefits of the system in actual production. Even today it is difficult to make castings so accurately to size that they can be used without machining, as Réaumur suggests, in any but the crudest assemblies.

longer make all the others useless. What is left of a very badly shattered musket will serve to repair another.

In time, the King may make use of the new art in an even more important field. I am referring to his artillery, especially the artillery on ships. I cannot report as many experiments concerning this subject as I should like. I have not been able to make the experiments with cannon which I should like to have undertaken; but I believe that there is no reason to fear that experiments would disprove what our art seems to promise in this field. Only two kinds of cannon are made. One is made of copper with an admixture of tin and zinc, etc. These are ordinarily called "cast" cannon; but they are also called "bronze" cannon, and I shall always call them that to avoid confusion with cast iron. The other kind is made of cast iron, of metal like that used for chimney backs—in other words, of gray iron. They are ordinarily called "iron" cannon. Both have their shortcomings, and many attempts have been made to produce a third kind without the faults of the other two. One has looked for methods of making them of wrought iron, which of all known materials has the greatest ability to resist high stresses. The most powerful resistance is not too great [540] if it has to meet the violent impact of gunpowder, and wrought iron is incomparably much better suited to resist this impact than cast bronze. Cannon made of wrought iron would be stronger, though lighter. For a special reason, we are even forced to reduce the strength by which the copper could resist the dilating force of the powder. The bore of a cannon must keep its diameter, its uniform roundness. If pure copper were used, it would not have enough hardness to withstand the drag of the ball. We are therefore forced to alloy it with tin and zinc, which makes it harder but at the same time more brittle. We increase its resistance to the drag of the ball but simultaneously decrease its resistance to the force of the powder. Furthermore, the priming holes then become more easily enlarged, which is another very great disadvantage.*

Nevertheless, at present the cannon made of bronze are still

* The greater erosion of gun metal, as compared with copper, was commonly obviated in eighteenth-century cannon by casting a copper insert for the touch hole.

better than those made of cast iron. The metal in the latter has greater resistance to the drag of the ball, but its brittleness is responsible for two very great disadvantages. (1) In order to make cast-iron cannon as strong as those made of bronze, they must be heavier than bronze cannon of the same caliber. (2) When these cannon burst, they do not simply split open, as the bronze ones do; their much more rigid metal splinters in bursting, and the splinters kill the gunners and spread terror among the survivors. After one cannon has burst, they no longer dare use the [541] regular charge for the others, and the shots fired thereafter no longer have any effect. The course of a battle at sea has often been reversed by such an accident.

If we could succeed without too much expense in forging cannon of iron, they would undoubtedly be incomparably much superior to the others. They would have greater resistance to the force of the powder as well as to the drag of the ball. Being stronger, they would not have to be so heavy. Many attempts have been made in this direction but so far without much success. They even have ruined a man who was rich as well as talented, but new attempts are made every day. It is hoped that they will have a happier ending; and there really is no reason for despair.

Whatever will develop, at present we only have cannon made of bronze or of cast iron. The artillery used on land is made of bronze, but most of the artillery used at sea, on the King's vessels as well as on merchant ships, is made of cast iron. It would cost enormous sums to have it made of bronze. The ships groan, however, under the weight of their cannon, which especially distresses our traders in wartime. They would be very happy if they could load their vessels exclusively with bronze cannon.

The objection to this increased load is not only [542] that it takes the place of an equal weight of merchandise. I have heard reasonable traders complain that it ruins their ships; that it is an important factor in causing them to split open. The strain on the vessel is not so great as long as it has the wind in the back. But, when the wind comes from the side, it is obvious that the weight of the cannon, which is borne by one half of the vessel, tends to separate this half from the other. The location of this weight is the reason why the force exerted by it is more powerful than if it were distributed all over.

There seems to be no question that by means of our new art cast-iron cannon will be improved over what they are today. Annealed cast iron will no doubt be less brittle. The important question is, however, whether annealing can bring them to the point where they no longer splinter when they burst open. I know that this desirable effect cannot be expected from every kind of annealed cast iron. I even have made a sort of test. Instead of a large cannon I had a pistol barrel cast in a mold. I softened it very thoroughly, and it became easily workable by the file. I put in a much larger charge than would ordinarily be used, and it did not burst. Finally, after increasing the charge even more, after filling the barrel almost full of powder, it burst, and unfortunately it splintered in bursting. I do not believe, however, that this experiment should make us give up hope that we shall ever succeed in producing cast-iron cannon which when they burst will open up like those made of bronze. The cast iron used for this pistol barrel had been chosen at random; [543] and I have pointed out that some irons are much tougher than others after annealing. It is therefore necessary to try out different cast irons. If we started by making tests on pistol barrels, they would not be expensive, and they will suffice as a first step before we go on to larger experiments.

In order to obtain the required degree of toughness in pieces of cast iron as thick as cannon, it would be necessary to anneal them for a long time in our compounds. But the annealing time will not be as long as one might think. There are places where it is already customary to anneal cannon for several days. After they have been removed from the molds, they are immediately surrounded by lighted charcoal, which has little effect. Perhaps the duration of our anneal will not have to be much longer, for we have seen that pieces thicker than an inch require only three days at most. The number of days will increase at a greater rate than the thickness, but it looks as if it could not be excessive, and the cost is immaterial compared with the advantages which we would derive from the process.

Furthermore, such annealing can be undertaken much more

boldly than when small pieces are treated. There is no danger that such thick pieces might melt, and scaling is nothing to be afraid of. One of the difficulties will be to find suitable furnaces. It would be possible [544] to use furnaces similar to those we have used so far. The necessary changes would be from small to larger and, especially, from low to higher. Let us assume that the crucibles are arranged as we had them arranged before and that the center crucible is deep enough to receive a cannon standing on end and long enough to accommodate several of them in a row. After all, this matter is important enough to make experiments, which would not be excessively expensive. One also could build something like towers, or construct something like the outer part of the mold used to cast cannon, only larger.

Because there is no reason to be afraid of scaling, perfectly sealed crucibles may not be so essential.

We have seen that the strength of iron castings can be increased by using wrought-iron inserts. Would not this expedient provide us with the means of producing cast-iron cannon which have all the improvements desired? Suppose we made a structure of wrought-iron bars which would be tied together at intervals with iron hoops, or perhaps it would be enough to make this structure by riveting, and then it could be done in a shorter time. This structure of wrought iron could form a sort of skeleton which would be covered inside and out with cast iron. After all his experiments with cannon made of wrought iron, M. de Villons concluded that it was impossible, without exorbitant cost, to make them [545] completely of this metal. It was his idea to make the inside of wrought iron, which on the outside would subsequently be covered by cast bronze.

After having discussed the possible uses of cast iron for the grandiose, the beautiful, and even the terrible, I shall now consider it in connection with a less noble application—its usefulness in the kitchen. I must confess, however, that this field seems at least as important to me. Fundamentally, it is better to perfect the utensils needed there than deadly weapons. This way of thinking may not be the most lofty, but it is at least the most human and perhaps the most sensible. It can be hoped that in the future almost the entire kitchen equipment will be made of cast iron—kettles, pots and saucepans, casseroles, warming pans, etc. The Kingdom, whose copper mines are neglected, could then save much money which is now leaving the country to acquire this metal. Pots and kettles of cast iron have been made for a long time; but they are hardly used except in villages and some small towns, and the only reason is to save the copper vessels. There are three reasons why cast-iron utensils of this sort have not been adopted for more general use. (1) They always look dirty. Because they are rough both inside and out, it is not easy to clean them. (2) They are thicker than vessels made of forged copper and [546] for that reason more difficult to heat. (3) Finally, they break easily. It would not be easy for the cook to handle them. They must be treated with care; it is risky to rap upon them sharply. If it were not for that, a pot or kettle of cast iron would be an almost everlasting container, for the fire does not burn it as it does copper vessels. Our new art does away with these three difficulties. Today these vessels are cast less thin than they could be made, in order to make them resistant to shock. But if those which will be cast from now on are not considered thin enough when they are removed from the mold, the rest can be accomplished after they have been annealed. They can be worked on the lathe as copper kettles are worked and can be made as thin as they must be in order to heat up rapidly. In short, as they will be made less brittle by annealing, the principal difficulty that has impeded their wide use is being removed. I do not dare hope that annealing will give them quite the same toughness as copper has, but it will give them enough not to break provided average care is used in handling them. There actually are many well-to-do households where pots cast of alloyed copper are used; these are thick and brittle but nevertheless very expensive. The advantage which compensates for these two bad qualities is that tinning is not required.

Thus, there is no other reason than necessity for [547] using ordinary copper in spite of its disagreeable smell and in spite of the nature of the rust to which it is subject and which is a dangerous poison. It has indeed been a very good idea to tin-coat the vessels made of this metal in order to protect them against verdigris and to prevent them from communicating their bad smell to the food cooked and cooled in them. The rust of iron is not objectionable, and only little is formed in cast-iron vessels. According to our housewives, these vessels confer no taste upon the food cooked in them. They assure us that soup from cast-iron pots is excellent. But, if it still seems desirable to protect them against rust, there is no reason why they should not be coated with tin just as locks and bolts are tinned by locksmiths, the cheeks and bits of bridles are tinned by spurmakers, and sheet ir ɔn is tinned. I do not say this without having tried it; I have asked some spurmakers to tin a number of cast-iron pots, which took the tin very well.*

The demand for the items that are called "kitchen utensils" is so great and so general that I do not hesitate to consider this as one of the most important fields of our art. It is important to make more beautiful grillwork, more beautiful railings for balconies, more beautiful locks, to produce in general more refined, more decorative work. One might ask, however, what would be gained by the human race if the number of objects we call "beautiful," and which are simply beautiful, [548] were increased beyond a certain limit. If we knew the secret of how to build palaces as cheaply and as quickly as cottages, if small houses were suddenly changed into magnificent buildings, we should be struck by the novelty of the spectacle. But soon it would be just as well if our common houses had remained unchanged. We should look with less pleasure and interest at the paintings of the great masters if daubers discovered how to paint similar ones. We can judge what we call "beautiful" only by comparison, but we can judge at all times the things directly connected with our occupation and decide whether they are good. There is always something with which to compare them.

Will somebody worry—for we are sometimes astonishingly humane when it is a case of raising objections—will somebody worry, I said, what would become of all the coppersmiths if most of the kitchen equipment were made of iron? I have seen a great magistrate refuse to license a new machine for such a

* See also Introduction, pp. xiii, xiv, and xvi.

reason. I shall answer this question as I answered the judge for
the man who had every justification in petitioning for a license
—that, if we had always been so considerate, we should have
neither windmills nor water mills nor mills worked by horses.
Grain used to be ground by hand in mortars before we knew
how to crush it under grindstones moved by [549] horses. How
many people were occupied doing that? Water mills, to the
great advantage of mankind, have necessarily restricted the use
of mills worked by hand or by horses. The pretty recent invention of windmills supplements the water mills, which cannot
be built everywhere. To come back to the coppersmiths, I do
not believe that many people would charitably buy their copper utensils only to assure them a living if utensils made of iron
were better and cheaper. But let us not worry. There will be
more than enough work for them. They already work in iron;
they make small stoves and other small pieces. They will make
an increased effort to work this metal; they will repair it, work
it on the lathe, etc.

If it were possible to make of wrought iron all the kitchen
utensils that are made of copper, there is no reason to believe
that copper would ever have been used. If the art had been able
to do it, pots, casseroles, and kettles would have been forged out
of iron as frying pans are forged. But iron is not ductile enough
to be shaped as much as is necessary, and the quality it lacks most
is the ability to be raised and hollowed under the hammer. It
is this quality which makes it possible to hammer out vessels
of lead, copper, gold, or silver. A frying pan can be forged out
of iron because the sides of the pan flare away from the bottom.
If a similar [550] pan were made of copper or silver, it could be
changed into a vessel of any shape desired. By hammering upon
its walls on the outside, one could shrink them so that they
would leave an opening that is much narrower than the bottom
from which they start. This is called "hollowing." But there
is no way by which iron can thus be hollowed. I have heard of
an artisan who was skilful enough to make of wrought iron
something like a bottle with a long neck—who had actually
succeeded in hollowing it to this extent. But this could have
been achieved only after a long time, after reheating a prodi-

gious number of times, and such a piece made of iron would be more expensive, because of the labor involved, than if it were made of silver and perhaps even of gold.

It is true that iron vessels are made which are narrower at the top than at the bottom. Our coffee pots are an example. But we know that the iron in such containers has not been hollowed. They sometimes are made of several pieces whose ends, after they have been folded upon another, are held together only by solder. This is the reason why we do not dare expose them to the fire except when they are full of water, which prevents the vessel from acquiring the degree of heat which would cause the solder to melt.

In the future it will be possible to make cast-iron stoves good enough to heat those apartments in which they have recently found a place in the Kingdom.

The large urns which beautify the flower beds in our gardens [551] will be made of cast iron and have the same very graceful shapes as those made of bronze and will be just as well finished. Finally, we shall be able to cast in iron an endless number of statues and busts. The little cast-iron horse which now stands in His Majesty's cabinet at Versailles will no longer be one of the objects which owe their rarity to the material of which they are made. If cast iron is suited for anything, it certainly is suited for objects which are made only to be exhibited and are not subject to strain.

Today we make of copper or of pot metal candlesticks and innumerable other objects which can also be made of cast iron.

If it should seem desirable to gild or silver our cast-iron objects, there is no reason why it could not be done—they can be gilded or silvered like copper. As with wrought iron, the gold can be applied in a special way—that is, it will be possible to damascene them with gold, as muskets and sword hilts are decorated. Fire grates, candlesticks, sconces, and chandeliers of cast iron could first be given a violet color, and light ornaments of gold damascene could subsequently be laid on, which would produce magnificent and highly artistic pieces.

Anything can be turned into an advantage. Even mishaps in work one had planned can often become useful. This happened when the first castings which I tried to soften were treated so that they scaled, a mishap which does not generally occur [552] with all castings. It is safe to employ bone ash alone for plain castings or for those which have no delicate ornaments; it will accelerate the softening. And there are plain castings for which scaling is even desirable. I mean those which are too thick when they are removed from the mold. Pots and casseroles belong in this class. If these vessels are not thin enough when they come out of the mold, anything that comes off as scale does not have to be removed by working them either by the file or on the lathe.

I therefore have undertaken experiments in which I not only purposely employed bone ash alone but also used clay, ordinary lime, and calcined gypsum. Lime alone has a much stronger effect than clay. Gypsum alone has too much effect and could lead to pitting. To moderate its action, I placed only a thin layer of this powder around the casting and filled the rest of the crucible with ordinary bone ash, whereupon the scale was of only the right thickness. This thickness will vary with the thickness of the layer of gypsum or plaster of Paris which is placed around the casting and also with the duration of the fire. But things must be so arranged that the castings which are meant to scale will heat uniformly; otherwise the thickness of the scale would be too unequal.

Speaking of gypsum, I shall describe an experience [553] which, however, affects in no way the fundamentals of our art. When I unstoppered the small crucibles in which I had packed cast iron in this powder alone, and turned them upside down before I had given the iron enough time to cool completely— that is, at a time when it was still of a very brownish, a very deep, red—under these circumstances, I mean, I have seen flames come out of this powder at more than twenty places. Their color was like that of the flame of common sulfur. In addition, cast iron that was packed in gypsum always took on an insufferable smell of sulfur. Another observation is that it seemed to me that gypsum always caused white irons to scale much more than gray irons and that it caused wrought iron to scale more and faster than cast iron.

Having reviewed in the preceding the principal applications of our new art, I should devote no less effort to arrest any over-optimistic hopes that might arise. I have felt the necessity for this ever since I revealed the fundamentals of this art at the opening meeting of the Academy in November, 1721.* I have had to object to extravagant expectations more frequently than I have had to allay misgivings about different types of cast-iron work. If we listen to some people, we ought to give up all forge work. They would like to see everything cast into molds, including the most [554] simple pieces—including, it seems to me, even iron bars. Some people want to use a new discovery for everything, and it is therefore often rendered useless. For instance, there is a remedy which is now ignored but would properly still be held in great esteem if it had been used only in the cases in which it was first so successful, if one had not tried also to use it for all other diseases. Lest our iron castings be misused as badly, I shall give solemn warning that cast iron must never be used for pieces for which very soft, very pliable iron is required. It would be an abuse, for example, to make musket barrels of cast iron, because even among bar irons there are many which are not suited for the purpose. I am not sure whether even the cock of the musket, which falls with very quick percussion, can be made of cast iron. Ironwork that is subject to much strain must, in general, be made of the softest kind of iron, and consequently cast iron is not suitable. Objects that are long and very thin, provided they have to support anything, must never be made of cast iron.

Furthermore, only those articles should be fashioned from this kind of iron which otherwise would require long working with the file or the hammer. All articles that do not require long fabrication should be made of wrought iron. I have said that elaborately ornamental keys will be made of cast iron; but there would be little profit in casting ordinary keys in iron, [555] and one might risk producing an article of lower quality. The advantage of cast iron increases the longer it takes to finish the article by the ordinary method; and there are enough of

* This is not referred to in the *Histoire* of the Academy for that year.

such cases to make the benefits derived from our new art far-reaching. Cast iron will be used in very many classes of iron-work which I have not mentioned. On the other hand, it is possible that it will be found unsuited for some of the applications for which I believe it to be fitted.

Cast-iron articles which are well molded and carefully worked with the file often should not be distinguishable to the eye from wrought iron. Although they may be as good as wrought iron, there are circumstances where it is necessary for the person who wishes to use them to know their origin, and it would be deceitful toward the buyer, because it would be to his loss, if cast iron were sold to him as wrought iron. Let me make this clearer by an example. If one sells elaborately ornate hinges to a locksmith or other individual, it will be easy for him to recognize that they are not made of wrought iron. But if one sells him plain hinges and wants to make him believe that they are wrought iron, although they are cast iron, it may be difficult for him to recognize the truth. These cast-iron hinges, after being put up, will hold the door as wrought-iron hinges would; but, in being installed, they sometimes require precautions which are unnecessary with the others. If [556] the part that is meant to be put on the wood must be straightened, the workman who thinks it is wrought iron will hammer it too sharply and may break it, whereas if he had known that it was cast iron, he would have struck it gently when cold or might even have heated it to treat it more carefully.

Avarice finds a way to make ill use of even the best things. To circumvent the abuse of which I have just spoken, it might be advisable to mark as such all the plain iron castings which will be sold in large cities. The guardians or jurymen of the locksmiths' guild or any other guild could be empowered to affix this mark; but it would be an even greater abuse than the one I am planning to circumvent if this mark fell into the hands of revenue farmers. If that happened, I should bitterly regret the advice I have just given. However, since these gentlemen think of everything that can make them rich by exploiting the people in the name of some often imaginary public service, they obviously would have thought of it themselves. Fortunately, we live under a regime that is little inclined to listen favorably to their propositions.

But let us come back once more to our cast-iron work. Each artisan could have his own furnace where he would anneal the castings with which his profession is concerned. However, since there are [557] few who like to do anything but their ordinary work, or who could do it, and it is also more profitable always to make the same thing, it would be of greater advantage to the public if there were established artisans whose task it would be to soften iron castings for everybody else, and who would be given the title of *annealers of cast iron*. If cabinetmakers, watchmakers, sword furbishers, locksmiths, and several other artisans need copper or silver castings, they do not themselves found these metals. (Only the goldsmith does not turn to the founder for help.) They take the models of the desired pieces to a foundry, and they know how much they have to pay for a pound of casting. In the same way, gunsmiths, locksmiths, sword furbishers, etc., would go to the common founder to have any needed iron castings made and would pay by the pound at a rate they would have agreed upon.

They would then take these same castings to the annealers of cast iron and would pay them more or less money, depending on the degree of annealing they require—either for toughness or for color—and depending further on the thickness of a piece. It would be easy to agree upon a price scale, and, as soon as there are such establishments, such a scale could easily be worked out.

The men who will have no other occupation than that of softening iron, who will make it their job, must be equipped with furnaces of different sizes. [558] When they have only small articles to anneal, which must be extremely soft, they will use their small furnaces. Even a very small furnace will hold a large quantity of sword hilts, gun locks, buckles, and other small pieces. Even a very small sum charged for the annealing of each of these pieces will be high enough to pay for the time and fuel spent. One cartload of wood is enough to anneal an enormous quantity of these small castings.

In conclusion I should like to say that so far I have only laid out the foundations of an art which must be perfected. I have only roughed it out. I could not have tried out everything, nor could I have foreseen everything. Much is still to be learned from often-repeated practical experience on a large scale. It is hoped that those who make discoveries which would contribute to the advancement of this art will share them with the public. As far as I am concerned, I shall not fail to publish anything new I may learn concerning this subject and also everything that I could still add now concerning several other related subjects which have furnished me with observations which, I believe, will be useful and which may be found rather interesting.

[GLOSSARY]

Explanations of Some Terms*

Adoucir le fer fondu, ou le fer forgé [to soften cast iron or wrought iron] means to decrease its hardness and its rigidity; to make it easier to work with the file, easier to cut with the chisel; and also to make it more flexible.

Bain [bath] indicates the state of complete liquidity to which a metal has been brought. Any metal rendered completely liquid by the effect of the fire is called a "metal bath."

Bille d'acier [a steel billet] is a rather short piece of steel forged into a rectangular section, which is often less thick than wide. A steel billet is seldom more than 6–7 inches long.

Bure d'un souflet [the nozzle of a bellows] is the end of the bellows, the tube by which the wind leaves the bellows.

Chaude is the degree of heat acquired by iron or steel. It is called "cherry-red" when the iron in the fire has become only cherry-red. One speaks of "welding heat," or "melting heat," when the iron has been heated to the point where it is ready to begin to drip.

Corroyer un morceau de fer ou d'acier [to double a piece of iron or steel] means to [562] bend it once or several times upon itself after it has reached a welding heat and to force the bent parts by hammering to combine with those upon which they have been bent.

Découvrir, se découvrir dans la trempe [to descale in quenching] means to become white at the surface when being quenched. Steel that is well descaled after quenching is steel with a white surface. No scale, nothing black, is to be seen on the surface.

Égrainer, s'égrainer [to crumble] is to break up into small pieces. Steel which is quenched too hot crumbles easily.

Étirer le fer, ou acier [to draw out iron or steel] means to make it longer by forging. We obtain a much greater length if we do not broaden the iron that is being drawn out.

Étoffe [composite steel] is a billet or some other piece of steel which is compounded of steels of different degrees of fineness by forge-welding them upon another. The finest steels are nearest to the center.

* The spelling of the French definitions is as in the original.

Évent [vent] is a foundry term meaning a channel hollowed out in the mold to permit the air to escape.

Fenton [nailrod] is an iron rod obtained by slitting a bar into several parts. This is done by very beautiful machines called "slitting mills." The rods are used by nailmakers, glaziers, and several other artisans who need thin iron.

Fonte de fer [563] is cast iron before it has been made into malleable [wrought] iron; in other words, it is iron which cannot be hammered either hot or cold and which is much harder than wrought iron.

Gersure de l'acier [cracks in steel] are rents or small fissures which owe their name to their resemblance to cracks in clay.

Gueuse [pig] is a long piece of cast iron whose shape resembles a prism with a triangular base. Some pigs are 10–12 feet long and weigh from 1,200 or 1,500 up to 2,000 pounds.

Jet [gate] is a foundry term describing any channel that conducts the metal into the mold which is to be filled. It also means the metal that has been cast in such a channel.

Laitier [slag] is vitrified matter, a kind of glass, which floats on an iron bath. There are slags of many different colors. Some contain much iron and others contain none or very little.

Pailles de fer, ou de l'acier [laps on iron or steel] are badly welded spots. The rents that form laps differ from those forming cracks insofar as the cracks, one might say, only notch the surface of the bar or billet, whereas laps are often rather large pieces [564] which are almost entirely separated from the metal on which they rest.

Paquet [box], when used in connection with quenching, is a box made of sheet iron, and coated with clay, in which steel is placed, packed in certain materials. The steel is heated in this box and then removed for quenching.

Quarillon [square merchant bar] is wrought iron forged into a rectangular section, which is as thick as it is wide. Each side measures approximately 8–10 lines [$\frac{3}{4}$ in.].

Recuire [to heat for annealing, tempering, or hardening] usually means to heat (anneal) iron and steel for a purpose other than subsequent forging. Frequently, steel is heated (tempered) to remove hardness, to be softened. Sometimes it is heated (soaked) to be hardened, as in pack-hardening.

Recuit [annealing or soaking]: "Annealing" means heating steel or iron to a mild degree when it is done at the forge. But, if the metal is heated in a box or some other similar container, this is always called "soaking," regardless of the degree of heat reached.

Refouler, se refouler [to be turned back] means to be flattened out, to yield [565] to pressure. A chisel made of bad steel is turned back when used to cut iron cold. Its edge becomes soft.

Ringard [poker] is any bar of iron, either straight or hooked, used to stir burning charcoal or wood or metal that is being heated or melting.

Souder [to hammer-weld] two pieces of iron or steel together, or one piece of iron and one piece of steel, means to force two pieces to be completely joined together, to constitute thereafter only one and the same piece. This is done by hammering upon the two pieces that are to be welded after they have been brought to almost a melting heat. To hammer-weld iron to iron is to be distinguished from joining them by means of solder. If solder is used, this operation is called "brazing."

Surchaufure [overheating] means that the steel has been heated too hot. Overheated steel loses part of its quality.

Trempe [the quench] may mean the quality of the quenched steel; or the medium in which it is quenched; or the treatment preceding the actual quenching operation. A steel is said to have a hard and brittle quench when it has become hard and brittle after having been quenched. The expressions "water-quench" and "tallow-quench" refer to tallow or water in which steel is quenched. To quench from the box (pack-harden) means [566] to soak steel in a box before quenching it.

Tremper l'acier [to quench steel] means to cool it suddenly, usually by plunging it, red-hot, into ordinary cold water.

Tuyère is a short tube shaped like a truncated cone in which rests freely the end or nozzle of one (or more) bellows in a forge or furnace.

Voiler [to billow] means to buckle. A clay plate has buckled when it looks like a sail.

FINIS

TABLE OF CONTENTS
OF THE MEMOIRS

Collected in the First Part of This Volume

* The page numbers shown are those of the 1722 edition. For the corresponding pages of this edition see p. v.

[568]

TABLE OF CONTENTS
OF THE MEMOIRS

Collected in the Second Part

Table of Contents of the Memoirs

END OF THE TABLE

Printed by P. A. Paulus-du-Mesnil, rue S. Severin, at the sign of the King's arms.

APPENDIX A

Units of Weight and of Length and Value of Currency

UNITS OF WEIGHT

The units of weight used by Réaumur are the *livre, once, gros,* and *grain.* Since his *livre* contained 16 *onces,* the *once* 8 *gros,* and the *gros* 72 *grains,* it has seemed permissible to use "pound," "ounce," "⅛ ounce," and "grain" in the translation, although the French pound actually weighed 17⅜, instead of 16, ounces avoirdupois.

UNITS OF LENGTH

The units of length used by Réaumur are *pied, pouce,* and *ligne,* which have been translated into "foot," "inch," and "line," respectively. The *pied* had 12 *pouces,* and the *pouce* had 12 *lignes.* The *pied* measured 1.066 feet.

VALUE OF CURRENCY

At Réaumur's time (since 1667) the *livre tournois,* a silver coin, was the recognized currency in France. Under the First Republic, in 1795, when the *livre* became the *franc,* it was worth about 19.1 cents (9⅖ *d*).

$$
\begin{array}{lll}
1\ écu & = 3\ livres \\
1\ livre & = 20\ sols\ (\text{or } sous) \\
1\ sol & = 12\ deniers \\
\tfrac{1}{2}\ sol & = 6\ deniers & = 1\ blanc \\
\tfrac{1}{4}\ sol & = 3\ deniers & = 1\ liard
\end{array}
$$

APPENDIX B
Bibliographic Notes

FIRST EDITION (1722)
The first edition of Réaumur's memoirs, and the only one to contain his essays on steel, is that published by Michel Brunet in 1722. The title page is reproduced as the frontispiece to the present translation. The colophon, on page 568, reads: "De l'Imprimerie de P.A. PAULUS-DU-MESNIL, ruë S. Severin, aux Armes du Roy." Uncut copies are 18 × 25 cm. There are 20 preliminary unnumbered pages, 566 pages of text, and 2 unnumbered pages of index. There are 17 plates, engraved by Phillippe Simonneau, bound in groups at the conclusion of the pertinent memoirs.

SECOND EDITION (1762)
The six memoirs on cast iron in the first edition were posthumously republished together with twelve entirely new ones in the *Descriptions des arts et métiers* of the Académie Royale des Sciences of Paris. The title page reads as follows:

NOUVEL ART
D'ADOUCIR
LE FER FONDU,
ET
De faire des Ouvrages de Fer fondu auffi finis
que de Fer forgé.

Par M. DE RÉAUMUR.

SUITE DE LA TROISIEME SECTION SUR LE FER.

M. DCC. LXII.

Folio (33 × 46 cm.), viii + 124 pp., 5 pls.

There is no indication of printer or place of publication, but there is little reason to doubt that it was printed by H. L. Guerin and L. F.

Delatour, whose names appear on adjacent parts of the *Descriptions* which are in identical format. All the parts bear rudimentary title pages, supposedly because they were considered merely as section headings, although they are separately paginated and were available for separate sale. The statement that Réaumur's work is a "sequel to the third section on iron" derives from the fact that it was placed after the third section of the *Art des forges et fourneaux à fer* by the Marquis de Courtivron and E. J. Bouchu, although it has no particular relation thereto. It was inserted there by Duhamel du Monceau, the editor of the series, who contributes a short introduction in which he says the work was found in good order among Réaumur's papers.

The plates were re-engraved by Patte from the pertinent plates of the 1722 edition, advantage being taken of the larger pages to reduce their number.

The new memoirs incorporated in this edition must have been written prior to May, 1726, for, in a paper on the fluidity of cast iron read in that month to the Academy, Réaumur says: "It seems that, instead of continuing to print separate memoirs, it would be better to assemble into a single collection the unpublished ones on iron that I have read to the Academy on different occasions. This collection has for its title *Le nouvel art d'adoucir le fer fondu*. In it will be found procedures for making cast-iron pieces amenable to working with the file, which I had not discovered when I published *L'Art d'adoucir le fer fondu* in 1722 and which are more easy to carry out in practice than the ones therein described; one will also find observations and reflections on this metal which will perhaps aid in their understanding" (*Mém. Acad. Sci.*, 1726, p. 287). The fact that Réaumur laid these memoirs aside and did not publish them perhaps reflects his uncertainty as to their value. We give below translations of the headings of the three parts into which this edition is divided and of the individual memoirs wherever they differ from those in the 1722 edition.

PART I. Which deals with the characteristics of different kinds of cast iron and the different methods of casting them into molds, and contains instructions on how intractable castings are softened by annealing them in containers into which the flame cannot reach.

This consists of five memoirs with the same titles and essentially the same content as Memoirs 1–5 in the 1722 edition. In Memoir 4 there is an added remark that reverberatory furnaces such as bronze founders use cannot be used for melting malleable iron, since duration of heating is not a substitute for the activity of a fire. There are relatively extensive paragraphs describing cupola-like furnaces urged by water-driven bellows and very large crucible and ladle furnaces for melting iron. There are minor changes dealing with the way in which salts operate in annealing and a number of comments on the nature of various kinds of iron. None of these changes, however, represents a significant change of viewpoint over that represented in the earlier edition. The sixth and last memoir of the first edition is reprinted as the last one, Part III, Memoir 9, of this edition; but in between there is a quantity of entirely new material as listed below.

PART II. Where it is shown how cast iron can be softened by simply coating the castings. The composition of these coatings. Different methods of annealing such articles. Precautions necessary to prevent warpage.

First Memoir. How iron castings can be softened without being inclosed in crucibles or chambers serving the same purpose. Two methods of doing it. The advantages of these methods. What light they shed on the cause underlying the softening.

Second Memoir. On different kinds of coatings for cast iron, and the method of applying these coats.

Third Memoir. On different methods of annealing and softening the coated castings. Description of a new furnace suitable for the purpose.

Fourth Memoir. Precautions to prevent the castings from warping while being annealed. On ways of straightening those which have warped.

PART III. Where it is shown how castings can be produced which come from the mold soft enough to be worked with the file and otherwise finished without the necessity of an anneal. What can be expected of castings made of steel or soft iron.

First Memoir. Attempts to soften iron while it is in the molten state; and to keep iron soft, throughout melting, that was already in this condition when it was charged in the crucible. Ways of succeeding with the latter.

Second Memoir. Selecting cast irons for the charge which will give soft cast iron. This property is natural to some irons. It can be conveyed upon others by application of the art. With still others it is practically impossible to give them this property.

Third Memoir. Cast irons produced in accord with the processes described in the preceding memoirs are sometimes unsatisfactory by being too gray. How this defect can be corrected, and they can be given the color of the whitest ironwork. How soft gray iron can instantly be made hard and white.

Fourth Memoir. A necessary precaution in casting iron that is soft. White iron is quenched iron. But some irons are more inclined to be hardened by quenching than others. The advantages of flasks made of iron.

Fifth Memoir. Iron flasks suitable for various molds. How the formation of thick fins in the molds can be prevented. How the two halves of the molds are held together.

Sixth Memoir. Furnaces in which sand molds can be properly heated or fired. How molds made of clay must be heated to reach the necessary state of being fired.

Seventh Memoir. Means of keeping down the expense for molding sands; how those which have been used once can be reconditioned. How suitable sands can be obtained in country where the earth does not naturally yield them. On substances of which molds can be made in which the iron will be more likely to come out soft than in sand molds. Molds made of clay and molds made of metal.

Eighth Memoir. Sequence of operations from the moment the molds have become hot until the castings have been withdrawn, with notes on every step. The method of annealing the castings in the molds themselves.

Ninth Memoir. [This is the sixth memoir of Part II of the 1722 edition reprinted without change.]

The remarkable thing about the second edition is that, in Parts II and III, Réaumur seems to be trying as hard as possible to depart from his really useful invention of making malleable cast iron. This involves essentially the making of a white cast iron, free from graphite, and subsequent annealing of the castings—after they have been removed from the molds and have been surrounded by special compounds and packed in closed containers—to produce either a mechanically harmless spheroidal form of graphite or the complete removal of carbon. The latter alone would meet his requirements for work of the highest quality that could take a finish similar to wrought iron.

Part II of this edition is designed to exploit the fact that castings can be softened without placing them in boxes and without the use of annealing compounds. Heat alone will do it, but only heat of an optimum temperature acting rapidly. Since this is hard to attain, scaling must be avoided by covering the castings with a simple refractory coating or plaster, graphite mixed with clay being preferred. Almost any kind of furnace can be used, even a forge fire, but an inclosed structure with shelves is preferable.

The theory of softening is developed in a fine manner. As "sulfurs" leave the surface of a hot cast-iron piece, they are continually drawn from inside to the surface. The coating is like the head of an alembic in which oily vapors assemble; if the head is removed, or the coating broken, they evaporate. Fire, which feeds on them, will soon absorb the sulfurs, but the sulfurs do not evaporate from iron or steel heated in a closed space. "The more the cast iron is charged with sulfurs and salts, the easier it is to remove an equal quantity in the same time. When first exposed to fire, it is flooded with these materials, but, when it has lost a certain quantity, not only are there fewer to provide for evaporation but also those sulfurs and salts that remain are more dif-

ficult to detach; they are the ones that are most intimately bound."
This section reflects a true, if intuitive, understanding of all the factors
involved in heterogeneous chemical reaction.

The experiments described in Part III are aimed at producing a cast
iron which is removed from the mold soft enough to be worked, instead of being softened by subsequent treatment. For this purpose,
two distinctly different methods of approach were tried: (1) to effect
the softening in the liquid state and (2) to control the fracture and
the hardness of the castings by annealing them in the mold.

In the first memoir Réaumur describes attempts to soften the iron in
the melt by making additions. More than a dozen groups of materials
were used as addition agents, but none had the desired effect. Iron
filings, for instance, gave a very sluggish melt, which could hardly be
cast, and the resulting iron was brittle. Among the experiments with
different salts, the one with saltpeter is particularly interesting. In
paraphrase, Réaumur says: It is well known that the addition of saltpeter causes certain substances to ignite, but with others it has no
such effect. It must be concluded that only those substances are set on
fire by saltpeter which contain an inflammable matter. The fact that
saltpeter reacts violently with charcoal and molten iron indicates that
both furnish this matter. It would seem logical, therefore, to consider
saltpeter as an addition which would "burn the sulfurs of iron," that
is, which would soften it. In reality, the effect produced was disap-
pointing to the foundryman. Iron to which saltpeter had been added
during melting formed a crust on the mold, and the remainder thickened and solidified very quickly. The resulting iron was very hard.
It seems, therefore, that saltpeter "burns some of the sulfurs in the
iron. These sulfurs take with them the disposition for being fluid, but
they do not remove the hardness."

Further on, Réaumur observes that gray irons on being remelted
tend to become white and hard. He suspected that common sulfur
from the crucible was a partial cause of this and tested graphite and
wrought-iron crucibles. He showed that gray iron melted when surrounded by charcoal, or by a mixture of charcoal and bone ash, would
remain gray indefinitely, although such melting would not soften a
previously white iron. The converse effect of making gray iron white
could be achieved, but not controllably, by the addition of sulfur to the
molten metal. "The composition of ordinary sulfur is known as well
as that of any other mineral. At least it is known that it is a mixture.
The inflammable part, the true sulfur, is not more than a very small
portion, an acid of the nature of that of vitriol dominating the mix-

ture. It is our concern to know whether it is the inflammable part which has hardened our cast iron so promptly, or if it is the saline part, or if it is the two together." Tests with oily materials showed that they burned on the iron without rendering it either more white or more gray, which suggested that the acid part of sulfur should certainly produce hardness. "We know that the acid of sulfur and that of vitriol are the same though entangled in different matrices, and we would therefore expect vitriol to have the same effect as ordinary sulfur as far as the hardening of cast iron is concerned." This it did, and so did alum when used alone or mixed with bone and charcoal and thrown on the top of the melt, although iron melted in a crucible packed with an alum-charcoal mixture did not become hard. Réaumur concluded that, to produce a white iron, one should throw pinches of a mixture of alum, bone, and charcoal onto the surface of the melt and continue until a sample showed the desired type of fracture.

The fourth memoir of Part III is important, for it greatly amplifies the observations in the first edition on the rate of cooling in relation to fracture. Puzzled by the fact that cast iron which was gray in the pig would become white in a casting, Réaumur remarks: "In matters of natural philosophy unforeseen occurrences, however opposed they may be to what was promised, should not cause alarm if one has the courage to seek remedies: They should even be seen with pleasure, for they usually put us on a new road for the acquisition of knowledge." After dismissing the idea that sulfur in the molding material was responsible for the white fracture, Réaumur came to realize that cast iron was essentially being hardened by the quenching action of the mold. He showed that very gray iron became completely white on pouring it into water. Arguing then that a hot mold should give a soft gray iron, he made some sand molds in flasks which were heated red-hot: a normally white iron cast in them came out gray. "Thus it appears in general that white iron is iron quenched. This is a new idea that should be further developed."

After these astute observations he proceeds to describe in great detail the design and operation of a foundry for making castings in red-hot sand molds and gives a good description of the foundryman's routine. This whole procedure indicates a curious lack of economic sense. The operation was designed merely to enable the use of a normally white cast iron in making soft castings. The product would have none of the virtues of Réaumur's earlier true malleable cast iron, and the use of red-hot molds would involve a great increase in cost, which would be justified only if there were a very large price differential in favor of white pig. It well may be that Réaumur himself was uncertain about this, for it must be remembered that he did not publish this work during his lifetime, but it was published posthumously simply because it was found "in good order" among his papers.

THIRD EDITION (1781)

Volume XV of the quarto reprint of the *Descriptions des arts et métiers* made under the editorship of J. E. Bertrand contains a simple reprint of the 1762 version. The title page of the section containing Réaumur's work is worded identically with that of the 1762 edition except for omission of the date. The volume itself is entitled:

Descriptions des Arts et Métiers, faites ou approuvées par Messieurs de l'Académie Royale des Sciences de Paris ... Nouvelle Édition ... Par J. E. Bertrand, Professeur en Belles Lettres à Neuchâtel ... à Neuchâtel dans l'Imprimerie de la Société Typographique, MDCCLXXXI.

Réaumur's nine memoirs occupy pages 71–314 inclusive. They are followed by other material, not in the original edition, translated from the additions to the German edition of the *Descriptions*, and some comments on Réaumur translated from Henry Horne's *Essays concerning Iron and Steel* (London, 1773).

The German edition of the *Descriptions* has the title *Schauplatz der Künste und Handwerke.* . . . It was published at Berlin, Leipzig, and elsewhere, commencing in 1762 under the editorship of J. H. G. von Justi. Volumes II (1763) and III (1764) contain a translation of de Courtivron and Bouchu's original work but omit both Réaumur and the long work by Swedenborg which in translation from the 1734 Latin was a useful part of the original.

ENGLISH TRANSLATION

No translation of Réaumur's metallurgical work *in extenso* has heretofore appeared. The single chapter on the hardening of steel (Part I, chap. ii) came out in a little pamphlet in 1771:

An Essay on the Mystery of Tempering Steel. Wherein the Effects of that Operation are fully considered. Extracted from the Works of the celebrated Monsieur Réaumur. By J. Savigny. London: Printed for G. Kearsly, at No. I in Ludgate Street. M.DCC.LXXI.
21 cm., xvi + 44 pp.

In the Preface the author apologizes for not knowing French very well, never having "had an opportunity of leaving his native kingdom to improve himself in the language." His errors, however, seem to be due to ignorance of metallurgy rather than of French.

INDEX

INDEX

Académie Française, 11 n.

Académie Royale des Sciences, viii–xxi, 5, 5 n., 8, 11, 11 n., 14, 178 n., 356
  Descriptions des arts et métiers, xii, xiii, xv, 5, 20, 61, 158 n., 178 n., 370, 371, 376
  Histoire, xii, 356 n.
  Mémoires, xii, 5 n., 32 n., 200, 222, 241, 371

Academy of Sciences; *see* Académie Royale des Sciences

Acid of sea salt, 146, 146 n.

Acids
  in carburizing compounds, 36, 37
  of iron, 146
  quenching in, 239

Aciers de Carme, 178 n.

Activity
  of carburizing compounds, 56
  of fire, 70, 71, 89
  of furnace, 275, 285

Activity versus quantity
  of air, 104
  of charcoal, 103
  of compounds, 56

Additions to molten iron, 174, 374, 375

Agate, 191

Agricola, Georgius, xix, xx, xx n., xxi

Agricultural steel, 20, 183, 229

Air
  cause of quench hardening, 210, 211
  effect on burning and scaling, 308
  effect on fire, 104, 105
  exclusion from carburizing boxes, 47, 48, 48 n., 62
  in furnace, 65, 71, 82, 84, 104, 105

Alchemy, xxi, xxv n., xxviii

Alicante soda, in carburizing compounds, 35

Alkalies
  in annealing, 153, 155, 294, 296–98, 333
  in carburizing compounds, 35, 36, 40
  effect on scaling, 295

Allevard, 120

Allium sativum, 42 n.

Allotropy of iron, xxviii

Alloys, nature of, xix

Alum
  in annealing compound, 297
  in carburizing compounds, 35

changes gray to white iron, 375
in quenching medium, 237

Amontons, Guillaume, 195

Anatomy, xv

Anchors, xiii

Angervilliers, ——— d', 29

Angoulême, 120

Angoumois, 120

Animal matter, in carburizing compounds, 25

Annealers of cast iron, 358

Annealing cast iron, 269 n.
  architectural, 342
  in bone ash, 294–96, 306
  cannon, 349, 350
  in chalk, 294, 296
  in compounds; *see* Annealing compounds
  degrees of, 328–30
  economics, 334, 335
  effect on fracture, 320–25
  furnace for; *see* Annealing furnace
  in iron scale, 306, 307
  melting during, 326–28, 350, Pl. 16
  overheating, 299
  temperature and time, 299, 300, 318, 333
  trials, 317
  wood consumption, 333

Annealing compounds
  alkalies in, 294, 296–98, 333
  alum in, 297
  amount used, 305
  animal shells in, 305
  antimony in, 297
  bone ash in, 294–306, 317, 318, 333
  chalk in, 294, 296–301, 333
  charcoal in, 296, 297, 302, 303, 305, 317, 318, 327
  clay in, 298, 333
  corrosive sublimate in, 297
  cost, 303
  crushed glass in, 298
  gypsum in, 298
  leather charcoal in, 297
  lime in, 298, 305
  non-oxidizing, 299 n.
  oily substances in, 297, 298
  potter's earth in, 298
  quicklime in, 298
  salts in, 296, 297
  slaked lime in, 298
  transparent plaster in, 298
  verdigris in, 297

PLATES

Explanation of PLATE 1

A B, small oblong crucibles suitable for the smallest trials.

C D, other oblong crucibles, which are a little larger.

*C*2, the cover for crucible *C* made like the cover of a box.

E, the cover of crucible *D*, of the rabbet type, seen from above.

F, a square or almost square crucible.

G, the cover of crucible *F* viewed upside down.

H, section through this cover.

I, an oblong crucible, the cover of which fits into a guideway. *K*, its cover, which has only partly entered the guideway.

L M, square crucibles, which are larger than the previous ones.

N, a crucible which alone can take the place of several because of the partitions, *OO PP QQ*.

R, a flat piece of iron ready to be put in one of the small crucibles.

S, the mold for a square crucible.

T, the same mold partly covered with clay.

V X X, a crucible filled with iron and compound and the cover luted on. The lute is seen at *X X*.

Y Z, a luted [78] crucible. One end has been cut off to show how the layers of iron are separated by layers of compound. This is seen in *Z*.

a, a round crucible of the common shape, filled with compound into which flat sections or small bars of iron have been inserted; *b*, a small bar of iron only partly inserted.

c, the mold, or form, on which crucibles like *a* are made.

d, a cylindrical crucible.

e, the stopper for the preceding crucible.

f, section through this stopper.

g, the mold, or form, for the cylindrical crucible.

Figure *h i k l* is not drawn on the same scale as the preceding ones; *h* is a workman who uses a pair of tongs to hold a cylindrical crucible like *d* over the fire; *i*, this crucible; *k*, the baffle inclosing the charcoal; *l*, this same baffle shown under the forge; *m*, the round crucible.

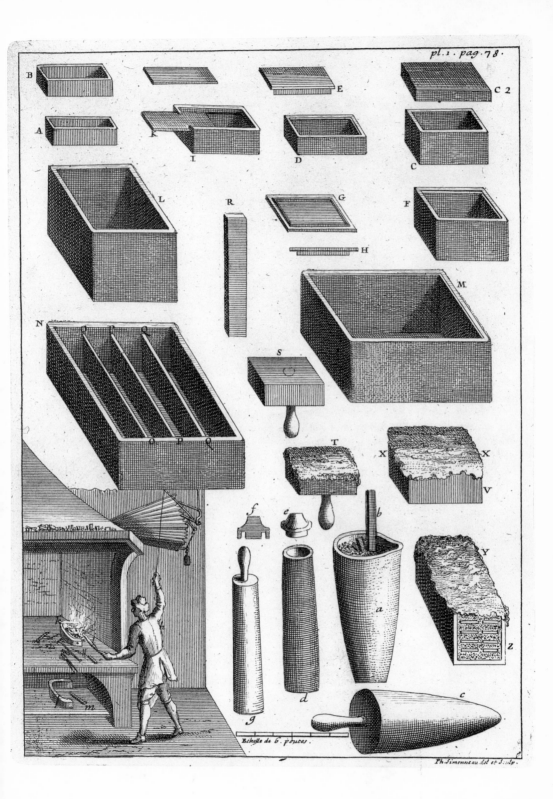

Echelle de 6. pouces.

Ph. Simonneau del. et Sculp.

Explanation of PLATE 2

A B, the same baffle as in Plate 1 drawn on a larger scale.

C, a round crucible lying in the baffle inclosure.

D E F, three small crucibles arranged so as to form the base of a stack.

G, a stack of small crucibles.

G2, a stack of small luted crucibles.

K K, two pieces of fired earthenware which together form a baffle.

I I, a baffle made of the two preceding pieces.

H, a stack of crucibles placed inside the baffle.

L, a baffle with an ordinary crucible inside.

M, two baffles, one put on top of the other so that they can inclose a higher stack of crucibles.

N N O O P is part of a forge where the bellows are not shown. It is easy to imagine where they must be.

O P, several pieces similar to those used as baffles, which are built up to form a kind of furnace into which the trial crucibles have been placed. The bellows drive the wind into the lower part of this kind of furnace.

Q, cover of exploratory furnace.

R R S is the front of an exploratory furnace of which no more detailed description is given here. The plans of the large steelmaking furnace, which will be given later, will satisfactorily explain the construction of the inside of this one, which [80] is practically identical except for size.

a a b c d d e, the furnace of the brass founders, used for all kinds of small work. The front of this furnace has been cut away to show the inside. It seemed unnecessary to draw the bellows. The wind is conducted through a flue into the cavity whose opening appears in *e*. This opening is closed when the bellows are worked; *e* is the mouth of the ashpit.

d d, rods supporting the iron plate which is the real bottom of the furnace. An ordinary crucible is standing on this plate; *aa ab bc* are the upper tiles facing the inside, forming part of the lining. Beyond the lining there is a layer of clay which can be increased or decreased in thickness depending on whether the capacity of the furnace is to be increased or decreased. The rest is brick.

f, an ordinary crucible.

g, its stopper.

k k is the same furnace, into which an oblong crucible *i* has been placed.

l, this crucible viewed outside the furnace.

m, its cover.

o, the plate on which the crucibles stand.

p q, two iron tie bars through which pass the rods that support the plate.

r s s t shows how the two iron rods (*r*) pass through the tie bars (*s*) and support the plate (*t*).

u, one of the rods that hold the plate.

Echelle de 6. pieds.

Ph. Simonneau del. et Scu.

Explanation of PLATE 3

It gives a horizontal section, a vertical section, and several elevations of the steelmaking furnace.

Figure 1 is a horizontal section [or plan] through this furnace.

Figure 2 is a vertical section through line *Ab* of the plan.

Figure 3 is an elevation, or a perspective view, of this furnace taken parallel to line *Ab* of the plan. Part of the furnace has been cut away to show the inside of the crucibles and the location of the spaces for the charcoal.

Figure 4 is another perspective view of a section similar to the preceding one. But in this one the crucibles are filled with iron bars and compound.

Figure 5 is a perspective section through the same furnace taken along line *dc*. The large crucible through which this section is taken is filled with iron bars and compound. In this figure these bars are viewed lengthwise, while in the preceding figure their ends are seen.

Since corresponding parts are lettered alike in these figures, they are all explained at the same time.

A c b d, Figure 1, is the shell of the furnace at ground level. If the wall is made thicker than it is here, the furnace will simply be more solid.

e e f f, Figure 1, is [146] the horizontal section through the cavity of the interior of the furnace.

gg hh ii kk, Figures 1–5, indicate the guideways into which the plates are set.

l l, Figures 1–5, are the two end plates, *m m*, the center plates.

n n, Figures 1–4, are the tuyères.

oo, Figure 1, is the horizontal section through a different type of tuyère which takes the place of several and which may, perhaps, be substituted for them with advantage. Although two types of tuyère are shown in the section, only one type will be used in every furnace.

p p p p, Figure 1, are the openings by which a poker with a crooked end may be passed into the furnace in order to open up the tuyères when that is necessary.

p p, Figure 2, are other openings located higher than the preceding ones. These can be made larger so that they come down to where the tuyères come out; then they will serve to pull out the vitrified matter and everything else that has collected on the bottom of the furnace. They are closed by a door.

q q2 q3, Figures 1, 2, and 5, are the openings through which we can withdraw test bars from the center crucible.

r r, Figures 1–3, are the openings through which we can withdraw test bars from the side crucibles.

s, Figure 4, the cover of the center crucible; *t t*, the covers of the side crucibles.

u, Figure 3, cover of the center crucible, of a shape suitable to let the charcoal fall down; *x*, cover of one of the small side crucibles, which has the same property; *y*, a similar [147] cover; the wall into which it is set has been cut away.

A, Figures 2–5, the ashpit. *A* [Fig. 1], the duct through which the wind of the bellows is conducted under the furnace or into the ashpit.

Figure 7, an ordinary tuyère shown on a larger scale than the rest. *D*, the flange that serves to hold it in the masonry.

Figure 8, oblong tuyère, seen from above.

Figures 10 and 11 are a horizontal and a vertical section, respectively, of a simple bellows, which have no relation to the scale [of the rest of the plate] and which are added here only to make the calculations on pages 98 ff. more easily understandable.

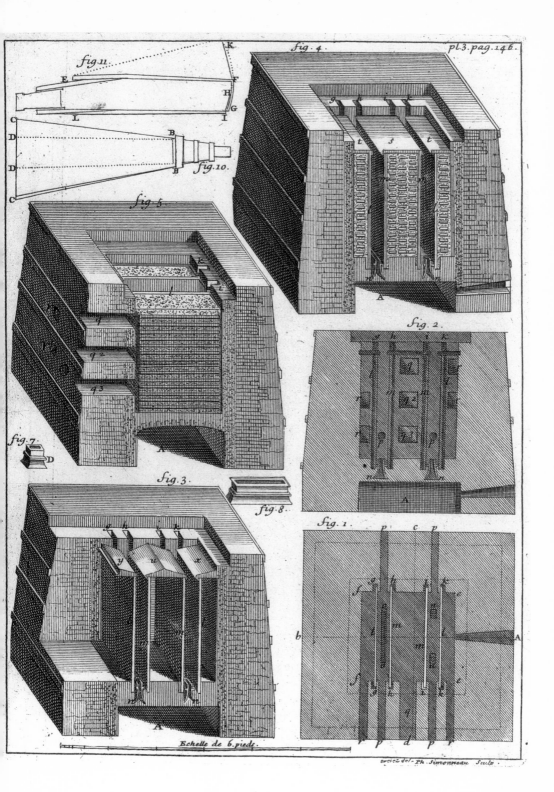

fig.11

fig.10

fig.4

fig.5

fig.7

fig.3

fig.8

fig.2

fig.1

Echelle de 6.pieds.

Breiel del. Ph. Simonneau Sculp.

A B C D E F G, etc., is the entire furnace, drawn to scale.

A, the center crucible. *A* also indicates the slot in which the end of the cover of this crucible can be set.

B B, the side crucibles.

C C, the fire chambers, or spaces for the charcoal.

D E E D, the guideways for the plates that form the crucibles.

F F2 F3, the windows or openings through which one can observe what goes on in the center crucible.

G G H H, similar openings for the side crucibles.

I I, small doors through which tools can be introduced into the fire chambers.

K K K K, the ties of the furnace; the stronger they are, the better.

L L, opening through which a poker is passed to open up the tuyères.

M, the blast pipe for the bellows.

N, the same, viewed separately.

O P Q, different stoppers for the openings *F G H*.

R, the stopper for one of these stoppers.

S T, stoppers which have stoppers of their own.

V X, one of these stoppers cut open.

Y (at the bottom of the plate), [149] the stopper of one of the openings marked *L*.

Z, cover of crucible *A* seen from above.

Z2, the same cover turned upside down.

d e, cover of a small crucible, seen from above and from below.

f, spanner for tightening the nuts on the ties.

g, one of the nuts.

h, one of the pieces of which the tie consists, joined to the end of another piece by a nut.

k i, pieces of the ties with openings at *i* and *k* for the threaded ends of the other pieces to pass through.

l m n are three covers the upper sides of which are sloping to facilitate the falling of the charcoal between the plates.

o p q r s t, the large cover of the furnace.

o q, its ties.

o p also indicate two pins by which it can be hung.

r, the hole by which the charcoal leaves.

s, the holes serving as registers.

t u, the holes through which iron rods are passed to help the charcoal go down.

x ꝣ ꝣ ꝣ ꝣ y, one of the ties of the cover viewed separately; *ꝣ ꝣ ꝣ ꝣ*, the pins; *y*, the piece connected with the pin, which grips the cover from below.

5, the cover upside down.

6, the grapple used to take off the cover.

7, the stopper of the cover fitted out with all its little stoppers.

8, the same, [150] with the little stoppers taken out.

9, the larger stopper of the stopper.

10, the big stopper upside down.

11, the small stoppers of the stopper.

a a, *b b* are two figures which have no other purpose than to make the discussion on page 103 more easily understood.

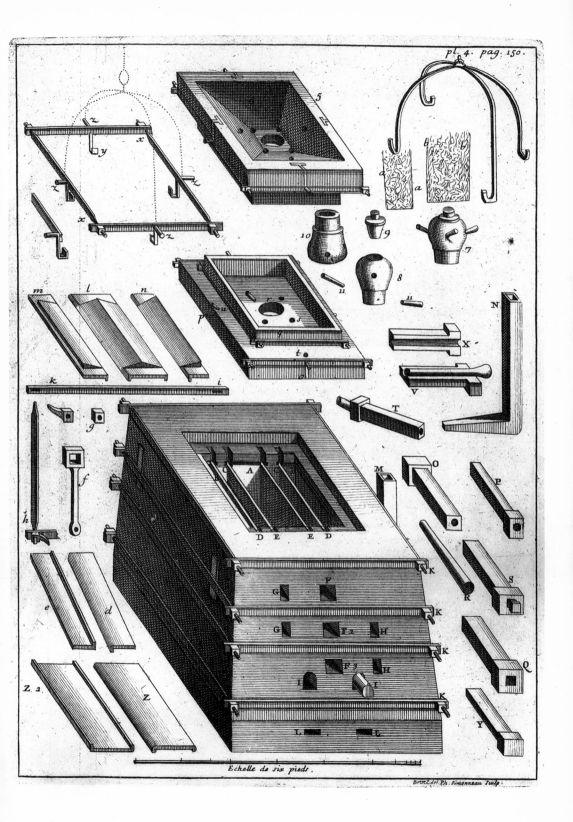

pl. 4. pag. 150.

Echelle de six pieds.

Bretez del. Ph. Simonneau Sculp.

Explanation of PLATE 5

Figure 1 shows the charged furnace; the cover has just been put on, or is ready to be taken off; for, when the fire is burning in the furnace, the grapple is not over the cover as it is here.

a, the hood of the flue.

b, the bellows; *d*, the chain by which it is pulled.

e e, grapple for lifting the cover.

f g, lever on which the grapple hangs.

h, the gallows-like support of the lever.

Figure 2 [shows a man who] beats clay to make plates. The place *o* where this man stands is lower than the table *p* on which he does his beating.

q, a pile of finished plates.

r s t, the iron framework supporting the plates which are to be fired.

x, a wooden table suitable for making plates drawn to the scale given below.

*x*2, section through the same table.

y y z, clay shaped into a plate, still on the table; it extends over the edge at *y y;* at *z y* the clay extending over the edge has been cut away.

Figure 3 is a horizontal section of a furnace with five crucibles.

A is the place where the pipe for the wind is cut away; this pipe divides into two branches, and [each of these] divides again into two more branches.

E D C B are [152] these four branches, or the four blast pipes; at *E D C B* are their dampers.

F G H are the horizontal sections of the three large crucibles.

I K, those of the two side crucibles.

L L L L, the four fire chambers.

M M, etc., the openings into the crucibles.

0 0, the openings leading into the fire chambers.

Figure 4 is the horizontal section of a furnace with a center crucible that is square or almost square. The available space was insufficient to make the furnace wall in this and the preceding figure as thick as it ought to be.

P, the center crucible; *Q Q*, the two side crucibles.

R R, the fire chambers in which wood may be used if desired.

Figure 5 is an elevation of this furnace above line *Q Q* [?].

X is a section through the center crucible; in it the ends of bars are seen alternately with the long sides of bars.

S T, two openings through which one can observe what happens in one of the side crucibles.

Z, the other side crucible, which has been cut open.

V, the door by which wood can be put in one of the fireboxes.

Y, the other firebox, with the front cut away to show the grating, which supports the wood.

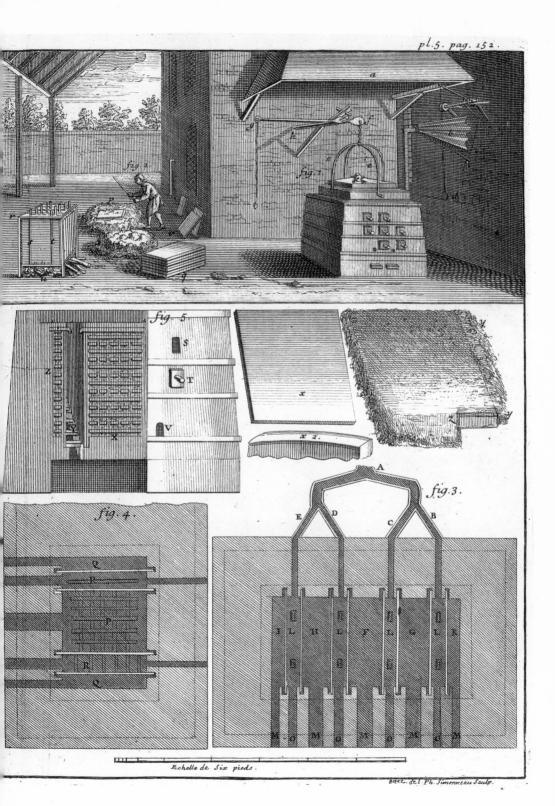

fig. 2

fig. 1

fig. 5

S

T

V

X

Z

Y

A

E   D   C   B

fig. 3

fig. 4

Q

P

P

P

R

Q

R

Echelle de Six pieds.

Brez. del. Ph. Simonneau Sculp.

Explanation of PLATE 6

It shows pieces of iron bars of different quality after they have been fractured. The purpose of these illustrations is to demonstrate the differences in shape, size, and arrangement of the parts perceptible in the fracture of different irons.

Figure 1 is the fracture of the iron which I have called "iron with large, or coarse, platelets."

Figure 2 is a piece of the fracture of the same iron but drawn as seen under a magnifying glass in order to bring out better the non-uniformity of the arrangement of the platelets and, especially, that there are some among them that are inclined at different angles.

Figure 3 is the fracture of a bar of iron of the second class. Here, the whole fracture is occupied by platelets, which are smaller and more uniformly arranged than those of the preceding figure.

Figure 4 is part of Figure 3 as seen under the magnifying glass.

Figure 5 is another fracture of a bar of iron of the second class, but the platelets are smaller than those of the iron of Figure 3.

Figure 6 is the fracture of an iron belonging in the third class. Platelets are here mixed with grains.

Figure 7 shows only the platelets of Figure 6.

Figure 8 shows only the grains of Figure 6.

Figure 9 is [200] the fracture of an iron belonging in the fourth class. The platelets occur in smaller quantity than the grains.

Figure 10 is the fracture of an iron containing grains—that is, an iron of the fifth class. The smooth-appearing part around the fracture is not a fracture. It shows where the bar was cut with a chisel so that the iron would break more easily.

Figure 11 is the grain of this iron as seen under the magnifier. Thus enlarged, the grain of this iron is almost representative of that of the iron of the sixth class.

Figure 12 is the fracture of a piece of merchant bar. This iron has been left in the fifth class, although its grain is finer than that in Figure 10, and it also has fine platelets.

Figure 13, the grains of Figure 12.

Figure 14, the platelets of Figure 12.

Figure 15 is the fracture of a bar of iron belonging in the seventh class; it consists of fibers which look like leaves.

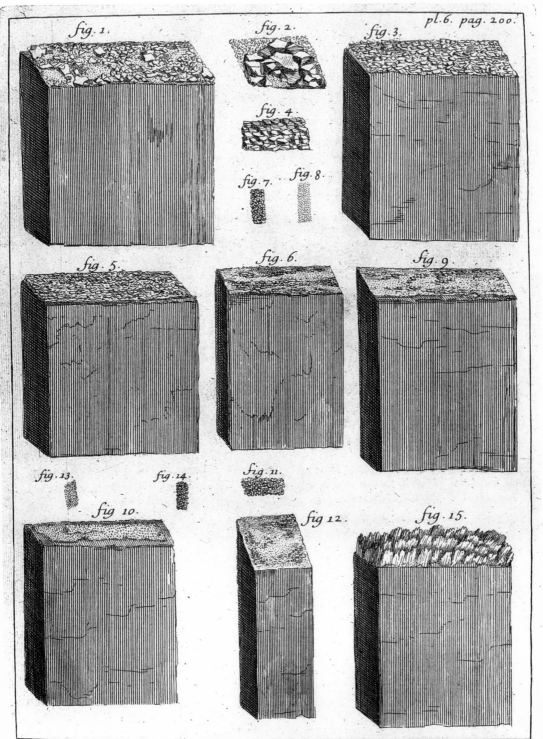

fig. 1.

fig. 2.

fig. 3.

fig. 4.

fig. 7.   fig. 8.

fig. 5.

fig. 6.

fig. 9.

fig. 13.   fig. 14.   fig. 11.

fig. 10.

fig. 12.

fig. 15.

Ph. Simonneau del. et Sculp.

Explanation of PLATE 7

Figures 1, 2, and 5 are more fractures of iron.

Figure 1 is the fracture of a fibrous iron which differs from Figure 15 [Pl. 6] by having coarser fibers and by the fact that, when several fibers combine, they do not form such distinct leaves.

Figure 2 is the fracture of an iron in which fibers and grains occur.

Figure 3 is [201] the fracture of an iron with a mixture of large and small platelets, grains, and fibers.

Figure 4 is the fracture of a bar of fibrous iron which has only partly been converted into steel. The outer border, which contains dull platelets and is marked in two places by the dotted lines *A A*, is steel. The dotted lines *B B* mark an area of brilliant white platelets; the fibers of the iron are broken up in this area, which is close to becoming steel but has not yet been completely converted. The center of the bar has preserved all its fibers.

Figure 5 is the fracture of a bar of iron of good quality which has been converted into steel. Platelets are seen throughout, but they are smaller and duller near the outside than toward the center.

Figure 6 is the fracture of a bar of which part *aabb* was nicely converted into steel, while part *aacc* has remained iron. The reason is that the compound covering this part was accessible to the air and was burned in the furnace. *G* is a large blister; *g*, a small one.

Figure 7 is the fracture of a bar of iron converted into steel; but it was overexposed to the fire. Its platelets are too dull and at some places too small; its grains are only as small as dots. *G* is a large bubble or surface blister; *g* are small blisters. The dotted line *O* points to a bubble, an ebulition that took place inside the bar.

Figure 8 illustrates the fracture of an iron that always forms very small platelets upon being converted into steel.

Figure 9 is the fracture of a bar of iron [202] of the second class. The whole interior still has its brilliant platelets and has in no way been changed into steel. The parts surrounding it have become steel; but instead of platelets, like the good steels, this one has only grains as small as dots.

Figure 10 shows a wide bar which on being forged on its side has become corrugated. Even if these corrugations are later eliminated by further forging, the steel is inclined to split open in quenching at the locations where the corrugations have been.

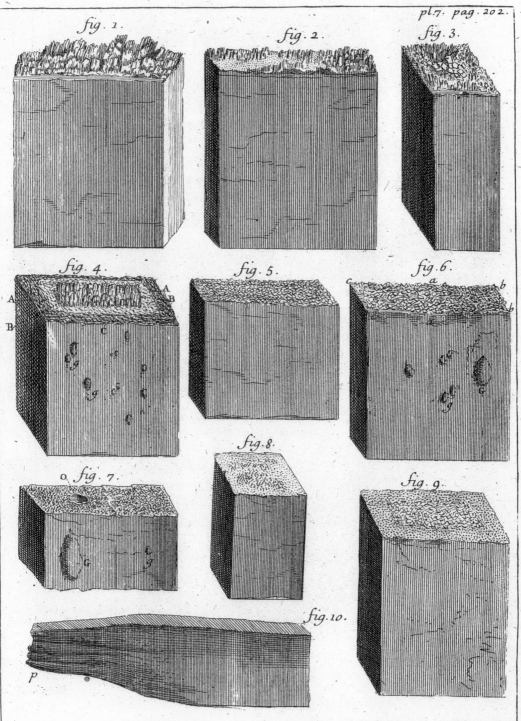

fig. 1.

fig. 2.

fig. 3.

fig. 4.

fig. 5.

fig. 6.

fig. 7.

fig. 8.

fig. 9.

fig. 10.

Pl. Simonneau del. et Sculp.

Explanation of PLATE 8

Figure 1 is a billet of intractable steel. Its surface is completely covered with cracks.

Figure 2 is another steel billet with cracks but with fewer cracks than the preceding one. Here they occur principally at the corners, as in *A*. The cracks are sometimes so fine that one has to look at them closely to discover them.

Part *D B* of the piece of steel shown in Figure 3 has been bent around to make it approach *D C*. This steel, being of bad quality and hardly fit to be worked, partly broke in the bend *D*, although it was bent hot.

Figures 4–7 are fractures of different bars of steel, each one of which has one of the spots called "roses." The rose of each bar differs from the others in color and shape.

Figure 8 is a small steel bar; the end *F* has been hammered out into a point. It then has been heated and quenched. If the thick end *L* is struck with a hammer, the point (*F G*) will break. In the same figure, *M* marks the defects called "laps," which are parts badly welded to the rest and which sometimes, when they are thin, can be lifted off.

Figure 9 consists of four separate pieces of steel, *fg*, *gh*, *hi*, and *ik*. They were obtained by striking the bar of Figure 8, which [302] successively broke at *G*, *H*, *I*, and *K*. It will be assumed that the point was almost melting-hot, while the end *L* remained almost cold or did not become colored at all. Consequently, the fractures near *F* have a coarser grain than those farther down, a fact which can be observed in *gh*, *hi*, and *ik*.

Figure 10 shows a flat bar of steel which was forge-welded to a bar of iron so that afterward the steel could be broken in such a way that the fracture would show the entire range of different grain sizes.*

Figure 11 is the iron bar.

Figure 12 shows how these bars are partly welded together. They are completely welded at *aa* and down to *b; dba* is the iron bar, *cba* is the steel bar, and *de* is the line along which the iron bar must be cut after it has been welded.

In Figure 13 the piece is ready; *ghh iik* is the groove cut into the iron. The part beyond the groove is steel. All that is still to be done is to heat one end of this piece melting-hot and then quench it. Thereafter it can be broken lengthwise.

Figure 14 shows the piece of the preceding figure, which has been partly cut at *l l*. With the chisel *n*, it is being forced to open up at *m m* and the surrounding area.

Figure 15 illustrates one of the two halves obtained by the division of the previous piece. Surface *pqss* shows where the iron was cut with the chisel or the file which made the groove; *opqr* is the fracture of the steel, on which all the different types of grain can be seen; *o,1* is the first type, the coarse grain. *1, 2* is the second type [303], or mixed grain; *2, 3* is the third type, the fine grain; *3, 4*, and everything thereafter is the grain of the grade of steel under consideration when it has not been affected by quenching; it is the fourth type. Part *o u* consists of grains of less whiteness and brilliance than those which follow within the same division, the reason being that the end was heated so hot that it was almost melting.

* Harry Brearley (*Heat Treatment of Tool Steel* [London, 1916], p. 91) refers to this test—modified only by milling a notch instead of welding on iron—as "Alling's method" and shows photographs of such fractured pieces which illustrate more clearly than Réaumur's engravings the sequence of fractures involved.

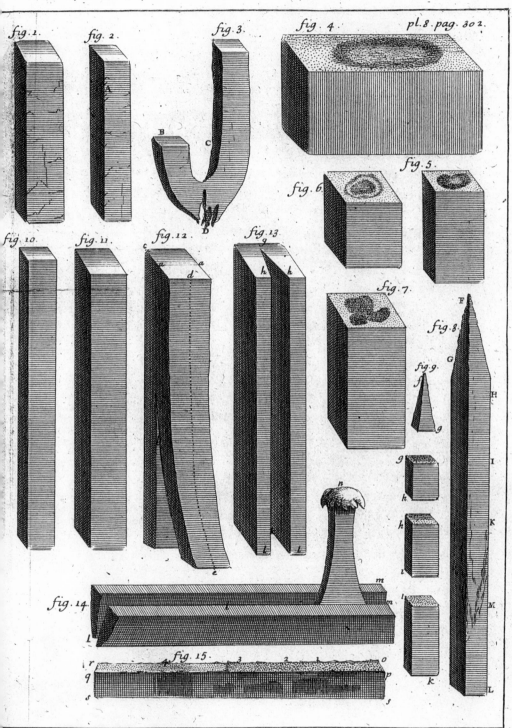

fig. 1.

fig. 2.

fig. 3.

fig. 4.

pl. 8. pag. 302.

fig. 5.

fig. 6.

fig. 7.

fig. 8.

fig. 9.

fig. 10.

fig. 11.

fig. 12.

fig. 13.

fig. 14.

fig. 15.

Ph. Simonneau del. et Sculp.

Explanation of PLATE 9

Figure 1 shows a steel bar forged razor-shaped, so that it can easily be broken lengthwise. *AA* is the back, which is much thicker than the rest. *BC* is a groove cut with the chisel along a line where this bar is to be broken. If end *C* is the one that is not supposed to be affected by the quench, no groove is cut near *C*.

Figure 2 shows the preceding bar, which now has been broken all along the groove, *BC*. The fracture, *DE*, shows the different types of grain. This is a coarse steel of very bad quality. Its coarse grain is neither so white nor so sparkling as that of some other steels. But it is even more noteworthy that these grains seem to be arranged in parallel layers, a fact which indicates the presence of iron. These layers are still more noticeable in the mixed-grain division (*1, 2*), where something like fibers can be seen, which are pure iron. These fibers are still more evident in the fine grain (*2, 3*). Here we have another rule—that the presence of iron in steel is always [304] more noticeable in the fine grain than in the preceding divisions. In the first division it exists as white grains that can hardly be distinguished from those of steel, except when they are tried with the file. The fracture of the fourth type of grain (*3, 4*) resembles that of fibrous irons.

Figure 3 consists of four pieces (*F F F F*) which have been separated from the bar of Figure 1.

Figure 4 is a bar of another steel. It is seen by its fracture that it is still coarse but less so than the previous steel. A small vein of iron (*i*) appears in the mixed grain (*1, 2*) and two larger ones in the fine grain (*2, 3*). The grains of the third division in this steel, and of the preceding one, are not as fine as those of the next figure. The fourth type (*3, 4*) consists partly of grains and partly of fibers.

Figure 5 shows (as the earlier ones) the fracture, *LM*, of a steel which is finer than the preceding ones and actually one of the finest kind. The coarse grain is in no way mixed, the mixed grain (*1, 2*) is very mixed, and the fine grain (*2, 3*) consists of very fine grains, which are well separated from each other. The unquenched part has only grains, which are very fine, so that this division actually equals the third division in some quenched steels, but the grains are grayer than the fine grains of this same steel. Such very fine grain at a location where the steel was not affected by the quench ordinarily indicates a steel which is hard to process and which has little body.

Figures 6 and 7 show the fractures of different steels. It was considered sufficient in this case to draw the surfaces of these fractures. It is assumed that the two steel bars on which the fractures have been drawn were heated equally by being plunged [305] up to *R R* into a bath of molten iron. *0, 1* is the first division of the one steel and *Q 1 M* of the other; *3* indicates the end of the fine grain in both steels. It will be noticed, and it is the purpose of these figures to point out, that the steel of Figure 7, which is the finer of the two, has a longer range of [quenched] grain (*Q, 3*) than the steel of Figure 6 (*0, 3*). It will also be noticed that in Figure 7 the ratio of the extent of fine grain (*2, 3*) to the extent of mixed grain (*2, 1*) is greater than the corresponding ratio in Figure 6. The unquenched grain (*s*) in Figure 7 consists of finer grains than the corresponding division in Figure 6.

Figure 8 shows the entire range of different types of grain of a steel as seen enlarged under a magnifying glass. The figure had to be short, because it is assumed that it was obtained on a piece of steel only a short end of which was quenched. *u, 1* is the first division, which seems to consist of platelets similar to those observed in certain irons by the unaided eye. This demonstrates that steel differs from iron less by the shape than by the smallness of its parts. *1, 2* is the second division, which has brilliant platelets mixed with dull grains. In the third division (*2, 3*) there seems to be nothing but some sort of grain. It should not be concluded, however, that the particles have not here, as elsewhere, the shape of platelets. The only conclusion that can be drawn is that the microscope, which in the first and second divisions shows platelets of the size indicated, does not show them in this one; but platelets would be seen under a much stronger microscope. *3, 4, T* is the structure unaffected by quenching.

[306] Figure 9 shows a steel bar the end of which was broken. This steel was treated [i.e., decarburized] as described in the eighth memoir. The circumference of the fracture is a layer of iron, and all the rest is steel.

Figure 10 shows a steel wire which is to be tested for body.

Figure 11 is the barrel of a small pistol, or a piece of a musket barrel, in which lead or tin can be melted, so that steel wires can be heated equally when their body is to be compared.

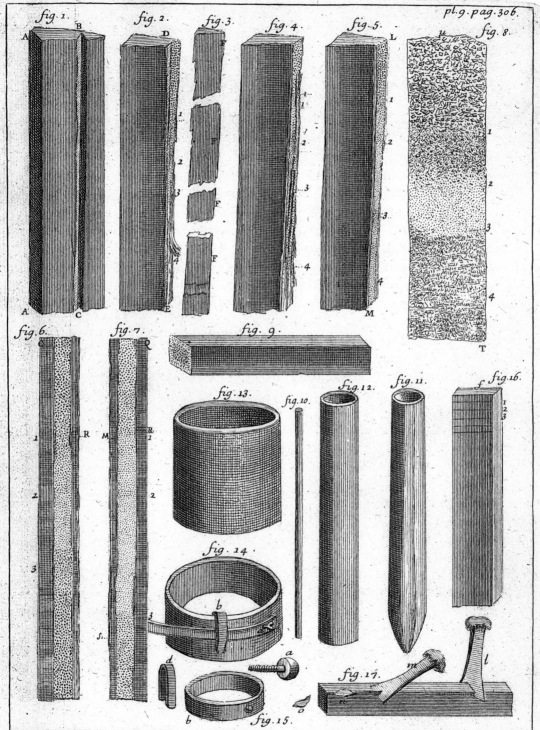

fig. 1. fig. 2. fig. 3. fig. 4. fig. 5. fig. 8.

fig. 6. fig. 7. fig. 9.

fig. 13. fig. 10. fig. 12. fig. 11. fig. 16.

fig. 14.

fig. 17.

fig. 15.

Ph. Simonneau del. et Sculp.

Figures 12 and 13 are crucibles which can be used for the same purpose or to keep iron molten, in which steel bars (forged into razors like those shown in preceding figures) can be heated equally to compare their body.

Figure 14 shows a ring, or hollow cylinder, upon which steel strip or steel wire can be wound to test its body. *a* is the screw that holds one end of the iron [*sic*] strip or wire; *b* is a hook which keeps the steel fastened to the ring; *d b* is the hook viewed separately.

Figure 15 shows another ring of smaller diameter. Experience will indicate what diameters should be given to different rings to make the tests.

Figure 16 is a bar of bad steel, or of hard iron, the end (*f*) of which has been quenched. It is graduated by parallel lines (*1, 2, 3*). It serves to test chisels made of different steels. The best ones are those that cut closest to *f* without spalling and without having their edges fold back.

Figure 17 shows a piece of iron [307] with two chisels resting on it; *l* is a chisel standing upright; *m* is a chisel placed obliquely; *n* is a cut which was previously made with the chisel held obliquely. The brighter and cleaner this cut looks, the better is the steel which has made it; *o* is a chip that has been lifted by the chisel.

Explanation of PLATE 10

Figure 1 is the little machine for testing the body of steel, as viewed from above. It can be held in one's hand, but it is much more convenient to fasten it in a vise.

Figure 2 shows the same machine, as viewed from below.

Some parts of this machine are also shown separately, but the same letters are used throughout for the same parts. *A A* are the two arms of the bent piece of iron that constitutes the base of the machine.

B B is the plate, made of iron or copper, which is attached to these two arms.

C is the small vise, the jaws of which hold one end of the wire that is to be tested for body.

D D are the two lunette guides, or holes, that receive the movable shaft.

E is this shaft, provided with a screw hole at *E*.

F G is the coarse screw.

H is the small fork which fits into the end of the coarse screw and turns in it freely.

I is a small [308] screw which serves to secure the shaft which holds the coarse screw. This screw is placed closer to the vise or farther away from it, depending on the length of the wire that is to be tested.

K L, in Figure 1, is the small rule, which is bent at *L*.

L M, in Figure 2, is the same rule. *M* is the screw that holds it to the plate.

N O, in Figure 1, is the iron [*sic*] wire in position to be broken. It will be broken when the screw *F G* has strained it to a certain extent.

Figure 3 shows two steel prisms which are equal in every respect, one placed upon the other. Both of them have been notched by the same blow which was applied to the upper one.

Figures 4 ff. explain matters discussed in the eleventh memoir. *g h i* is a steel wire; its upper end is hung up at *g; h* is a small plate on which one or two pieces of red-hot charcoal are placed to heat the wire at this location to the point that is required to quench it; *k l* is a lever around which the lower end of the steel wire is wrapped. The arm *i k* is much longer than the other one; it is made as long as one finds it necessary. The arm *i l* is stopped at *l* by any suitable body. The arm *k i* is loaded to break the steel wire.

Figure 5 shows a grain of steel as it would look if it were vastly enlarged. Its natural size is shown in G. *M M M* are the molecules of which this grain is composed. *V V* are the voids left between them.

Figure 6 shows part of this grain, or one [309] molecule, by itself; *p p* are the parts of which this molecule is composed.

Figure 7 consists of two rows (*R R*) of equal spheres, some of which do not touch.

Figure 8 consists of two rows (*S S*) of smaller spheres than the preceding ones, all of which touch.

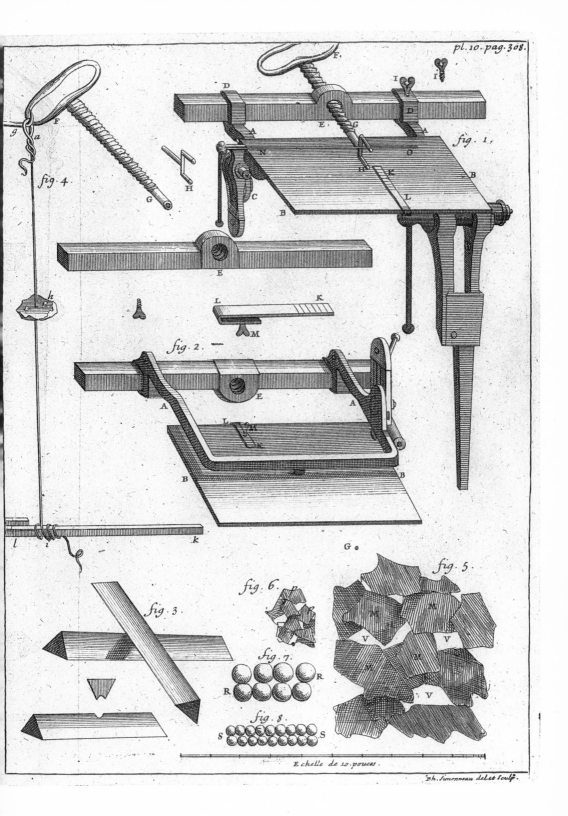

fig. 1.

fig. 4.

fig. 2.

fig. 3.

fig. 6.

fig. 5.

fig. 7.

fig. 8.

Echelle de 10. pouces.

Ph. Simonneau del. et sculp.

Explanation of PLATE 11

It shows the fractures of different kinds of pig iron or cast iron.

Figure 1 illustrates the fracture of one kind of white iron which, however, has some non-uniformities on its surface.

Figure 2 is the fracture of another white iron, the kind of fracture commonly found in irons that have been refined a second time.

Figure 3 is the fracture of another white iron, which for some reason has radii. Most often, these radii, which are directed toward the center, are not as pronounced as they are here.

Figure 4 is another fracture of a white iron where something like radii can be observed which are directed toward the center; but here they are weaker than in Figure 3.

Figure 5 is the fracture of a gray iron resembling rather closely the fracture of a coarse steel in the quenched condition; but the color of this fracture is much browner and the grains are larger.

Figure 6 is the fracture of one of the irons called "mottled." The matrix is white but interspersed with something like small stars.

Figure 7 is the fracture of a very brown, almost black, iron. In addition to differing from that of Figure 5 in its color, it also differs from it by being less distinctly granular. Its grains are less clearly defined, and the fracture is interspersed with platelets.

Figure 8 is [407] a small part of Figure 5 taken from one of its corners. It is shown as magnified under the microscope; it seems to be composed of an infinite number of small branches.

Figure 9 is one of the branches of Figure 8 drawn separately in order to show that each branch seems to be made entirely of small platelets placed one upon another.

Figure 10 is the fracture of a gate from an iron casting. The iron had not been thoroughly refined. It is very white only near the thin ends *B B* and around the circumference, while the entire inside has remained gray.

Figure 11 is the fracture of another casting gate of refined iron where some gray iron has remained but less than in the preceding figure. *A* is the remaining gray iron.

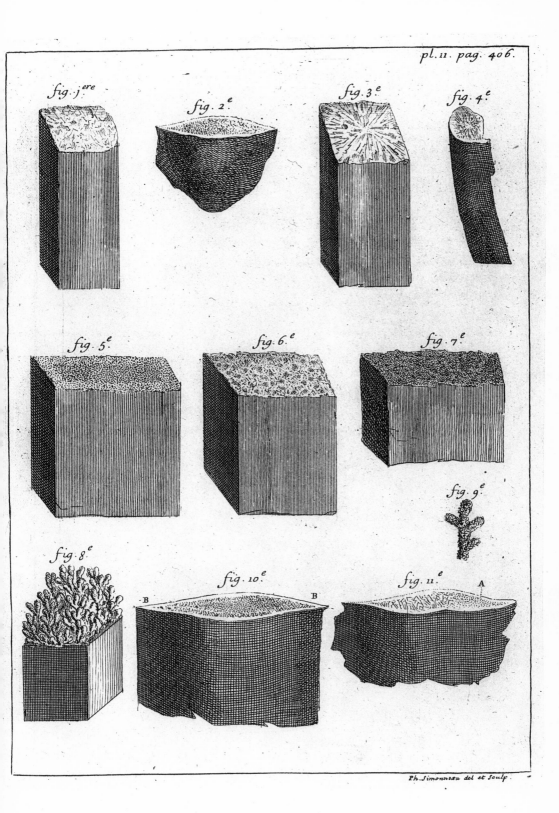

fig. 1.ᵉʳᵉ

fig. 2.ᵉ

fig. 3.ᵉ

fig. 4.ᵉ

fig. 5.ᵉ

fig. 6.ᵉ

fig. 7.ᵉ

fig. 9.ᵉ

fig. 8.ᵉ

fig. 10.ᵉ

B   B

fig. 11.ᵉ   A

Ph. Simonneau del et Sculp.

Explanation of PLATE 12

The upper part of the Plate shows two small foundry furnaces and artisans doing all the work connected therewith.

a b is a shed under which is the kind of furnace which is generally used in the shops of foundrymen producing small castings.

c is the furnace of these artisans. It is the same of which sections are shown in Plate 2.

The man in Figure 1 works the bellows of this furnace.

d d is the box, a sort of bin, containing the sand with which the molds are filled.

e e are molds put out to dry.

f is a small movable furnace to which the bellows of a forge supplies the wind.

g is the tube through which the wind of the bellows, *h*, is conducted into the furnace.

i k is a forge on wheels. If it is used as a forge, the bellows are rearranged so that they blow toward *k*.

The man in Figure 2 pours the liquid metal from the crucible, which has just been taken from the furnace, *f*, into a mold.

m is the clamp in which the molds are locked.

n, three molds held in this press.

o, an open mold.

The man in Figure 3 places into a heap of charcoal, *p*, the castings [442] which he has just removed red-hot from the mold, *o*.

q is an oven, resembling a baker's oven, in which the castings may be placed as they are removed from the molds.

LOWER PART OF THE PLATE

A, the small portable furnace.

B, the base upon which it is placed.

C, its cover.

D E F G H IK are all the separate pieces of which the furnace is built.

D, the base.

E, the piece that forms the ashpit, which is the only one with a flange at the inner rim to hold the iron plate with cut-out corners.

F, this iron plate.

G H IK, the remaining pieces of the furnace.

L, a piece of soft clay, shaped into a square block, which only has to be cut out in the middle to be turned into a piece like those just described.

M, a baffle of a more useful shape than ordinary baffles. If this is put on a forge, it takes the place of a furnace.

N, a mold into which metal has just been poured.

O P is mold *N* when it is open. These are the frames of which it is made, filled with sand on which the shape of the casting is seen.

Q R S T V [*X*] *Y Z*, the castings made in mold *N*. [443] The different castings are held together by the gates. *R S* is one cheek of a bridle, *T* is an escutcheon, *V* a sword guard, *X Y* are gunlocks. *Q Z* is the trunk of the gate which has opened up into branches through which all these castings were fed. The places where, according to my recommendation, the gates should be kept thin are those where they touch a casting.

Echelle de 3. pieds

This illustrates the ordinary furnace in which cast iron is melted by charging it together with charcoal, without placing it in a special crucible.

The upper part of the Plate shows one of these furnaces, in which iron is actually melted. It also shows how iron melted in a second furnace is being poured into molds.

The men in Figures 1 and 2 work the bellows.

a b, the upper part of the furnace. Its lower part is buried in charcoal breeze, or charcoal dust.

b is the opening into which the charcoal and the pieces of iron are charged.

c c is the heap of charcoal dust around the bottom of the furnace.

d, the tuyère into which the nozzles of the bellows are laid.

e, a heap of charcoal; *e2*, a heap of broken pieces of cast iron.

f, the post which holds the lever by means of which the ladle, or crucible, which is the bottom of the furnace, is easily [444] lifted out.

g g, this lever.

h is the hook over which one slides the handle used to lift the crucible.

The men in Figures 3 and 4 are casting iron that has been melted in another furnace, which, however, is entirely identical with the first one. The man in Figure 3 turns the lever. The ladle, or crucible, with the molten iron is hanging on one side of this lever.

The man in Figure 4 holds the handle of the cradle and, by tilting the ladle, casts its metal into a mold.

i i, the hole where the ladle had heretofore been.

k k, the ladle, or crucible.

l, the stack which covered the ladle, after it has been knocked off.

m, the bail of the cradle.   *n*, a mold into which iron is poured.

o, the mold after it has been filled.   *p*, a mold that is to be filled.

The lower part of the Plate illustrates more clearly the construction of some of the parts shown above.

A A B B C D, the ladle, or crucible, which is the bottom of the furnace. *A A B B* is the old kettle. *C* is the clay which rises above its rim. *D* is the opening cut out to receive the tuyère.

E F G H I, the stack of the furnace, the part that fits on the ladle. *F G H I* are the different pieces of which it is put together, which generally are not so well suited to be assembled into a unit as they are here. *E* is the opening that will receive the tuyère.

K, the tuyère shown separately.

L L M M N 0 is a section [445] through the crucible, or ladle.

M L L M is the old iron kettle, or pot, lined on the inside with a layer of sandy clay. *M N*, the part of the clay that rises above the kettle. *0*, the tuyère in its place. The part above *N* is a section through the piece *F* of Figure *E F G H I*.

P P Q Q, section through the pieces *G* and *H* of the stack. The part from *P P* to *Q Q* is lined with clay.

R is the upper part, *I*, of the stack. In its opening, pieces of pig iron have been placed as they are placed for every charge which is made directly on the charcoal.

S, several pieces of broken-up cast iron.

T V X X, the cradle in which the ladle is placed.   *Y*, the bail of this cradle.

Z V, its iron handle, which is partly inclosed by a wooden handle.

1, 2, 3 shows the ladle placed into the cradle.

4, the bail hanging from a hook.

5, 6, different hooks which hold the cradle suspended from one side of the lever (*7*), only part of which is shown.

8, 9, 10, 11 is a section through part of Figure *F* in the upper half of the Plate.

8, the ring through which the lever is passed.

9, 10, the head of the pin that holds the ring.

11, 11, cut through the shaft in which this pin (*10*) is inserted. It turns freely.

12, weights that [446] are hung on the end of the lever to counterbalance the weight of the crucible.

13, mold.   *14*, a mortar which has been cast in this mold.

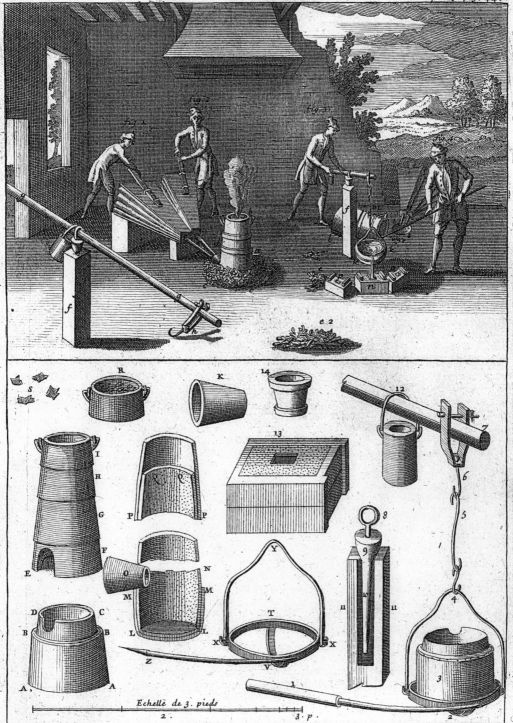

Echelle de 3. pieds

Ph. Simonneau del. et sculp.

Explanation of PLATE 14

The upper part of the Plate illustrates in perspective the kind of iron-melting furnace under which the molds are moved. Two views are given, representing different stages in the operation.

Figure 1 shows the furnace in the position it will have when the metal is being melted.

Figure 2 represents the position it will have when the molten metal is poured.

a a a a in Figures 1 and 2 are the wheels on which the whole assembly is mounted.

b b c d are four posts which are usually held by transverse bars.

d is a post which is higher than the others because it supports pieces that serve to operate the bellows.

f, the bellows. In Figure 1 its end or nozzle is inside the tuyère of the furnace. In Figure 2 the same nozzle is outside the furnace. Before the furnace is tilted, as in Figure 2, the bellows is pushed back. This is easy, because the two parts of the bent iron bar, which holds it up in back, slide in grooves cut all along the transverse bars (*h h*) from one end to the other.

g, the furnace—upright in Figure 1 and tilted in Figure 2. At *i i* [447] there are two rack bars with the two trunnions which hold the furnace and on which it can turn. By means of the rack bar the furnace can be placed higher or lower as necessary. At *g* in Figure 2 a heavy iron hoop circles the furnace. At two places which are diametrically opposite each other on this hoop the poles can be engaged with which the artisans (*k*) pull the furnace downward. They can easily hold this weight; but they could be relieved of part of the load by the use of counterweights.

The artisan *l* in Figure 2 holds the two screws of a clamp in which the mold or molds are confined.

o, the ladder used to charge the furnace with charcoal or iron.

p, the pole serving as a spring, which forces the bellows to collapse.

LOWER PART OF THE PLATE

I consider it unnecessary to give any details of all those parts that belong to the framework on which the furnace is supported. This is a completely arbitrary construction and will be used only by those who wish to move their furnaces, which would hardly be attempted in commercial plants. But everything concerning the furnace itself has here been developed a little further.

A A B B C is the whole furnace shown separately.

A A B B is the stack, *B B C* the ladle or crucible—the bottom part of the furnace; *B B* are the two trunnions by which it is held.

D, the opening [448] through which the molten iron is poured. If this were its only purpose, it would not have to be so large, but it also serves to let the rakes enter with which the dross and the charcoal that float on the iron are pulled out before the iron is cast.

D 2, [the plug for] this opening shown separately.

E E, iron bars whose two ends are fastened by screws [*sic*] to the stack and the ladle, respectively.

F, the iron hoop in which the poles are engaged with which the stack is pulled downward.

F 2, this hoop shown separately.

G, one of the poles used to tilt the stack.

H H I K is a section of the entire furnace showing the inside. *I*, the opening by which the molten metal runs out. *L*, the tuyère which is directed as shown by the dotted line.

0 H H 2 shows on each side of the section a thin iron bar, fastened by its two ends to the wall of the stack and thus helping to support the clay. There are more of these inside, quite close to each other, but they cannot be seen here because they are covered with clay.

*H*3, one of these iron bars by itself.

M M, the stack shown separately, where *D* is the opening through which the dross is removed.

N N 0 0, the crucible, or ladle, shown separately. The inside is completely lined with clay. *0 0*, the openings through which pieces of charcoal are put to keep the bottom of the crucible warm.

P P, the outer shell [449] of the ladle, the outer case, not yet fitted out inside.

Q Q, the cone-shaped sort of cage which is placed inside the empty vessel, *P P*.

S, the cage in its place in the ladle, ready to be covered with clay to become the crucible of Figure *N N 0 0*.

T T X, the cart on which the large molds can be placed. *V*, a mold on the cart.

X, the funnel that is set on the mold. In order better to conduct the metal into the mold *Z*, a pipe could be used to convey it from the furnace, but it would have to be heated before the metal is cast.

Y, the piece of iron that is fitted on the mold and supports the funnel.

Z, a mold, with the funnel in place.

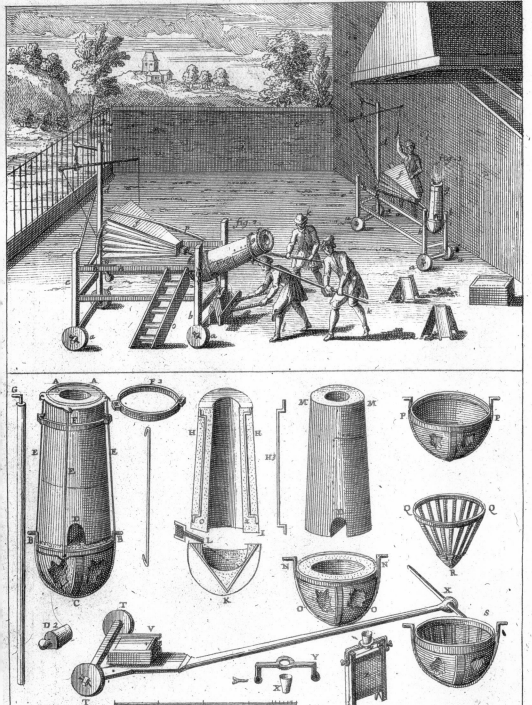

Echelle de ..... 4. pieds.

Ph. Simonneau del et Sculp.

It shows a furnace used to soften cast iron. The crucibles are charged from the side. This same furnace can also be used for the conversion of iron into steel. It must stand free so that one can easily move all around it.

Figure 1 is the plan of this furnace.

A A A A are the four ducts through which the air enters the furnace. They will be made as long as the ground around the furnace permits; and they will also get wider to varying extents [see p. 311].

B B, the openings through which the wood is charged.

C D, the two plates or partitions which together form the center crucible.

E F, the two plates which with one of the inside walls of the furnace form the end crucibles, *EH FG*.

EC DF, two plates which keep those between which they are placed straight; they prevent warping. Note that where they touch these other plates, the plates of the crucibles, there are slots which prevent them from slipping toward the right or left.

FG, a small plate which, like plates *DF* and *EC*, buttresses plate *F* of the end crucible.

Figure 2 shows the furnace in perspective. It is a view [494] of the side with the opening through which the center crucible is charged.

A, the opening by which the wind enters.

B B, doors used for the wood.

C D E E, the opening through which the large center crucible is charged.

F F, the two small plates inserted to prevent the plates of the crucibles from curving in such a way that they would project into the fire chambers. They do not extend, by a considerable amount, to the lower ends of the large plates.

G, the casting with which one has started to charge this crucible.

IH IH IH, the ties of the furnace, the number of which can be increased at will. They are cut at *H*, where each one forms a sort of ring.

KK, one of the vertical bars whose two ends are anchored in the masonry of the furnace and to which the tie rods are fastened from above either by rivets or by screws.

TT is the surrounding ground, which on both sides is higher than the plane of the furnace. It could also cover the opening *A;* it could bury it.

Figure 3 again shows the furnace in perspective. It is a view of the side opposite the one shown in the preceding figure. It is a view of the side from which the small crucibles are charged.

A is again one of the openings by which the air enters the furnace.

F F, the small plates which support the large ones.

G, another [495] small plate by which the plates of the end crucibles are also buttressed if desired.

IK, the opening of one of the end crucibles. The part of each tie rod that must be placed over the crucible when it has been charged is not shown here.

LM shows all the clay pieces in position, which, as a whole, close the opening of the crucible when it has been charged. Here the ties are placed over these pieces of clay.

Figure 4 consists of all these pieces made of clay which, when fitted upon another, form the connecting wall that in Figure 2 must close the opening *C D E E*.

Figure 5 is one of these earthenware pieces. *P P* are the knobs by which it is pulled out of the furnace.

Figure 6 is the same piece with its stopper removed. *Q*, the stopper.

Figure 7 illustrates how the cut-out parts of the ties, which fit over the openings of the crucibles, are assembled.

Figure 8 is a section through three plates placed one upon another. Plate *a* is inserted in the grooves of plates *b b*.

Figure 9 illustrates how the two plates of the center crucible can be connected to avoid warpage.

It is assumed that covers like those shown in Plates 3, 4, and 5 are used on the crucibles and the furnace. It would have been useless to reproduce them here.

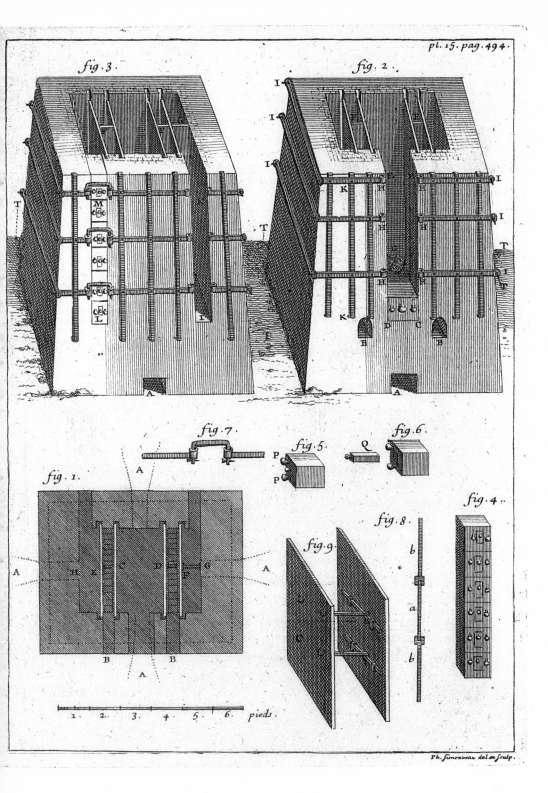

fig. 3.

fig. 2.

fig. 7.

fig. 5.

fig. 6.

fig. 1.

fig. 4.

fig. 8.

fig. 9.

1. 2. 3. 4. 5. 6. *pieds.*

Ph. Simonneau del. et sculp.

A B C are bars of cast iron of different section size intended to serve for tests. One of their ends is pointed. This pointed end makes it possible to use the large bars instead of smaller ones.

D, the fracture of one of these bars before softening.

E, the fracture of a bar that has started to soften. There are fine grains near the rim. Other locations also begin to be dotted with them. But there are so far no grains at the center.

F, the fracture of a bar where softening is more pronounced. Grains appear all through the fracture, and they are closer together than in the preceding figure.

G, the fracture of a bar where softening is still more pronounced. There is a surface layer, in the form of a white band, which is of the nature of wrought iron. The rest of the fracture is occupied by grains that are browner and coarser than those of the preceding figure.

H, the fracture of a bar in a still more advanced stage of softening. Where there are grains, they are coarser and blacker than in Figure *G*.

I, the fracture of a bar in a still more advanced stage of softening. The white color begins to reappear; the grains are no longer so black.

K K L L is the fracture of a bar of cast iron of larger section than the bars of the preceding figures. There [528] is a rather wide band around the rim. The texture and the color of this band resemble some wrought irons. The core is still granular and of the nature of steel. *L L* point by dotted lines to spots that are blacker than the rest. To the unaided eye, they appear to be grains, but under the microscope they prove to be holes.

M, the fracture of a specimen showing white grains similar to those in the wrought irons which I have called "irons with a granular structure."

QQ OO PP is one of the knockers for carriage-drive gates which became completely hollow except at *QQ*. Because this part is considerably thicker than the rest, the fire apparently was not strong enough to melt it.

R S T is one part of this knocker, which has been cut from the rest to show to what extent the entire piece has become hollow. It has been drawn to a larger scale than the knocker. The openings at *R* and *V*, which are the places where this piece was cut off from the rest of the knocker, sufficiently illustrate the shape of what might be called this hollow tube. At *T* there is a small opening which was made by the liquid metal and through which the metal has run out.

X Y is a piece of cast-iron test bar similar to those on which I purposely repeated what happened to me accidentally with the knocker of the preceding figure. *Y* is the spot at which the iron will flow out more easily if it is coated with sand or some other substance that retards softening. *Z* is the same cylinder changed into a hollow tube; *aa* is the tube cut open along its entire length.

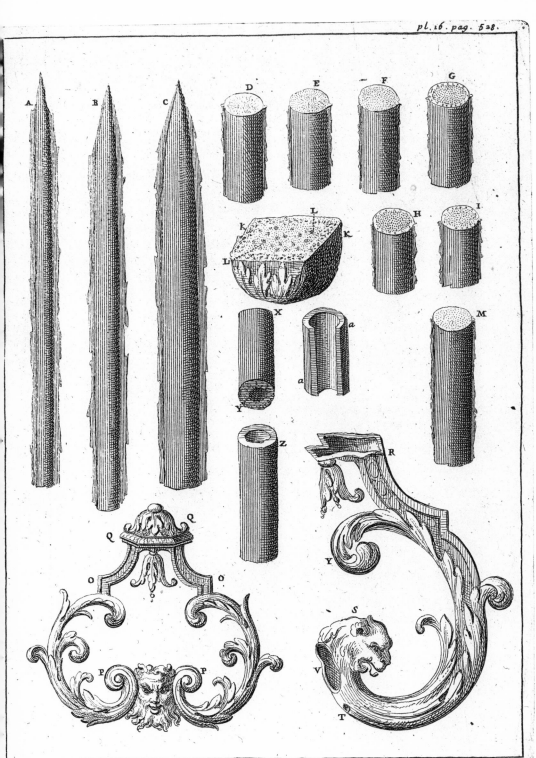

Ph. Simonneau f.

Explanation of PLATE 17

Figure 1 shows the striker, or door knocker, from the carriage entrance of the Hôtel de la Ferté, rue de Richelieu.

Figure 2 is the same knocker, turned around. *AA* are two pieces of wrought iron which are part of the hinge by which this knocker is hung on the door.

B CC, a wrought-iron staple placed in the mold for this knocker; the legs, *CC*, are the parts *AA* in Figure 2.

Figure 3 shows another door knocker. It is assumed that the ornament *D* has come out badly and that it was necessary to replace it by a piece of wrought iron.

Figure 4 is the knocker of Figure 2, which is supposed to have some defects that must be repaired. *E* is a hole into which screw threads have been cut in order to insert an ornament, the one marked *D* in Figure 3.

FG is the little substitute ornament made of wrought iron whose tail, *G*, has been cut to be a screw.

At *H*, Figure 4, there was a blister which has left a hole which the metal has not filled. It is planned to pour molten metal into this hole. *I I* shows a small rim of clay which forms a sort of funnel and covers the places on which the molten metal must not be applied.

Figure 5 is part of a fire grate. *L* is a piece of wrought iron which reaches into the grate and was inserted there in the mold.

Figure 6 is [560] the upright part of a candlestick. Its part *M* is likewise of wrought iron and was inserted by using the same expedient as described in Figures 5 and 2.

Figure 7 shows a cast-iron key as it comes out of the mold. *0* is its bit; the notches are not yet cut.

Figure 8 is the same key, with the notches cut into the bit after the key had been annealed.

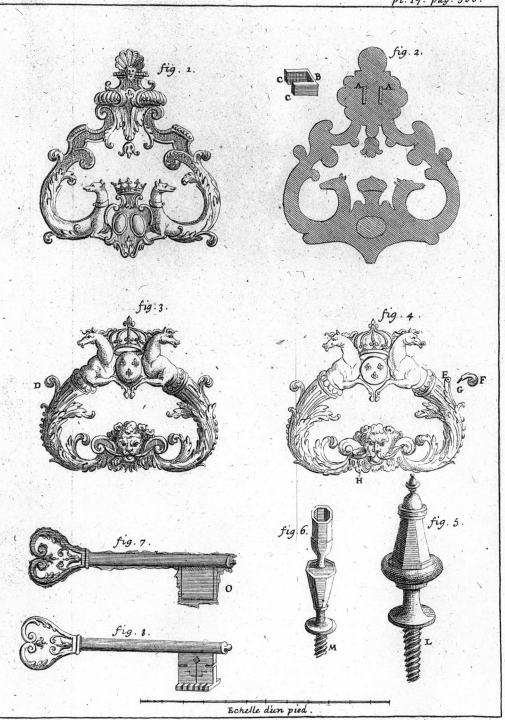

fig. 1.

fig. 2.

fig. 3.

fig. 4.

fig. 7.

fig. 8.

fig. 6.

fig. 5.

Echelle d'un pied.

Ph. Simonneau del. et Sculp.